THE BOOK OF CLASSIC PUZZLES AND WORD GAMES

THE BOOK OF CLASSIC PUZZLES AND WORD GAMES

GYLES BRANDRETH

CHANCELLOR
PRESS

First published by J. M. Dent & Sons Ltd in two separate volumes under the titles *Everyman's Classic Puzzles* and *Everyman's Word Games*.

This omnibus edition first published in 1992 by
Chancellor Press
Michelin House
81 Fulham Road
London SW3 6RB

ISBN 1 85152 114 3

Printed in Great Britain by The Bath Press

CONTENTS

KEY TO DIFFICULTY OF PUZZLES

☆ Very easy
☆☆ Easy
☆☆☆ Average
☆☆☆☆ Difficult
☆☆☆☆☆ Fiendish

CLASSIC PUZZLES

CONTENTS

1. OLD MASTERS

THE ANCIENT GREEKS

The ancient Greeks took mathematics quite seriously. The names of Euclid and Pythagoras, for example, are familiar to every scholar. But when they were not busy dropping perpendiculars and constructing squares on hypotenuses, they could relax with an entertaining puzzle, like the five that follow.

1. The Statue of Pallas ☆☆

The following inscription was on a statue of Pallas Athene: 'I, Pallas, am made of beaten gold, the gift of the poets. Half was given by Kariseus, an eighth by Thespis; Solon gave a tenth, and Themison a twentieth. The remaining nine talents were the gift of Aristodicus.'

How many talents of gold were there in the statue?

2. The Mule and the Donkey ☆

According to legend, Euclid was the author of this puzzle. 'A mule and a donkey were carrying a load of sacks. The donkey groaned, so the mule said to him: "Why are you complaining? If you gave me one sack, I would have twice as many as you; and if I gave you one of my sacks, then we would have equal loads." '

How many sacks was each carrying?

3. The House of Pythagoras ☆☆

Polykrates the money-lender said to Pythagoras: 'Blessed Pythagoras, scion of the Muses, answer my question. How many scholars dwell in your house?'

Pythagoras replied: 'I will tell thee, Polykrates. Half of the scholars are dedicated to literature; a quarter apply themselves to the study of the wonders of nature; and one-seventh contemplate in silence. There are also three women, of whom the greatest is Theano. That is the number of scholars beneath my roof.'

How many scholars were in the house of Pythagoras?

4. The Graces and the Muses ☆

The three Graces were carrying baskets of apples, in each basket the same number of apples. They met the nine Muses, and gave them each the same number of apples, and so the nine Muses and the three Graces had each the same number.

How many apples were in each basket?

5. Demochares ☆

Demochares has lived one-fourth of his life as a boy, one-fifth as a youth, one-third as a man, and has spent thirteen years in his dotage. How old is Demochares?

SOME OLD ARAB AND HINDU PUZZLES

Other ancient civilizations, too, produced their share of mathematics and mathematical puzzles. The following two puzzles, one from the Arabic, the other from the Hindu tradition, both existed for centuries before they were ever written down.

6. The Hungry Hunter ☆☆

A hungry hunter chanced to meet two shepherds, one of whom had three small loaves, and the other five small loaves, all the loaves being of equal size. When the hunter asked them for food, they decided to divide the loaves equally among the three of them. The hunter thanked the shepherds and gave them eight piastres. How should the shepherds divide the money?

7. The Dish of Potatoes ☆☆

Three travellers stopped at a tavern and ordered a dish of potatoes for supper. When the landlord brought in the potatoes, the men were all asleep. The first of the travellers to awake ate a third of the potatoes and went back to sleep without disturbing his companions. The second traveller awoke, ate a third of the remaining potatoes and went back to sleep. A little later the third traveller did the same. When they were all three sleeping again, the landlord came in to clear the table and found eight potatoes left.

How many potatoes had the landlord provided initially?

SOME OLD FRENCH PUZZLES

The following five puzzles come from two French collections of mathematical problems, written by Chuquet in 1484 and by Clavius in 1608.

8. A Length of Cloth ☆

Out of a length of cloth one-third is black, one-quarter is bleached, and the remaining 8 yards are red. How long is the length of cloth?

9. A Man and His Money ☆

A man spends one-third of his money, and loses two-thirds of the remainder at dice, leaving 12 ducats in his pocket. How much money did he have originally?

10. The Value of a Cloak ☆

As wages for a year's work, a servant is promised 100 ducats and a cloak. The servant, however, leaves after only seven months, and receives the cloak and 20 ducats as his due.

How much is the cloak worth?

11. The Merchant ☆☆

A merchant visits three markets. At the first he doubles his money and spends 30 ducats. At the second he trebles his money and spends 54 ducats. At the third he increases his money fourfold and spends 72 ducats. If he has 48 ducats left, how much did he have to start with?

12. Customs Duties ☆☆

Two wine merchants arrive at the gates of Paris. One has 64 and the other 20 barrels of wine. Since they have not enough money to pay the customs duties, the first pays 40 francs and 5 barrels of wine, and the second pays 2 barrels of wine but receives 40 francs in change.

What is the value of each barrel of wine, and what is the duty payable on it?

PUZZLES OF LEWIS CARROLL

Lewis Carroll, the creator of *Alice In Wonderland*, was also Charles Lutwidge Dodgson, mathematician and logician. His puzzles bring together the strands of fantasy and logic, as is demonstrated by the following eleven puzzles.

13. A Stick I Found ☆

A stick I found that weighed two pound:
I sawed it up one day
In pieces eight of equal weight!
How much did each piece weigh?

(Everybody says 'a quarter of a pound', which is wrong.)

14. The Governor of Kgovjni ☆☆

The Governor of Kgovjni wants to give a very small dinner party, and invites his father's brother-in-law, his brother's father-in-law, his father-in-law's brother, and his brother-in-law's father. Find the number of guests.

15. Up Hill and Down Hill ☆☆

Two travellers spend from 3 o'clock till 9 in walking along a level road, up a hill, and home again: their pace on the level being 4 miles an hour, up hill 3, and down hill 6. Find the distance walked: also (within half an hour) the time of reaching the top of the hill.

16. A Circular Railway ☆☆☆

(a) Two travellers, starting at the same time, went opposite ways round a circular railway. Trains start each way every 15 minutes, the easterly ones going round in 3 hours, the westerly in 2. How many trains did each meet on the way, not counting trains met at the terminus itself?

(b) They went round as before, each traveller counting as 'one' the train containing the other traveller. How many did each meet?

17. Five Sacks ☆☆

There are 5 sacks, of which Nos. 1 and 2 weigh a total of 12 lbs; Nos. 2 and 3, 13½ lbs; Nos. 3 and 4, 11½ lbs; Nos. 4 and 5, 8 lbs; Nos. 1, 3 and 5, 16 lbs.

Find the weight of each sack.

18. Scarves ☆☆

L makes 5 scarves, while M makes 2: Z makes 4 while L makes 3. Five scarves of Z's weigh one of L's; 5 of M's weigh 3 of Z's. One of M's is as warm as 4 of Z's; and one of L's as warm as 3 of M's.

Which is best, giving equal weight in the result to rapidity of work, lightness and warmth?

19. A Spiral Walk ☆☆☆

An oblong garden, half a yard longer than wide, consists entirely of a gravel-walk, spirally arranged, a yard wide and 3,630 yards long. Find the dimensions of the garden.

20. Casualties ☆☆

If 70 per cent have lost an eye, 75 per cent an ear, 80 per cent an arm, 85 per cent a leg, what percentage, at least, must have lost all four?

21. Three Sons ☆☆

A man has three sons. At first, two of the ages are together equal to the third. A few years afterwards, two of them are together double the third. When the number of years since the first occasion is two-thirds of the sum of the ages on that occasion, one age is 21.

What are the other two ages?

22. The Monkey and the Pulley ☆☆

A weightless and perfectly flexible rope is hung over a weightless, frictionless pulley attached to the roof of a building. At one end is a weight which exactly counterbalances a monkey at the other end.

If the monkey begins to climb, what will happen to the weight – will it remain stationary, will it rise or will it fall?

23. The Captive Queen ☆☆☆

A captive queen and her son and daughter were shut up in the top room of a very high tower. Outside their window was a pulley with a rope around it, and a basket fastened to each end of the rope of equal weight. They managed to escape with the help of this and a weight they found in the room, quite safely. It would have been dangerous for any of them to come down if they weighed 15 lbs more than the contents of the other basket, for they would do so too quick, and they also managed not to weigh less either.

The one basket coming down would naturally of course draw the other up.

The queen weighed 195 lbs, daughter 105, son 90, and the weight 75 lbs.

How did they all escape safely?

SAM LOYD

Sam Loyd (1841–1911) was America's (and possibly the world's) greatest creator of puzzles. He produced his first chess problem at the age of fourteen, and within a few years was acknowledged as the best in this field. For more than fifty years his puzzles appeared in countless newspapers and magazines. He also pioneered the use of puzzles as novelty advertising giveaways, demonstrating his unique blend of creativity and flair for publicity.

None of Loyd's puzzles appeared in book form during his lifetime. It was only after his death that his son, Sam Loyd Junior, collected his father's work to form the *Cyclopaedia of Puzzles*, which was published in 1914. The following eleven puzzles come from that mammoth opus.

24. The Stenographer's Salary ☆☆

Here is a problem from the ordinary affairs of life which is as interesting as it is puzzling to all who tackle it. The 'Boss' was feeling pretty good the other day, so he said to his stenographer:

'Now, Mary, in view of the fact that you never indulge in useless vacations, I have determined to raise your salary $100 every year. Beginning from today, for the ensuing year you will be paid weekly at the rate of $600 a year; next year at the rate of $700, the next at $800, and so on, always increasing $100 per year.'

'On account of my weak heart,' replied the grateful young woman, 'I suggest that it would be safer to make the change less abrupt. Start the salary from today on the basis of $600 a year, as suggested, but at the end of six months raise the yearly salary $25, and continue to give me a $25 yearly raise every six months, so long as my services are satisfactory.'

The boss smiled benignly upon his faithful employee as he accepted the amendment, but a twinkle in his eye set some of the boys to figuring whether or not the boss made a wise move by accepting her proposition. Can you tell?

25. Carnival Dice Game ☆☆

The following dice game is very popular at fairs and carnivals, but since two persons seldom agree on the chances of a player winning, I offer it as an elementary problem in the theory of probability.

On the counter are six squares marked 1, 2, 3, 4, 5, 6. Players are invited to place as much money as they wish on any one square. Three dice are then thrown. If your number appears on one die only, you get your money back plus the same amount. If two dice show your number, you get your money back plus twice the amount you placed on the square. If your number appears on all three dice, you get your money back plus three times the amount. Of course if the number is not on any of the dice, the operator gets your money.

A player might reason: the chance of my number showing on one die is 1/6, but since there are three dice, the chances must be 3/6 or 1/2, therefore the game is a fair one. Of course this is the way the operator of the game wants everyone to reason, for it is quite fallacious.

Is the game favorable to the operator or the player, and in either case, just how favorable is it?

26. Texas Drovers ☆☆

Three Texas drovers met on the highway and proceeded to dicker as follows.

Says Hank to Jim: 'I'll give you six pigs for a hoss; then you'll have twice as many critters in your drove as I will have in mine.'

Says Duke to Hank: 'I'll give you fourteen sheep for a hoss; then you'll have three times as many critters as I.'

Says Jim to Duke: 'I'll give you four cows for a hoss; then you'll have six times as many critters as I.'

From these interesting facts can you tell just how many animals were in each of the three droves?

27. Jack Sprat ☆☆☆

According to Mother Goose, Jack Sprat could eat no fat and his wife could eat no lean.

Together they could eat a barrel of fat pork in sixty days, whereas it would take Jack thirty weeks to perform this feat alone.

Together they could consume a barrel of lean pork in eight weeks, although his wife alone could not dispose of it in less than forty weeks.

Assuming that Jack would always eat lean pork whenever it was available and this his wife would do the same with fat, how long would it take both of them to eat a barrel of mixed pork, half fat and half lean?

28. The Leaning Tower of Pisa ☆☆☆

If an elastic ball is dropped from the Leaning Tower of Pisa at a height of 179 feet from the ground, and on each rebound the ball rises exactly one tenth of its previous height, what distance will it travel before it comes to rest?

29. The Shy Storekeeper ☆

'Give me three skeins of silk and four of worsted,' said little Susie as she placed 31 cents, the correct amount, on the counter.

As the storekeeper went to get the goods, Susie called out, 'I've changed my mind. I'll take four skeins of silk and three of worsted.'

'You're just one cent shy,' remarked the storekeeper as he placed the goods on the counter.

'Oh no,' said Susie as she picked up the goods and skipped out of the store. '*You* are just one cent shy!'

What was the price of silk and worsted?

30. Carousel ☆

While enjoying a giddy ride on the carousel, Sammy propounded this problem: 'One-third of the number of kids riding ahead of me, added to three-quarters of those riding behind me gives the correct number of children on this merry-go-round.'

How many children were riding the carousel?

31. Mrs Wiggs' Cabbages ☆☆

Mrs Wiggs explained to Lovey Mary that she has a larger square cabbage patch now than she had last year and will therefore raise 211 more cabbages. How many of our mathematicians and agriculturalists can guess the number of cabbages Mrs Wiggs will raise this year?

32. How Wide Should the Strip Be? ☆☆

Farmers and laborers who have no great skills in mathematics will often solve, in a practical way, some very difficult problems. I call the attention of our puzzlists to the clever way in which a couple of farmers adjusted their affairs.

A Texas ranchman, who owned more land than he could conveniently farm, leased half of a certain field to a neighbor. This field was 2,000 yards long by 1,000 yards wide, but because of certain bad streaks which ran through the land it was decided that a fairer division would be obtained by cutting a band around the field than by dividing it in half.

I presume our puzzlists will find no great difficulty in determining the width of a border strip, to be cut all round that field, that will contain exactly half of the total crop. There is a simple rule which will apply to any rectangular field.

33. Quick Deal ☆☆

While the suburban boom is on, we will take occasion to tell how a real-estate speculator stopped off at a wrong station and, having a couple of hours to wait for the next train, made a quick and profitable deal. He bought a piece of land for $243 which he divided into equal lots, then sold them at $18 per lot, cleaning up the whole transaction before his train arrived. His profit on the deal was exactly equal to what six of the lots originally cost him.

How many lots were in that piece of land?

34. Sam Loyd's Boxes ☆☆☆☆☆

(Equipment: Sets for several of these games have been produced commercially, but you can make your own cardboard versions very simply.)

1. The 14–15 Box was probably Sam Loyd's most famous – and frustrating – creation:

   As you can see, fifteen blocks are arranged in a square box in regular order, but with the 14 and 15 reversed. The game consists of moving the blocks about, one at a time, to bring them back to the present position in every respect except that the error in the 14 and 15 is corrected.

2. Once you have solved the original problem, have a go at this one. Start again with the blocks as in the original puzzle and move them so as to get the numbers in regular order, but with the vacant square at the upper left-hand corner instead of the lower right-hand corner.

3. This time, start with the blocks as before, but turn the box a quarter way round and move the blocks until they are as shown below.

	4	8	12
3	7	11	15
2	6	10	14
1	5	9	13

4. Finally, start as before, then shift the pieces until they form a magic square, the numbers adding to thirty along all vertical and horizontal rows, and the two diagonals.

5. In this box we have nine letters rather than fifteen numbers and the game begins with the box looking like this:

G	E	F
H	C	B
D		A

Now the aim of the game is this: moving one block at a time, restore the letters to their correct alphabetical order:

A B C

D E F

G H

H. E. DUDENEY

Henry Ernest Dudeney (1847–1930) was England's greatest creator of puzzles, and the only contender with Sam Loyd for the world title. Dudeney and Loyd corresponded frequently during their lifetimes and were friendly rivals

35. Mistaking the Hands ☆☆☆

'Between two and three o'clock yesterday,' said Colonel Crackham, 'I looked at the clock and mistook the minute hand for the hour hand, and consequently the time appeared to be fifty-five minutes earlier than it actually was.' What was the correct time?

36. The Leap-year Ladies ☆☆☆

Last leap-year ladies lost no time in exercising their privilege of making proposals of marriage. If the figures that reached me from an occult source are correct, the following represents the state of affairs in this country.

A number of women proposed once each, of whom one-eighth were widows. In consequence, a number of men were to be married, of whom one-eleventh were widowers. Of the proposals made to widowers, one-fifth were declined. All the widows were accepted. Thirty-five forty-fourths of the widows married bachelors. One thousand two hundred and twenty-one spinsters were declined by bachelors. The number of spinsters accepted by bachelors was seven times the number of widows accepted by bachelors. Those are all the particulars that I was able to obtain. Now, how many women proposed?

37. Exploring the Desert ☆☆☆

Nine travellers, each possessing a car, meet on the eastern edge of a desert. They wish to explore the interior, always going due west. Each car can travel forty miles on the contents of the engine tank, which holds a gallon of fuel, and each can carry nine extra gallon cans of fuel and no more. Unopened cans can alone be transferred from car to car. What is the greatest distance at which they can enter the desert without making any depots of fuel for the return journey?

38. The Labourer's Puzzle ☆☆

Professor Rackbrane, during one of his rambles, chanced to come upon a man digging a deep hole.

'Good morning,' he said. 'How deep is that hole?'

'Guess,' replied the labourer. 'My height is exactly five feet ten inches.'

'How much deeper are you going?' said the professor.

'I am going twice as deep,' was the answer, 'and then my head will be twice as far below ground as it is now above ground.'

Rackbrane now asks you if you could tell how deep that hole would be when finished?

39. Mr Gubbins in a Fog ☆☆

Mr Gubbins, a diligent man of business, was much inconvenienced by a London fog. The electric light happened to be out of order and he had to manage as best he could with two candles. His clerk assured him that though both were of the same length one candle would burn for four hours and the other for five hours. After he had been working some time he put the candles out as the fog had lifted, and he then noticed that what remained of one candle was exactly four times the length of what was left of the other.

When he got home that night Mr Gubbins, who liked a good puzzle, said to himself, 'Of course it is possible to work out just how long those two candles were burning today. I'll have a shot at it.' But he soon found himself in a worse fog than the atmospheric one. Could you have assisted him in his dilemma? How long were the candles burning?

40. The Railway Station Clock ☆☆☆

A clock hangs on the wall of a railway station, 71 ft 9 in long and 10 ft 4 in high. Those are the dimensions of the wall, not of the clock! While waiting for a train we noticed that the hands of the clock were pointing in opposite directions, and were parallel to one of the diagonals of the wall. What was the exact time?

41. The Spot on the Table ☆☆☆

A boy, recently home from school, wished to give his father an exhibition of his precocity. He pushed a large circular table into the corner of the room, so that it touched both walls, and he then pointed to a spot of ink on the extreme edge.

'Here is a little puzzle for you, pater,' said the youth. 'That spot is exactly eight inches from one wall and nine inches from the other. Can you tell me the diameter of the table without measuring it?'

The boy was overheard to tell a friend, 'It fairly beat the guv'nor'; but his father is known to have remarked to a City acquaintance that he solved the thing in his head in a minute. I often wonder which spoke the truth.

42. The Fifteen Orchards ☆☆☆

In the county of Devon, where the cider comes from, fifteen of the inhabitants of a village are imbued with an excellent spirit of friendly rivalry, and a few years ago they decided to settle by actual experiment a little difference of opinion as to the cultivation of apple trees. Some said they wanted plenty of light and air, while others stoutly maintained that they ought to be planted pretty closely, in order that they might get shade and protection from cold winds. So they agreed to plant a lot of young trees, a different number in each orchard, in order to compare results.

One man had a single tree in his field, another had two trees, another had three trees, another had four trees, another five, and so on, the last man having as many as fifteen trees in his little orchard. Last year a very curious result was found to have come about. Each of the fifteen individuals discovered that every tree in his own orchard bore exactly the same number of apples. But, what was stranger still, on comparing notes they found that the total gathered in every allotment was almost the same. In fact, if the man with eleven trees had given one apple to the man who had seven trees, and the man with fourteen trees had given three each to the men with nine and thirteen trees, they would all have had exactly the same.

Now, the puzzle is to discover how many apples each would have had (the same in every case) if that little distribution had been carried out. It is quite easy if you set to work in the right way.

2. CHILD'S PLAY

43. ☆

If a brick weighs 9 lb and half a brick, what is the weight of a brick and a half?

44. ☆

Rearrange the following eleven letters to make just one word:
USTOODWERNJ

45. ☆

The windows on all four sides of my house face south. How is that possible?

46. ☆

Can you punctuate the following sentence in order to make sense of it?
SMITH WHERE JONES HAD HAD HAD HAD HAD HAD HAD HAD HAD HAD HAD THE EXAMINERS' APPROVAL

47. ☆

A man, looking at a portrait, said:
'Brothers and sisters have I none,
But this man's father is my father's son.'
What is the relationship between the speaker and the subject of the portrait?

48. ☆

When the day after tomorrow is yesterday, today will be as far from Sunday as today was from Sunday when the day before yesterday was tomorrow. What day is it?

49. ☆

Can you translate this:
YYURYYUBICURYY4ME

50. ☆

A frog at the bottom of a well climbs up 3 ft every day, but slips back 2 ft during the night. How long will he take to reach the top, if the well is 20 ft deep?

51. ☆

If it takes five men six hours to dig seven holes, how long does it take one man to dig half a hole?

52. ☆

Take the letters ERGRO. Put three letters in front of it, and put the same three letters after it, to form a common English word.

53. ☆

What is the next letter in this series?

O T T F F S S . . .

54. ☆

Arrange the numbers from 1 to 9 in a square grid, as shown, so that each row and each column and the two main diagonals add up to 15.

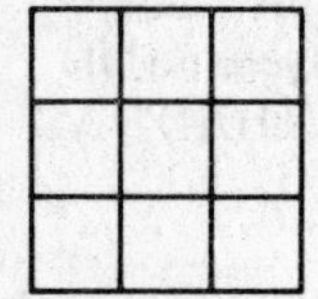

55. ☆

Now arrange the numbers from 1 to 16 in a four by four square, so that each row and each column and the two main diagonals add up to 34.

56. ☆

Ken Tucky is 40. Louise Yanner is 13. How many years ago was Ken four times as old as Louise?

57. ☆

A combined collection of dogs and chickens has 43 heads and 120 feet. Of the collection, how many are dogs and how many are chickens?

58. ☆

If a third of six were three, what would the half of twenty be?

59. ☆

A farmer, when asked what number of animals he had, replied: 'They're all horses but two, all sheep but two, and all pigs but two.'
How many animals had he?

60. ☆

Three-fourths of a cross, and a circle complete,
Two semi-circles at a perpendicular meet;
Next add a triangle which stands on two feet,
Two semi-circles and a circle complete.

What is being described in this verse?

61. ☆

Seven ears of corn are in a hollow stump. How long will it take a squirrel to carry them all out, if he carries out three ears a day?

62. ☆

A son asked his father how old he was, and received the reply: 'Your age is now one-quarter of mine, but five years ago it was only one-fifth.'
How old is the father?

63. ☆

If it takes three minutes to boil one egg, how long will it take to boil two eggs?

64. ☆

What are the next two letters in this series:
A E F H I K L M . . . . . .

65. ☆

What common chemical compound is represented by the following letters?
H I J K L M N O

66. ☆

How many times does the letter S occur in the name of the longest river in the world?

67. ☆

What number gives the same result when it is added to 1½ as when it is multiplied by 1½?

68. ☆

How many times can you subtract the number 2 from the number 25?

69. ☆

What is the closest relation that your mother's brother's brother-in-law could be to you?

70. ☆

A man drives his car a certain distance at 60 mph and arrives at his destination one hour earlier than if he had driven at 50 mph. What was the distance?

71. ☆

A soldier is on parade and facing due west. The sergeant-major shouts at him:

'Right turn!'
'About turn!'
'Left turn!'

In which direction is the soldier now facing?

72. ☆

Mary had a tiny lamb,
Its wool was pallid as snow,
And any spot that Mary did walk
This lamb would always go.
This lamb did follow Mary to school,
Although against a law;
How girls and boys did laugh and play,
That lamb in class all saw.

In what way is this odd? Think!

73. ☆☆

Two cyclists, twenty miles apart, start at the same instant and ride towards each other along a straight road at a speed of ten miles per hour. At the same instant a fly on the forehead of one of the cyclists starts to fly at fifteen miles per hour directly towards the other cyclist, lands on his forehead, and then flies back and forth over the continuously decreasing distance between the two cyclists until it is finally squashed as the foreheads of the two cyclists bump together.

How far has the fly flown, when all his journeys are added together?

74. ☆

There are three ordinary playing cards in a row. A diamond is on the left of a spade (though not necessarily next to it); an Eight is on the right of a King; a Ten is on the left of a heart; a heart is on the left of a spade.

What are the three cards?

75. ☆

If on January 1st you go to sleep at eight o'clock at night, having set your alarm clock to wake you at 9 a.m., and you sleep soundly until woken by the alarm, how many hours sleep will you get?

76. ☆

A tramp makes his own cigarettes from cigarette ends he collects. Seven ends will make a cigarette. He has collected 49 ends. How many cigarettes can he make from these?

77. ☆☆

Three missionaries and three cannibals have to cross a river. They have a boat, but it will only hold two people at a time. Cannibals must never be allowed to outnumber missionaries on either bank.

How do they get across the river?

78. ☆

Bill could never tell the truth. Tom could never tell a lie. One of them said, 'The other one said he is Bill.' Which one said that?

79. ☆

In a drawer there are five identical pairs of black socks and five identical pairs of brown socks, all jumbled together. If it was completely dark, how many socks would you need to take from the drawer to be sure of getting a matching pair?

80. ☆

There are five packets of sweets on a table. Four of the packets contain a total of 84 sweets. The fifth packet contains 4 sweets less than the average of the five packets.

How many sweets are there in the fifth packet?

81. ☆

Find a three-letter word which can go in front of any of the following words to form a new word.

TON PET ROT

82. ☆

Rearrange each of these words to form a girl's name:

ARMY	DINE	YACHT
TEAK	SAIL	IDEAL
YAM	HURT	AIRMAN

83. ☆

Rearrange each of these words to form a boy's name:

RICE	LINE	LYRIC
EEL	SAILS	NAILED
ANTS	EVENTS	WANDER

84. ☆

The following words have had all their vowels removed. Can you work out what the words should be?

PL	A game played on horseback
PL	A game played on a table
NN	A vegetable
B	A musical instrument
KLL	A musical instrument
CLL	A musical instrument
CN	A type of boat
S	Relaxation

3. NUMBER PUZZLES

85. Pocket Money ☆☆

A father divided a certain number of pounds among his four children. To the first he gave a part, to the second one-third of what was left after the first's share, to the third he gave five-eighths of what was left, and to the fourth the balance, which equalled two-fifths of the first child's share. No child received as much as £20.

How much money did the father distribute, and how much did each child receive?

86. Boat Race ☆☆

In a time race, one boat is rowed over the course at an average of 4 yards per second, another moves over the first half of the course at the rate of 3½ yards per second, and over the last half at 4½ yards per second, reaching the winning post 15 seconds later than the first. Find the time taken by each.

87. 1105 ☆☆

The sum of the squares of two consecutive numbers is 1105. What are the two numbers?

88. Division ☆☆

Divide 100 into two parts, so that a quarter of one exceeds one-third of the other by 11.

89. Find Three Numbers ☆☆

Find three numbers such that the first with half of the other two, the second with one-third of the other two, and the third with one-fourth of the other two, shall each be equal to 34.

90. Strange Squares ☆☆☆

The square of 45 is 2025. If we split this in two, we get 20 and 25. 20 plus 25 is 45 – the number we started with.

Find two other numbers with four-digit squares that exhibit the same peculiarity.

91. December and May ☆☆

An old man married a young woman. Their combined ages amounted to 100. The man's age multiplied by 4 and divided by 9 gives the woman's age.

What were their respective ages?

92. A Walking Expedition ☆☆

Jim and Bill set out on a walking expedition at the same time – Jim from X to Y, and Bill from Y to X.

On reaching Y, Jim immediately sets off back to X. Now, Jim reaches Y four hours after meeting Bill, but he reaches X three hours after their second meeting. In what time did each perform the journey?

93. Banker's Order ☆☆

A man went into a bank with exactly $1000, all in $1 bills. He gave the money to a cashier and said, 'Put this money into ten bags in such a way that if I call and ask for any number of dollars up to $1000, you can give me the exact amount by handing over one or more bags, without having to open any of the bags.'

How was the cashier to comply with these instructions?

94. Paintings by Numbers ☆☆

An art dealer has a certain number of paintings for sale. He sells half the paintings and one more to one customer, half the remainder and one more to a second customer, half the remainder and one more to a third customer, half the remainder and one more to a fourth customer – by which time he has sold all the paintings. How many had he?

95. Groceries ☆☆

My five grocery items each weighed a whole number of ounces, and the total weight was less than two pounds. With a balance scale, I found the following three inequalities, and in each case, the addition of the banana to the lighter side turned it into the heavier side.

(a) tomato and apple together failed to balance the orange.
(b) apple and orange together failed to balance the tomato.
(c) tomato and orange together failed to balance the potato.

I also found the following instances of equality:

(d) apple balanced the banana and tomato together.
(e) tomato and potato together balanced the other three items.

What was the weight of each item?

96. State of the Poll ☆☆☆

In a constituency in which each elector may vote for two candidates, half of the constituency vote for A, but divide their votes among B, C, D and E in the proportion of 4,3,2,1. Half the remainder vote for B, and divide their votes between C, D, E in proportion 3, 1, 1. Two-thirds of the remainder vote for D and E, and 540 do not vote at all.

Find the state of the poll, and the number of electors.

97. A Certain Number ☆☆☆

There is a certain number consisting of three digits which is equal to 36 times the sum of its digits. 7 times the leftmost digit plus 9 is equal to 5 times the sum of the remaining digits. 8 times the second digit minus 9 is equal to the sum of the first and third.

What is the number?

98. Rope ☆☆

A man ordered a length of rope by telephone, but when he went to collect it he found that the assistant had miswritten the order by interchanging feet and inches. As a result, the rope was only 30 per cent of the length that the man wanted.

What length of rope did he order?

99. A Powerful Number ☆☆☆☆

There is a certain number whose third and fourth powers, taken together, use all the digits from 0 to 9, each once and once only. What is the number?

100. Pairs of Weights ☆☆☆

With a pair of each of four different weights, any whole number of pounds from 1 pound up to 170 pounds can be weighed. What are the weights?

101. Four Dresses ☆☆☆

A woman has four dresses for which she paid a total of £80. The first dress cost as much as the second plus half of the third. The second cost as much as the fourth minus the cost of the third. The third cost one-third of the first. The fourth cost as much as the second and third together.

What was the price of each dress?

102. What is the Number? ☆☆

There is a certain number such that the square of its half is equal to the number with its digits reversed. What is the number?

103. Gamblers ☆☆

Three gamblers – Abe, Bert and Cal – sit down to play cards. As a result of the first game, Abe lost to each of Bert and Cal as much money as they started the game with. In the second game Bert lost similarly to each of Abe and Cal. And in the third game – you guessed it – Cal lost similarly to each of Abe and Bert. Each man then had $40.

How much money had each man when they started to play?

104. Escalation ☆☆☆

On one of the escalators on the London Underground, I find that if I walk down 26 steps I need 30 seconds to get to the bottom; but if I make 34 steps then I need only 18 seconds to reach the bottom.

If the time is measured from the instant that the top step begins to descend to the time I step off the last step at the bottom on to the level platform, what is the height of the stairway in steps?

105. Fours and Fives ☆☆☆

Find the smallest number that, when divided by 45, 454, 4545 and 45454, leaves the remainders 4, 45, 454 and 4545 respectively.

106. Going Home ☆☆☆

My friend Alex, who lives in the country, caught an earlier train home than usual yesterday. His wife normally drives to the station to meet him. But yesterday he set out on foot from the station to meet his wife part way. He reached home 12 minutes earlier than he would have done had he waited at the station for his wife. The car travels at a uniform speed which is five times Alex's speed on foot. Alex reached home at exactly six o'clock. At what time would he have reached home if his wife, forewarned of his change of plan, had met him at the station?

107. Life Spans ☆☆☆

The life span of a whale is 4 times that of a stork, which lives 85 years longer than a guinea pig, which lives 6 years less than an ox, which lives 9 years less than a horse, which lives 12 years longer than a chicken, which lives 282 years less than an elephant, which lives 283 years longer than a dog, which lives 2 years longer than a cat, which lives 135 years less than a carp, which lives twice as long as a camel, which lives 1,066 years short of the total of all the creatures' life spans.

What is the life span of each creature?

108. Circuits ☆☆☆

David and Jonathan start together from the same point on a circular path and walk round, each at his own pace, until both arrive together at the starting point.

If David performs the circuit in 3 minutes 44 seconds and Jonathan in 6 minutes 4 seconds, how many times does each go round the path?

109. 365 ☆☆☆

If we multiply 64253 by 365 we get the product 23452345, where the first four digits are repeated. What is the largest number that can be multiplied by 365 to produce a similar product of eight digits with the first four digits repeated in the same order? There is no objection to a digit being repeated within the first four.

110. Coaches ☆☆

A coach operator, not having room in his garage for eight of his coaches, increased the size of his garage by 50%, and then had room for eight more coaches than the number he owned.

How many coaches did he own?

111. Loading a Cart ☆☆

If a man can load a cart in ten minutes, and a friend can load it in five minutes, how long will it take them both to load it, working together?

112. Measuring Sticks ☆☆

A measuring stick, 13 inches long, needs only four marks on it so that it can measure any whole number of inches from 1 to 13. The marks are at the 1, 2, 6 and 10 inch positions. From 0 to 1 measures 1 inch, from 0 to 2 measures 2 inches, from 10 to 13 measures 3 inches, from 2 to 6 measures 4 inches and so on.

On a measuring stick 36 inches long, what is the smallest number of marks needed so that it can measure any whole number of inches from 1 to 36? And where should the marks be placed?

113. Burning the Candle at Both Ends ☆☆

One-third of an hour after a candle was lighted, the other end was also lighted. It took a further one-third of an hour for the candle to burn out. If the candle was lighted at both ends at the start, and one end was extinguished when only the middle one-third of the candle remained, how long in all would it take to burn the candle out?

114. Ferry-Boats ☆☆☆

Two ferry-boats start at the same time from opposite sides of a river, travelling across the water on routes at right angles to the shore. Each boat travels at a constant speed, though their two speeds are different. They pass at a point 720 yards from the nearest shore. Both boats remain at their slips for ten minutes before starting back. On the return trips, they meet 400 yards from the other shore.

How wide is the river?

115. Find Two Numbers ☆☆☆

Find two numbers such that the square of the first plus the second equals 11, and the square of the second plus the first equals 7.

116. Wine and Water ☆☆☆

There are two barrels, one of which holds thirty gallons more than the other. The larger barrel is filled with wine and the smaller one with water.

Ten gallons are drawn from each barrel. That from the first barrel is poured into the second, and vice versa. Each barrel is shaken thoroughly to mix the contents. Again ten gallons are taken from each barrel, and that from each is poured into the other.

If the larger barrel now contains thirteen gallons of water, what is the total capacity of the smaller barrel?

117. Palindromic Pairs ☆☆☆

Did you know that certain pairs of two-digit numbers have the same product when both numbers are reversed? For example:

$12 \times 42 = 24 \times 21$
$12 \times 63 = 36 \times 21$
$12 \times 84 = 48 \times 21$
$23 \times 96 = 69 \times 32$
$24 \times 63 = 36 \times 42$
$24 \times 84 = 48 \times 42$
$26 \times 93 = 39 \times 62$
$46 \times 96 = 69 \times 64$

There are six other sets of numbers of this nature. How many can you find?

118. A Way to Weigh ☆☆☆

Five children found a method of getting themselves all weighed on an automatic weighing machine with just one coin. Two of them got on the stand at the same time, and one child changed places with another until all the ten possible pairs had been weighed. The weights, in pounds, were as follows: 114, 115, 118, 119, 121, 122, 123, 125, 126 and 129. Can you work out their individual weights?

119. One to Nine ☆☆☆

A puzzle which has long been popular is to place plus and minus signs, wherever one cares to, between the digits 1, 2, 3, 4, 5, 6, 7, 8 and 9 so as to make the resulting expression equal in value to 100. The digits must remain in the original sequence. A typical solution is:

$$12 + 3 - 4 + 5 + 67 + 8 + 9 = 100$$

In this solution, six plus and minus signs were used. Can you find another solution, using the fewest possible signs?

120. Nine to One ☆☆☆

This is similar to the previous problem, the difference being that the digits have to be in the sequence 9, 8, 7, 6, 5, 4, 3, 2, 1. Here is one typical solution:

$$98 + 7 - 6 + 5 - 4 + 3 - 2 - 1 = 100$$

But the aim is to find a solution using the fewest possible plus and minus signs.

121. A Question of Age ☆☆

A man and his wife had three children – John, Ben and Mary. The difference between the parents' ages was the same as between John and Ben and between Ben and Mary. The ages of John and Ben, multiplied together, equalled the age of the father, and the ages of Ben and Mary multiplied together equalled the age of the mother. The combined ages of the family amounted to ninety years.

What was the age of each person?

122. The Bag of Nuts ☆☆

Three boys were given a bag of nuts, and they agreed to share out the nuts in proportion to their ages, which together amounted to 17½ years. The bag contained 770 nuts, and for every four nuts Joe took, Jack took three, and for every six that Joe took, Jim took seven.

How many nuts did each boy take, and what are their respective ages?

123. Strange Multiplication ☆☆☆

If I multiply 51,249,876 by 3 (thus using all the nine digits once and once only) I get 153,749, 628 (which again contains all the nine digits once).

Similarly if I multiply 16,583,742 by 9, the result is 149,253,678.

Now, take 6 as your multiplier and try to arrange the remaining eight digits so as to produce by multiplication a number containing each of the nine digits.

124. Curious Numbers ☆☆☆☆

The number 48 has this peculiarity, that if you add 1 to it, the result is a square number (49, the square of 7) and if you add 1 to its half, you also get a square number (25, the square of 5).

Can you find the next three smallest possible numbers that also have this peculiarity?

125. Find a Square ☆☆☆

What is the smallest square number that ends with the greatest possible number of identical non-zero digits?

126. Pandigital Fractions ☆☆☆

Using all the digits from 1 to 9 (each digit being used once and once only) it is possible to form a fraction equal in value to a half, thus:

$$\frac{6729}{13458}$$

Using these nine digits, see if you can form fractions equal in value to:

(a) a third

(b) a quarter
(c) a fifth
(d) a sixth
(e) a seventh
(f) an eighth
(g) a ninth

127. Four Primes ☆☆☆

A, B, C and D represent four different digits such that ADDD, AACA, BCDB and BDAC are prime numbers.

What digits do the letters represent?

128. ABCD ☆☆☆

Once again, A, B, C and D represent four different digits. These digits may be combined in different ways to give 24 different four-digit numbers. These 24 numbers include:

Four prime numbers
7 products of two odd primes
1 square of a prime
8 numbers divisible by 2, but not by 4
2 numbers divisible by 4, but not by 8
1 number divisible by 8, but not by 16
1 number divisible by 16

What are these numbers?

CRYPTARITHMETIC

In the following five puzzles, each letter represents a different digit. Your task is to discover which digit each letter represents.

129. Send More Money ☆☆

```
  SEND
  MORE +
 MONEY
```

130. Sixty ☆☆

```
     T E N
     T E N
 F O R T Y  +
 ---------
  S I X T Y
 ---------
```

131. Scrabble ☆☆

```
    L E T T E R S
  A L P H A B E T  +
  ---------------
  S C R A B B L E
  ---------------
```

132. Not Red Jam ☆☆

$\frac{NOT}{3} = ME \qquad \frac{RED}{6} = ME \qquad \frac{JAM}{9} = ME$

133. Presidential ☆☆

```
  L Y N D O N
            B  ×
  -------------
J O H N S O N
  -------------
```

134. A Long Division ☆☆☆

See if you can reconstruct this long division, given only one of the digits. There is a unique answer.

```
             * 7 * * *
         ---------------
 * * *  |  * * * * * * * *
           * * * *
           -------
             * * *
             * * *
             -------
             * * * *
               * * *
               -------
               * * * *
               * * * *
               -------
```

4. CIRCLES, SQUARES AND ANGLES

135. Cross Cut 1 ☆☆

Divide a cross, such as that shown in the diagram, into four pieces with two straight cuts, so that the pieces may be put together to form a perfect square.

136. Cross Cut 2 ☆☆

Can you divide this shape into four pieces, identical as to size and shape, so that the pieces may be put together to form a perfect square?

137. Seven Lines ☆☆☆

What is the largest number of non-overlapping triangles that can be produced by drawing seven straight lines? The diagram shows how seven lines can produce six non-overlapping triangles, but you ought to be able to find a much better solution than this.

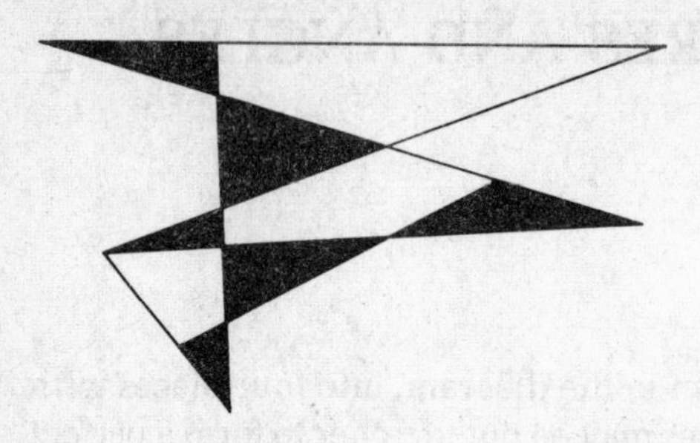

138. Folding a Triangle ☆☆☆

Given a perfectly plain square piece of paper, how would you fold it so as to form the largest possible equilateral triangle? The triangle with sides equal in length to the sides of the square, as shown in the diagram, will *not* be the largest possible. No markings or measurements may be made except by the creases themselves.

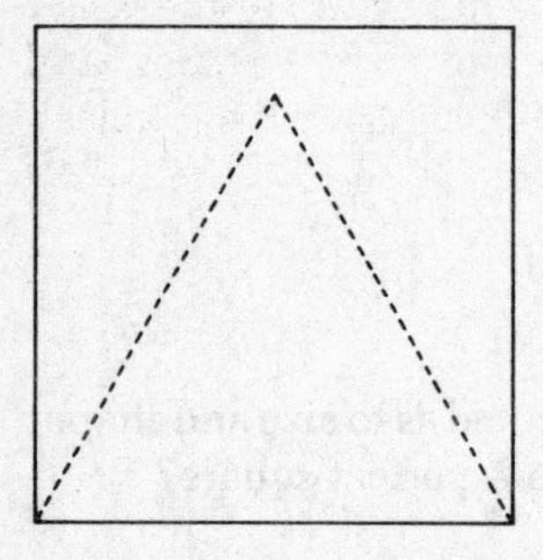

139. Folding a Hexagon ☆☆☆

You are given a perfectly plain square sheet of paper. How would you fold it so as to make creases that will form a regular hexagon, as shown in the diagram? You are not permitted use of a ruler or a pencil or any other instrument whatever.

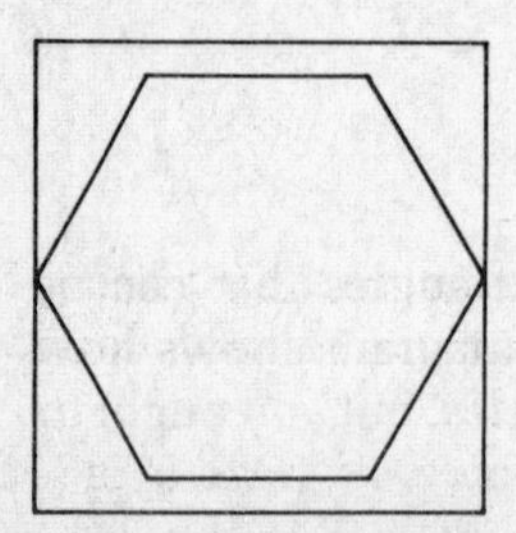

140. The Side of a Square ☆☆

How long is the side of a square whose area is equal to twice the sum of its sides?

141. A Strange Island ☆☆☆

There is an island in the form of a semi-circle. Two men start from a point on the diameter; one walks along the diameter, and the other at right angles to it. The former reaches the extremity of the diameter after walking 4 miles, and the latter the boundary of the island after walking 8 miles. Find the area of the island.

142. The Crescent Puzzle ☆☆☆☆

The crescent is formed by two circles, and C is the centre of the larger circle. The width of the crescent between B and D is 9 inches, and between E and F 5 inches. What are the diameters of the two circles?

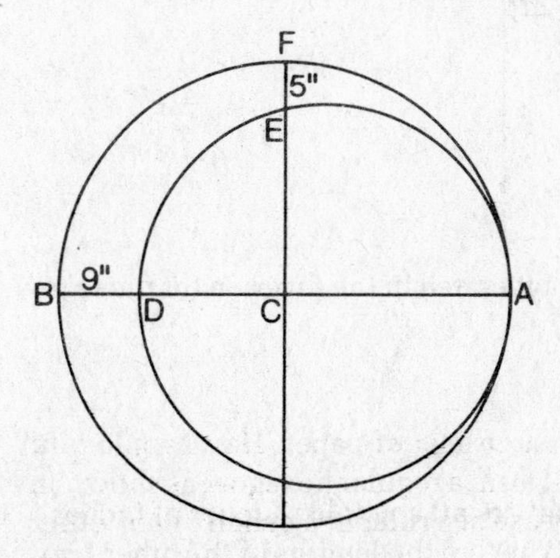

143. The Six-Sided Field ☆☆☆

A farmer owns a field in the shape of a regular hexagon, each side being 40 yards in length. He has a donkey tethered by a rope 50 yards long which is fastened to a post in one corner of the field.

How many square yards of the field may the donkey graze over?

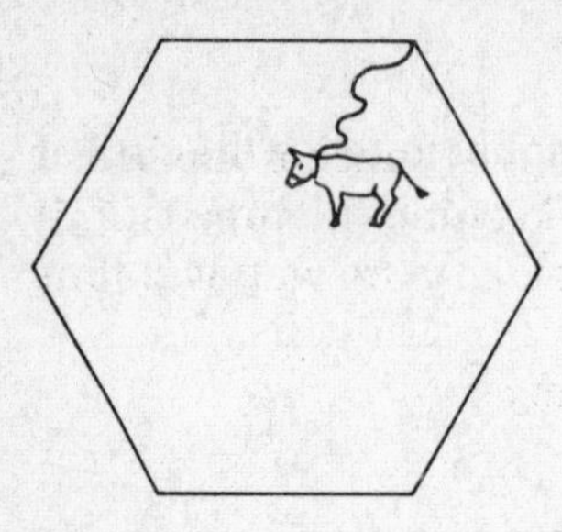

144. The Garden Path ☆☆☆☆

A man has a rectangular garden, 55 yards by 40 yards, and he makes a diagonal path, one yard wide, exactly in the manner indicated in the diagram. What is the area of the path?

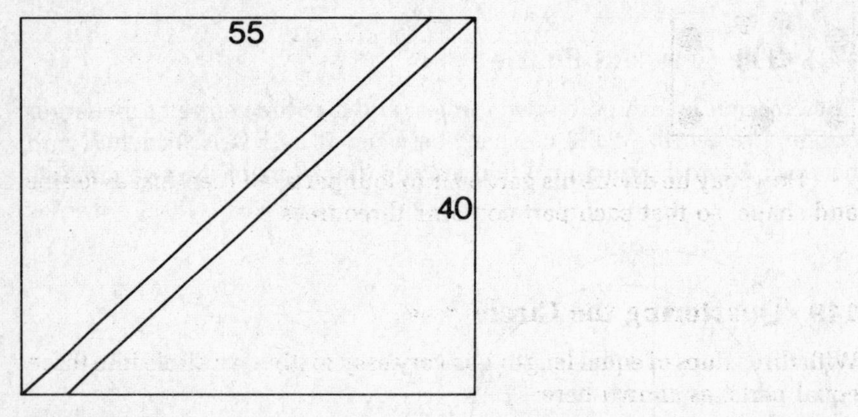

(Note that the width of the path is exaggerated in the diagram for the sake of clarity.)

145. A Triangular Question ☆☆☆

A right-angled triangle has sides that are all a whole number of inches. One of the sides is 47 inches long. What are the lengths of the other two sides?

146. The Ladder ☆☆☆

A ladder was fastened against a high wall of a building. A man unfastened it and pulled it out four yards at the bottom. It was then found that the top of the ladder had descended just one-fifth of the length of the ladder. What was the length of the ladder?

147. The Bell Rope ☆☆☆

A bell rope, passing through the ceiling above, just touches the belfry floor, and when you pull the rope to the wall, keeping the rope taut, it touches a point just three inches above the floor, and the wall was four feet from the rope when it hung at rest.

How long was the rope from floor to ceiling?

148. Dividing a Garden ☆☆

Mr Budd has a square garden, containing twelve trees, as in the illustration.

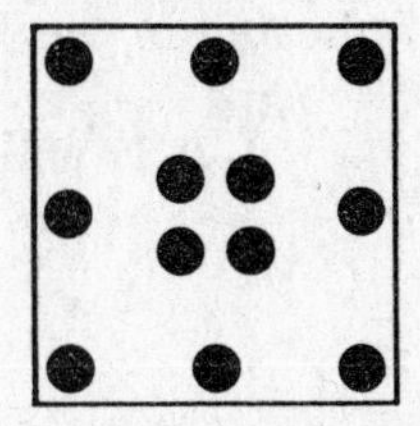

How may he divide his garden into four parts, all identical as to size and shape, so that each part contains three trees?

149. Quartering the Circle ☆☆☆

With three lines of equal length it is very easy to divide a circle into three equal parts, as shown here:

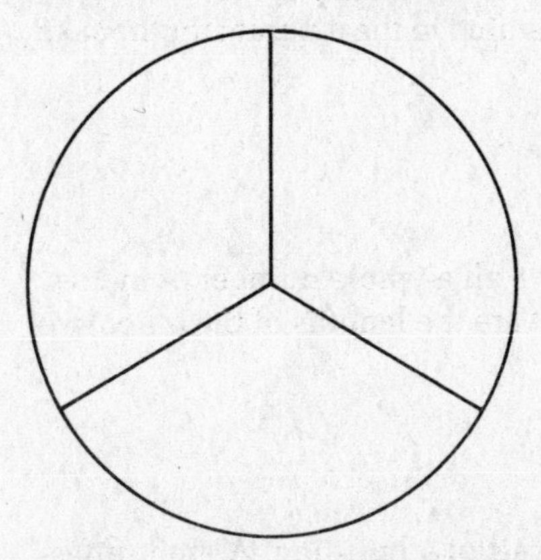

The problem, however, is to divide a circle into *four* equal parts, using three lines of equal length. The lines do not have to be straight, but they must not cross.

150. The Potato Puzzle ☆☆☆

Take a circular slice of potato, place it on the table, and see into how many pieces you can divide it with six cuts of a knife. Of course you must not readjust the pieces or pile them after a cut. What is the greatest number of pieces you can make?

The illustration shows how to make sixteen pieces. This can, of course, be easily beaten.

151. Splitting a Horseshoe ☆☆

With two straight-line cuts, can you divide a horseshoe, such as that illustrated, into six pieces?

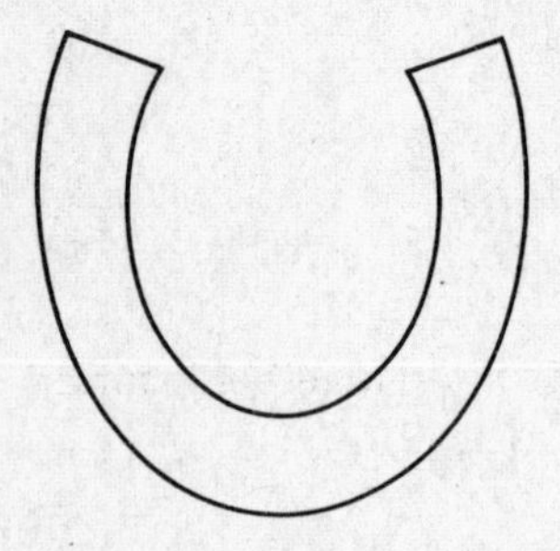

152. The Carpet-Fitter's Problem ☆☆☆

A carpet-fitter had a piece of carpet shaped like this:

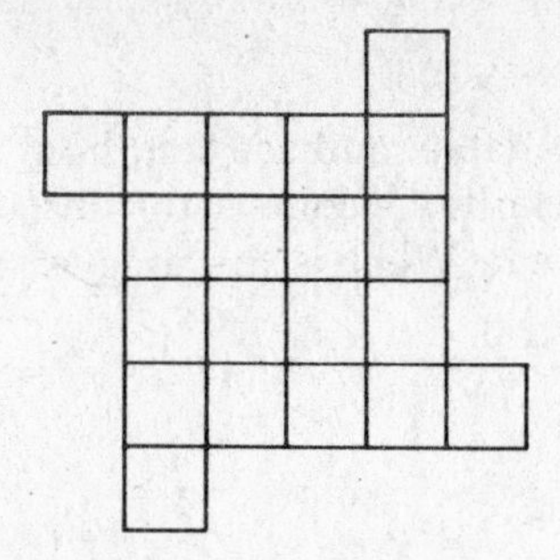

How could he cut it into four pieces, so that they could be rearranged to form a square?

153. The Joiner's Problem ☆☆☆

A joiner has a piece of wood as shown in the diagram.

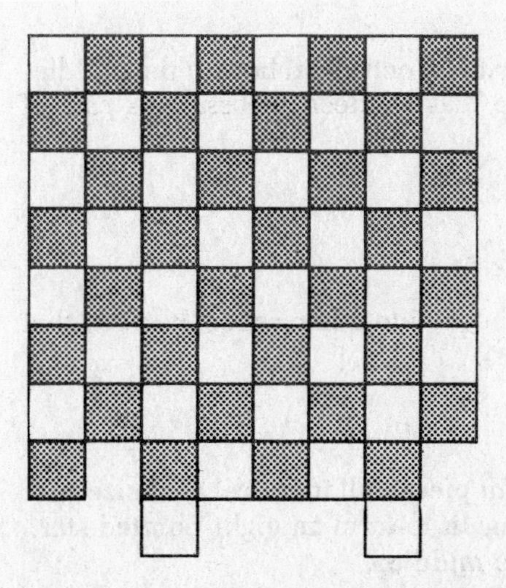

How can he cut it into only two pieces that can be fitted together to form a chessboard?

154. The Dressmaker's Problem ☆☆☆

A dressmaker has a piece of checkered cloth with four buttons attached, as illustrated here.

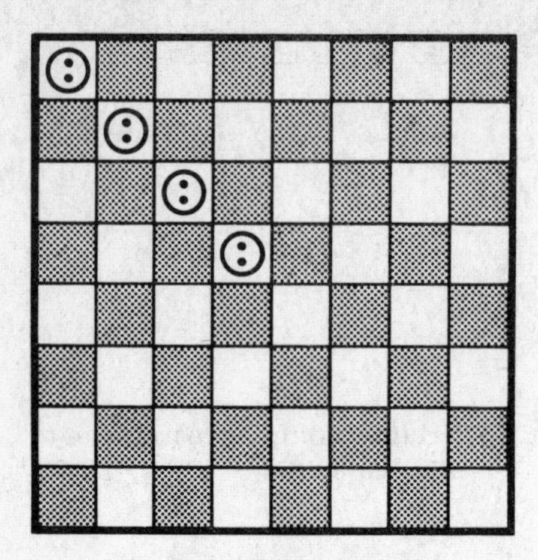

How can she cut it into four pieces, identical as to size and shape, each piece to contain one button?

155. Star-Maker ☆☆☆☆

You are given an octagonal shape with an octagonal hole in the middle.

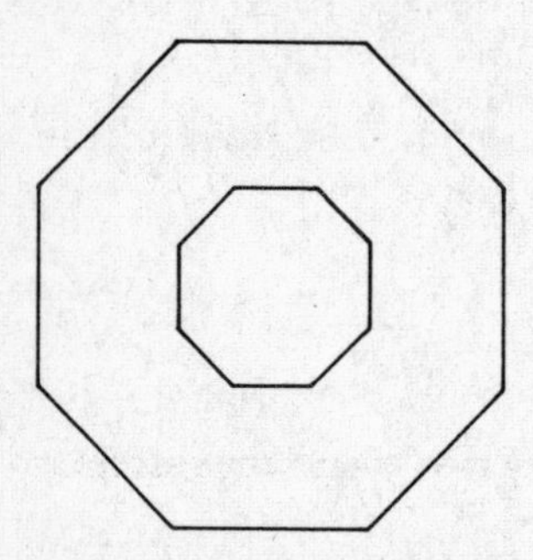

The problem is to cut it into eight pieces, all identical as to size and shape, which can be put together again to form an eight-pointed star, again with an octagonal hole in the middle.

156. Cigarette Boxes ☆☆☆☆

A manufacturer sends out his cigarettes in boxes of 160. They are packed in eight rows of 20 each, and exactly fill the box. Could he, by packing differently, get more than 160 into the box? If so, what is the greatest number that he could add? At first sight it sounds absurd to expect to get more cigarettes into a box that is already exactly filled, but a moment's consideration should give you the key to the paradox.

5. THREE-DIMENSIONAL PUZZLES

COIN PUZZLES

157. Coin Triangle ☆☆

Arrange ten coins in the form of a triangle, as shown in the diagram.

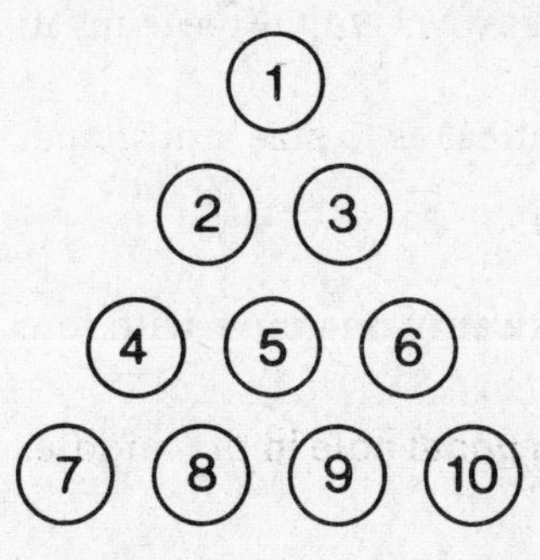

Now turn the triangle upside down by moving just three of the coins.

158. Eight in a Row ☆☆

Place eight coins in a row, the first four showing heads and the last four showing tails.

In four moves – each move consisting of moving two adjacent coins to a new position – you have to rearrange the coins so that the heads and tails are alternating. You are not allowed to turn over any of the coins, and when you have finished you must not be left with any gaps in the row.

159. Seven-Coin Rounders ☆☆

Place seven coins, all heads up, in a circle. Starting from any coin, count 1, 2, 3 in a clockwise direction and turn the third coin over. Repeat the process, beginning from any of the coins that are still heads up. Continue until all but one of the coins are tails up.

160. Five Rows ☆☆

Take ten coins and arrange them in five rows with four coins in each row.

161. Nine Rows ☆☆☆

Take twenty-seven coins and arrange them in nine rows with six coins in each row.

162. Twelve Rows ☆☆☆

Take thirteen coins and arrange them in twelve rows with three coins in each row.

163. Twenty-One Rows ☆☆☆

Take twenty-two coins and arrange them in twenty-one rows with four coins in each row.

164. Star Trek ☆☆☆

On a sheet of paper draw an eight-pointed star, and number the points as shown in the diagram. Place a coin heads up on point 1, another coin

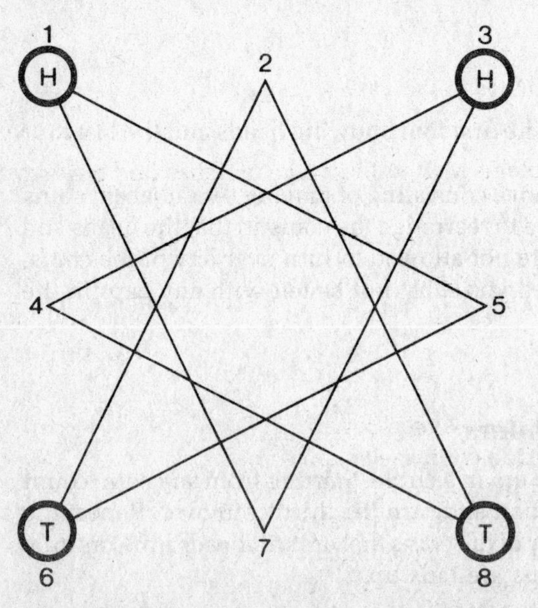

heads up on point 3, a coin tails up on point 6, and another coin tails up on point 8.

The puzzle is to transfer the two coins that are heads up to the points occupied by the coins that are tails up, and vice-versa. You are allowed seven moves. You may only move one coin at a time, although in each move you may move the coin along one line to a vacant point, or along more than one line in succession provided that the coin rests in a vacant point at the end of each line.

MATCH PUZZLES

165. Leave Three Triangles ☆☆

Arrange twelve matches as shown in the diagram.

Now move four matches so as to leave just three equilateral triangles.

166. Twelve Matches ☆☆☆

For each of these little problems start with twelve matches laid out like this:

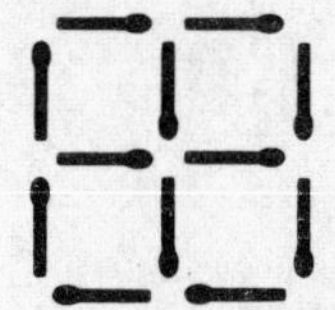

(a) Move two matches and make seven squares.
(b) Move three matches and leave three squares.
(c) Move four matches and leave two squares.
(d) Move four matches and leave three squares.
(e) Move four matches and make ten squares.
(f) Remove two matches so as to leave two squares.

167. Match Spiral ☆☆

With thirty-five matches form a spiral as shown in the diagram.

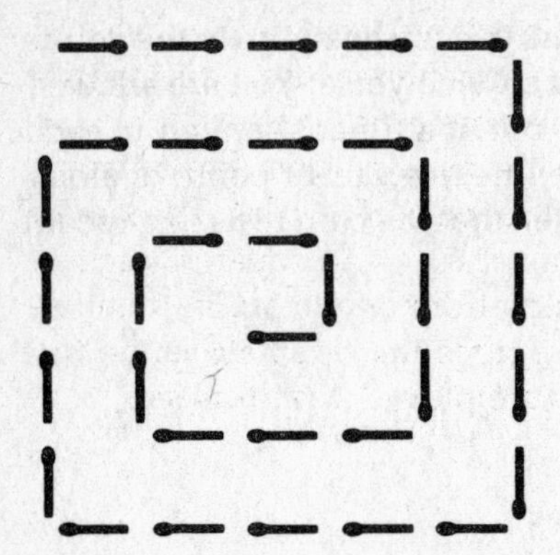

Now transform the spiral into three squares by moving just four of the matches.

DOMINO PUZZLES

The oldest known set of dominoes was discovered in 1922 in the tomb of King Tutankhamen of Egypt (c. 1371–c. 1352 BC) and can be seen today

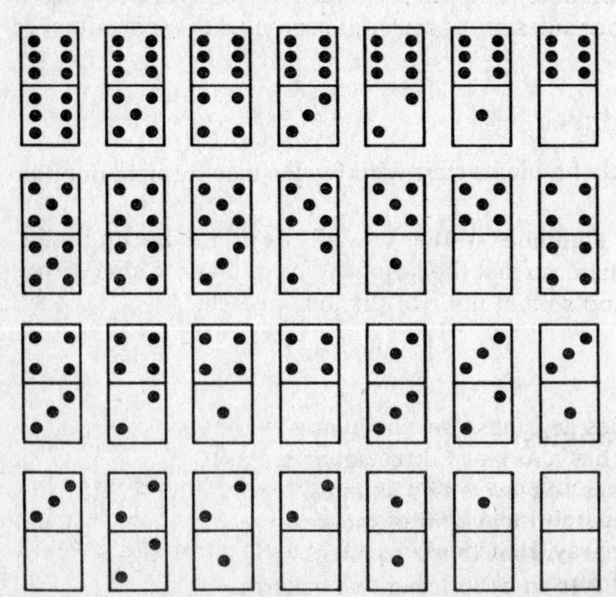

in the Tutankhamen Museum in Cairo. It seems generally agreed that dominoes actually originated in China and were introduced into Europe by Venetian traders in the fourteenth or fifteenth century AD. From Italy they were introduced into France, and it is believed that the English first learned about dominoes from French prisoners-of-war during the Napoleonic Wars at the beginning of the nineteenth century.

Dominoes are rectangular tiles, made usually from bone, ivory, wood or plastic. A standard European set consists of 28 tiles. The face of each tile is divided by a central line into two equal squares, each of which is either blank or marked with pips from one to six in number. This set is also known as the Double-6 set, as the double-6 is the top domino in the set. All the puzzles here are played with this set.

168. Six Square ☆☆

Take the 6 lowest dominoes in the set – the 0/0, the 0/1, the 0/2, the 1/1, the 1/2 and the 2/2 – and arrange them in a square, so that each side of the square contains the same number of pips.

169. Six Rectangle ☆☆

Using the same 6 dominoes as in the previous puzzle, form a rectangle, so that each of the four sides of the rectangle contains the same number of pips.

170. Ten Square ☆☆

Using the 10 lowest dominoes in the set – all the dominoes up to the double-3 – form a square, so that the number of pips on each side of the square is the same and so that none of the joins match.

171. Three Rectangles ☆☆☆

Using the 15 lowest dominoes in the set – all the dominoes up to the double-4 – form 3 separate rectangles of 5 dominoes each so that each of the 12 sides (that is to say, all 4 sides of each of the 3 rectangles) contain the same number of pips.

172. Five Lines ☆☆☆

Using the same 15 dominoes as in the last puzzle, form 5 lines, with 3 dominoes in each line, so that in each of the 5 lines the joins match and there are exactly the same number of pips in each line.

PENTOMINOES

Pentominoes were introduced to the world by a Californian mathematician, Solomon W. Golomb, in an article published in the *American Mathematical Monthly* in 1954.

Starting from the definition of a domino as two squares 'simply connected' (i.e. joined along their edges) he coined the word polyomino to describe the class of shapes formed by squares connected in this way. A monomino is a single square, a domino 2 squares simply connected, a tromino 3 squares, a tetromino 4 squares, a pentomino 5 squares, a hexomino 6, and so on.

From the family of polyominoes, it is the pentomino which has attracted the most interest because of its considerable recreational potential.

There are twelve distinct ways in which five squares can be joined together to form a pentomino. These twelve shapes constitute a set of pentominoes, which can either be bought from a shop or made at home. The twelve pieces in the set look like this:

These pentominoes form the basis of a number of interesting puzzles.

173. Pentomino Puzzles ☆☆☆☆

(a) Using any four pentominoes, form a 4 by 5 rectangle.
(b) Using any five pentominoes, form a 5 by 5 square.
(c) Using any six pentominoes, form a 5 by 6 rectangle.
(d) Using any seven pentominoes, form a 5 by 7 rectangle.
(e) Using any eight pentominoes, form a 4 by 10 rectangle.
(f) Using any nine pentominoes, form a 3 by 15 rectangle.
(g) Use all twelve pentominoes to form a 4 by 15 rectangle.

174. A Square with a Hole ☆☆☆

Using all twelve pentominoes, form an 8 by 8 square with a 2 by 2 square hole in the centre.

175. Pentomino Triplication ☆☆☆☆

Select any one of the pentominoes. Using nine of the remaining pentominoes form a large-scale version of the selected pentomino, each dimension being three times greater than the original.

CHESS PROBLEMS

176. ☆☆☆

These five classic chess problems are all the work of Sam Loyd. See if you can solve them.

(a) How can White play and mate on his third move at the latest, against any black defence?

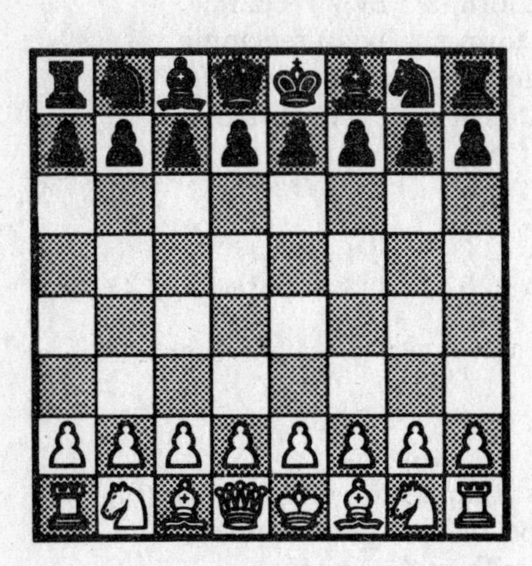

(b) If both sides make exactly the same moves, how can White mate in four? See if you can find both the possible solutions.

(c) How can White play and force mate on his third move, against any black defence?

(d) How can White play and force mate on his third move, against any black defence?

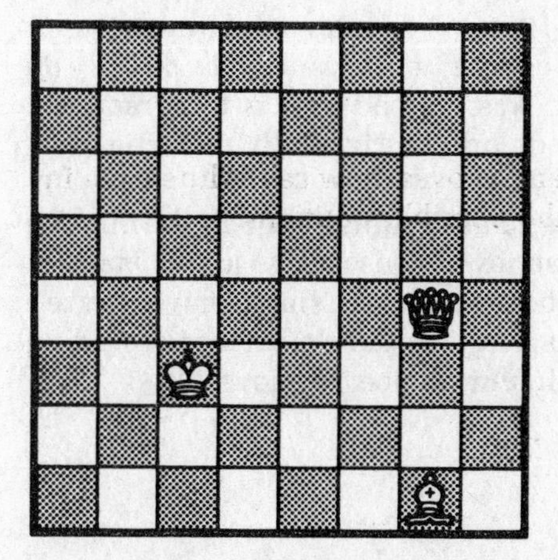

(e) (i) Place the black king where he would be stalemated.
(ii) Place the black king where he would be checkmated.
(iii) Place the black king where he would be checkmated next move.
(iv) Place the black king on a square where he can never be checkmated.

SOLITAIRE PUZZLES

The *Solitaire* board is normally made of wood or plastic and has 33 holes to hold the pieces, which are usually small marbles or pegs. (The French board has 37 holes, and is hexagonal in shape.)

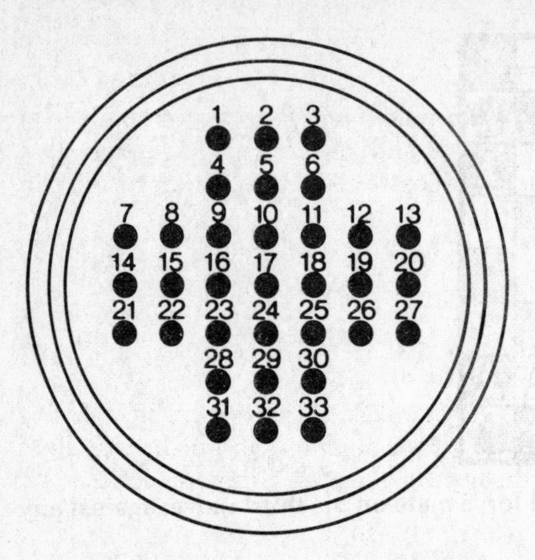

There are a number of puzzles for the solitaire board, but the method of making moves is common to all of them. A counter may be moved only by jumping it over a neighbouring counter to a vacant space directly on the other side. The counter which was jumped over is then removed from the board. Jumps may be made only horizontally or vertically – diagonal moves are not permitted.

The number of jumps made in a game of solitaire equals the number of counters removed. However, a series of consecutive jumps made at one time with a single counter can be regarded as a single move; hence a player can aim not merely at solving a given puzzle but also at finding the solution that requires the minimum number of moves.

177. The Latin Cross ☆☆

Start with six counters forming the shape of a cross, filling holes 5, 9, 10, 11, 17 and 24. The object is to remove five counters in five moves and leave the remaining counter in the centre of the board (hole 17).

178. The Greek Cross ☆☆

Start with nine counters arranged in the form of a cross, filling holes 5, 10, 15, 16, 17, 18, 19, 24 and 29. The object is to remove eight counters and leave the remaining counter in the centre of the board (hole 17). It is possible to do this in six moves.

179. The Triangle ☆☆☆

For this puzzle you start with sixteen counters forming a triangle over holes 5, 9, 10, 11, 15, 16, 17, 18, 19 and 21–27. Can you reduce this formation to a solitary counter in the centre of the board? Can you do it in eight moves?

180. The Square ☆☆☆☆

Start with the board set out as for standard solitaire – all the squares occupied, except the central one (17). The aim is to finish with eight counters left on the board, in the form of a square, occupying holes 9, 10, 11, 16, 18, 23, 24 and 25.

[illegible]

[illegible]

[illegible]

[illegible] Question [illegible]

[illegible]

[illegible] The Missing Dollar

Three men [illegible] at a hotel [illegible] thirty dollars [illegible] so the clerk [illegible] The next day the clerk found that [illegible] twenty-five dollars instead of thirty dollars [illegible] and gave him the five dollars [illegible] boy, however, who was not [illegible] and kept two dollars for himself. This meant [illegible] paying [illegible] dollars [illegible] dollars [illegible] three men [illegible] page boy [illegible] 29. So where did the other dollar go?

[illegible]

[illegible]

6. LOGIC PUZZLES

181. One Question ☆☆

A hiker comes to a fork in the road and doesn't know which way to go to reach his destination. There are two men at the fork, one of whom always tells the truth while the other always lies. The hiker doesn't know which is which, though. He may ask one of the men only one question to find his way. Which man does he ask, and what is the question?

182. The Missing Dollar ☆☆

Three men registered in a hotel and asked for three separate rooms at ten dollars each, so the clerk received thirty dollars from the three men. The next day the clerk found that these three rooms should have been let for twenty-five dollars instead of thirty dollars, so he called the page boy and gave him the five dollars rebate to give back to the three men. The boy, however, who was not very honest, gave the men one dollar each and kept two dollars for himself. This meant that each man, instead of paying ten dollars, actually paid nine dollars. This makes twenty-seven dollars for the three men; the page boy had two dollars; 27 plus 2 equals 29, so where did the other dollar go?

183. King Arthur's Knights ☆☆☆

King Arthur sat at the Round Table on three successive evenings with his knights – Beleobus, Caradoc, Driam, Eric, Floll and Galahad – but on no occasion did any person sit next to anyone who had sat next to him before. On the first evening they sat in alphabetical order round the table. But afterwards King Arthur arranged the two next sittings so that he might have Beleobus as near to him as possible and Galahad as far away from him as could be managed. How did he seat the knights to the best advantage, remembering that rule that no knight may have the same neighbour twice?

184. Mary's Age ☆☆☆

The combined ages of Mary and Ann are 44 years, and Mary is twice as old as Ann was when Mary was half as old as Ann will be when Ann is three times as old as Mary was when Mary was three times as old as Ann.

How old is Mary?

185. Shunt ☆☆☆

A locomotive, L, is on the main line of a railway. The trucks, marked 1 and 2 in the diagram, are on sidings which meet at the points, where there is room for one truck only but not for the locomotive.

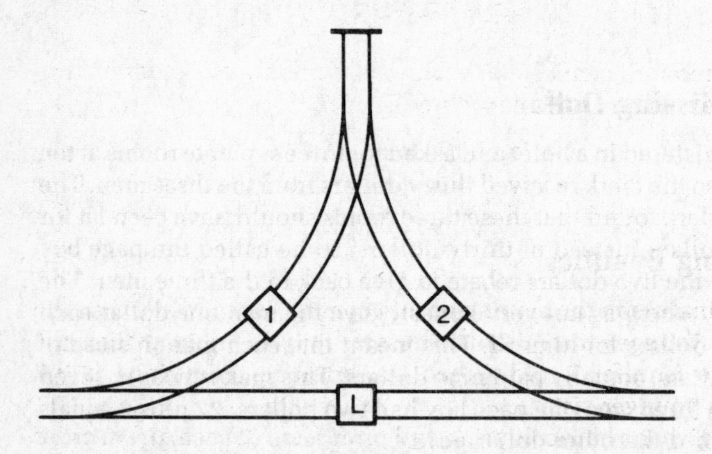

The problem is to swap the positions of the two trucks and leave the locomotive in its original position on the main line. The locomotive may push or pull the trucks – it may go between them, pulling one and pushing the other – but no truck may move without the locomotive.

186. The Eight Engines ☆☆☆

The diagram represents the engine-yard of a railway company under eccentric management. The engines are allowed to be sationary only at the nine points indicated, one of which is at present vacant. It is required to move the engines, one at a time, from point to point, in seventeen moves, so that the engines shall be in numerical order round the circle, with the central point left vacant. But one of the engines has had its fire

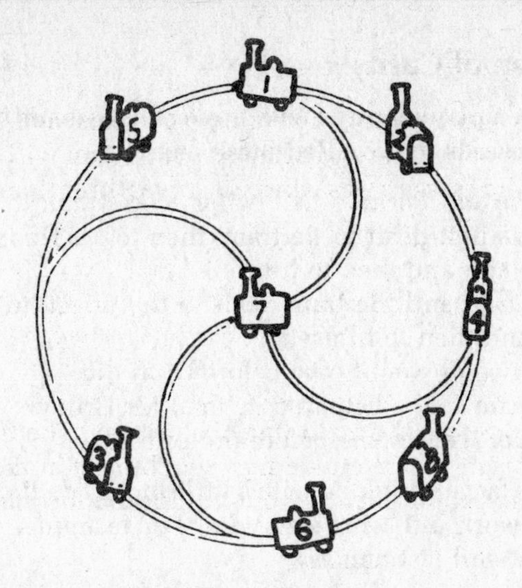

drawn and therefore cannot move. How is the thing to be done? And which engine remains stationary throughout?

187. Bathing Beauties ☆☆☆

Of the three finalists in the bathing beauty contest, Jane is older than the redhead, but younger than the hairdresser. Judy is younger than the blonde, while Jennifer is older than the brunette. The typist is the receptionist's younger sister.

Can you give the hair-colouring and profession of each girl in order of age?

188. Weight Lifters ☆☆☆

Boris, Sergei, Tam and Viktor are weight lifters. Viktor can outlift Tam, but Sergei can outlift Viktor. Tam can outlift Boris, but Sergei can outlift Tam. Therefore:

(a) Both Boris and Sergei can outlift Viktor.
(b) Viktor can outlift Boris but can't outlift Tam.
(c) Viktor can outlift Boris by more than he can outlift Tam.
(d) None of the above.

Which of these is correct?

189. A Game of Cards ☆☆☆

Dwight had been playing cards with three of his friends. Thinking about the game afterwards, he recalled these facts:

1. Ambrose and Bertram had better scores than the doctor.
2. Ambrose first dealt to Bertram, then to Mr Hooper, then to the accountant, and then to himself.
3. In the last hand, Bertram dealt to the priest, to Mr Hooper, to Clint, and then to himself.
4. Mr Eastwood went home before Clint did.
5. The doctor had a better score than Mr Grimm.
6. Mr Fuller went home before the priest.

With these facts, sprinkled with a little logical deduction, you ought to be able to work out who was who. For example, what were the musician's first and last names?

190. Take Four Girls ☆☆☆

1. Ann is younger than the dancer, who lives directly west of Barbara.
2. The dancer lives directly north of Miss Green, who lives exactly five miles from Cathy, who lives exactly two miles from the singer.
3. The pianist is older than Miss White and Diana is older than the actress.
4. Cathy is older than Miss Brown, who lives exactly three miles from Barbara, who lives directly south of Miss Black.

How far does Diana live from Ann? And which of the four girls is the oldest?

191. The Triple 'A' Club ☆☆☆

The membership of the Triple 'A' Club is drawn from three professions – auditors (who always tell the truth), advertising men (who always lie), and actors (whose statements are alternately true and false, or false and true).

Although I am not a member, I have occasion to visit the club from time to time. Here is what happened on four of my recent visits.

(a) I was introduced on one occasion to three new members, one being from each profession. Their names were John, Paul and George. Each of them made two statements as follows:

John: 'I am not an advertising man'.
'Paul is not an actor'.
Paul: 'I am not an advertising man'.
'George is not an auditor'.
George: 'I am not an advertising man'.
'John is not an actor'.

What was the profession of each new member?

(b) On another occasion I met three members, a representative of each profession, whose names were Tom, Dick and Harry. When I enquired about their professions and ages, each made two statements as follows:

Tom: 'Harry is an auditor'.
'Dick is older than Harry'.
Dick: 'Harry is an actor'.
'Harry is older than Tom'.
Harry: 'Tom is an advertising man'.
'Tom is older than Dick'.

What is the profession of each member, and how do their ages compare?

(c) On yet another occasion I asked three members, one from each profession, about their earnings. Their names were David, Lloyd and George, and each made two statements as follows:

David: 'I am an actor'.
'I earn more than George'.
Lloyd: 'I am an auditor'.
'I earn more than David'.
George: 'I am an advertising man'.
'I earn more than Lloyd'.

What is the profession of each member and how do their earnings compare?

(d) The club committee consists of three members, one from each profession, who fill the roles of chairman, secretary and treasurer. The present committee members are Freeman, Hardy and Willis. I asked two of them about the composition of the committee, and this is what they told me:

Freeman: 'I am not an actor'.
'Hardy is not the chairman'.
Hardy: 'I am not an auditor'.
'Willis is not the secretary'.

Can you name the person who fills each post on the committee, and identify his profession?

192. Islands in the Sun ☆☆☆

In the Gulf of Lug there are five islands, each with a different number of inhabitants. A different language is spoken on each island (reflecting the chequered colonial past of the area), and each island's economy is based on a different exported commodity.

From the facts below, see if you can work out the details of each island's population, language and export.

1. Cetri has 1 million inhabitants.
2. The island which exports bananas has a smaller population than the island on which Dutch is spoken.
3. The island on which Spanish is spoken does not export precious stones.
4. The island which exports coffee has a population of 2 million.
5. Auni's population is double that of the island on which English is spoken.
6. The island which exports emeralds has a population of 5 million.
7. Bebi is not the island with 3 million inhabitants.
8. The population of the island which exports amethysts is half that of the island on which French is spoken.
9. Equin has 1 million fewer inhabitants than the island which exports dates.
10. Dequar's 4 million inhabitants outnumber the population of the island on which Portuguese is spoken.

193. Do It Yourself ☆☆☆

On my bookshelves I have five books concerned with do-it-yourself subjects. From the facts below, see if you can work out the title and author of each book, the colour of its cover and the number of pages it contains.

(Note: the name of an author is not a reliable guide to the name of the book written by that author.)

1. *Painting and Decorating* has 50 more pages than the book with the white cover.
2. The book by Walter Wall has a blue cover.
3. The book by Bernard Cole has 20 more pages than *Domestic Insulation*.
4. *Carpet Fitting* does not have a blue cover.
5. The book with the yellow cover has 170 pages.
6. The book by Matt Coates has 70 fewer pages than the book with the green cover.

7. *Improve Your Garden* has 300 pages.
8. *Indoor Heating* was written by Celia Holmes.
9. The book with the white cover has 190 pages.
10. The book by Anita Lawn has a red cover and 220 pages.

194. Lewis Carroll's Symbolic Logic ☆☆☆

In each of these problems by Lewis Carroll, you have to find the 'ultimate conclusion' that can be drawn from the statements given. You do this by taking any two statements with a common term and seeing what conclusion can be drawn from them. Combine the result with another statement that has a term in common and draw another conclusion from them. Continue in this way until you reach the final conclusion that can be drawn – this will be the same no matter in which order you combine the statements.

Perhaps an example will make the process clearer. Take the following statements:

a. There are no pencils of mine in this box.
b. No sugar-plums of mine are cigars.
c. The whole of my property, that is not in this box, consists of cigars.

From (a) and (c) we may conclude 'All my pencils are cigars'. Combining this result with statement (b), we obtain the ultimate conclusion that 'No pencils of mine are sugar-plums'.

1
a. No acrobatic feats, that are not announced in the bills of a circus, are ever attempted there.
b. No acrobatic feat is possible, if it involves turning a quadruple somersault.
c. No impossible acrobatic feat is ever announced in a circus bill.

2
a. No birds except ostriches are 9 feet high.
b. There are no birds in this aviary that belong to any one but *me*.
c. No ostrich lives on mince-pies.
d. I have no birds less than 9 feet high.

3
a. No interesting poems are unpopular among people of real taste.
b. No modern poetry is free from affectation.
c. All *your* poems are on the subject of soap-bubbles.
d. No affected poetry is popular among people of real taste.
e. No ancient poem is on the subject of soap-bubbles.

4 a. I call no day 'unlucky', when Robinson is civil to me.
b. Wednesdays are always cloudy.
c. When people take umbrellas, the day never turns out fine.
d. The only days when Robinson is uncivil to me are Wednesdays.
e. Everybody takes his umbrella with him when it is raining.
f. My 'lucky' days always turn out fine.

5 a. Animals are always mortally offended if I fail to notice them.
b. The only animals that belong to me are in that field.
c. No animal can guess a conundrum unless it has been properly trained in a Board-School.
d. None of the animals in that field are badgers.
e. When an animal is mortally offended it always rushes about wildly and howls.
f. I never notice any animal unless it belongs to me.
g. No animal that has been properly trained in a Board-School ever rushes about wildly and howls.

6 a. The only animals in this house are cats.
b. Every animal is suitable for a pet, that loves to gaze at the moon.
c. When I detest an animal, I avoid it.
d. No animals are carnivorous, unless they prowl at night.
e. No cat fails to kill mice.
f. No animals ever take to me, except what are in this house.
g. Kangaroos are not suitable for pets.
h. None but carnivora kill mice.
i. I detest animals that do not take to me.
j. Animals that prowl at night always love to gaze at the moon.

7. VISUAL PUZZLES

195. Distances ☆☆☆

Which is the greatest distance: from A to B or from B to C?

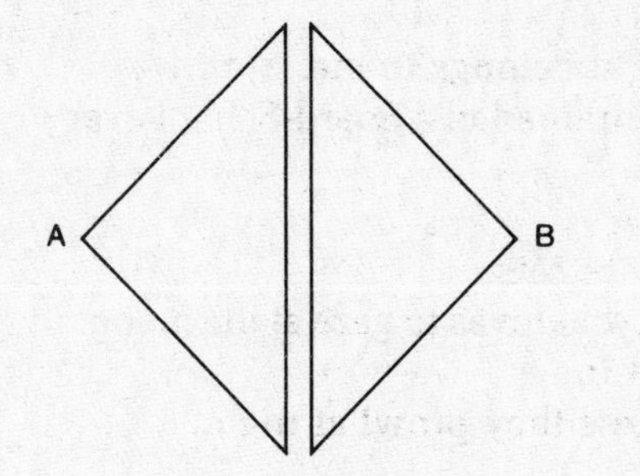

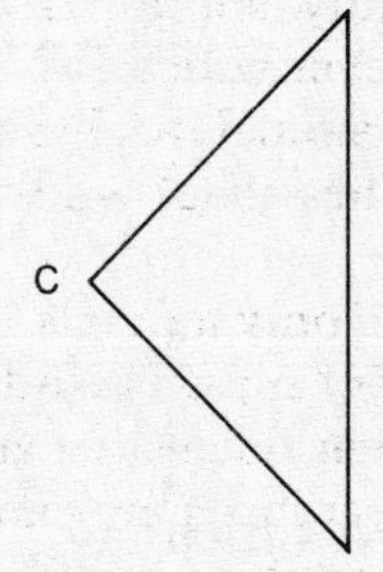

196. Arcs ☆☆

If the circle represented by arcs A, B and C were completed, which would have the greatest diameter?

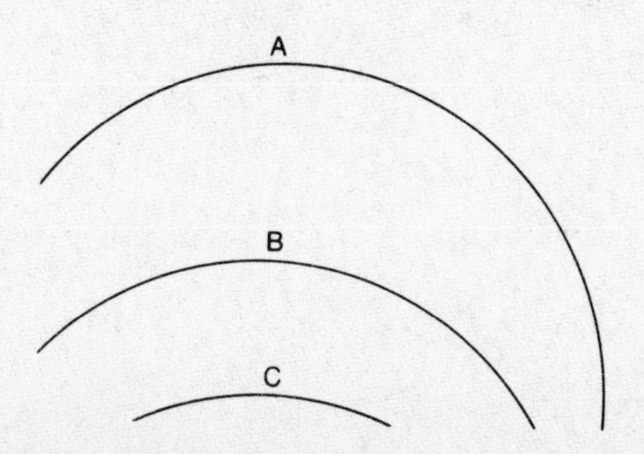

197. A Curious Cube ☆☆

(a) Is the cube viewed from above or below?
(b) Is the line across the corner of the cube straight or bent?

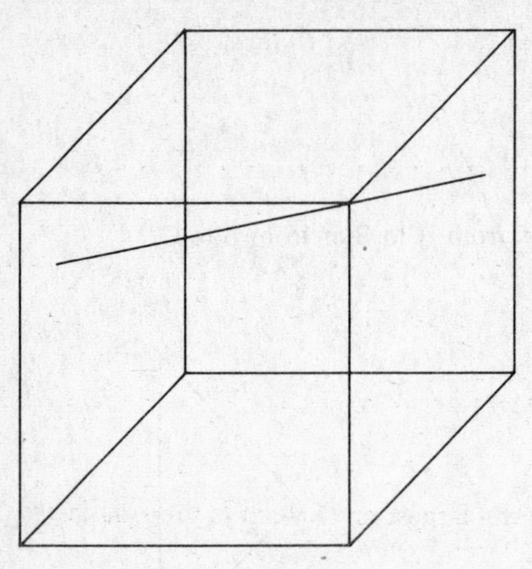

198. Two Lines ☆☆

Which line is the longer: AC or BD?

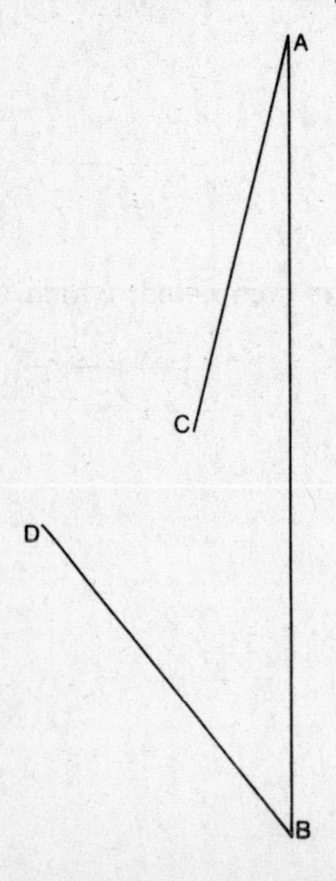

199. Three Lines ☆☆

Which of these three lines is the longest: the top one, the middle one or the bottom one?

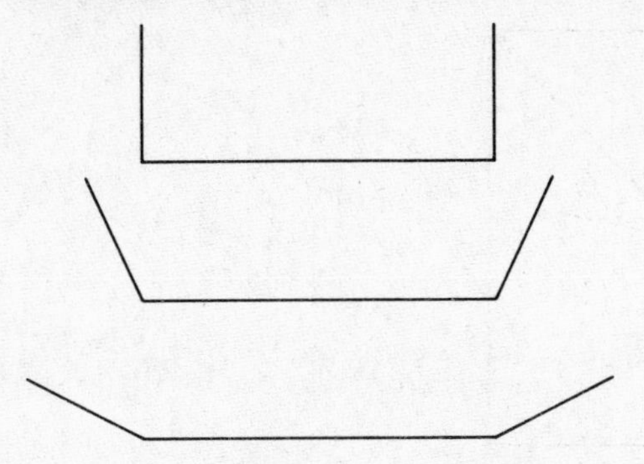

200. Five Shapes ☆☆

Which of these five shapes is the largest and which is the smallest?

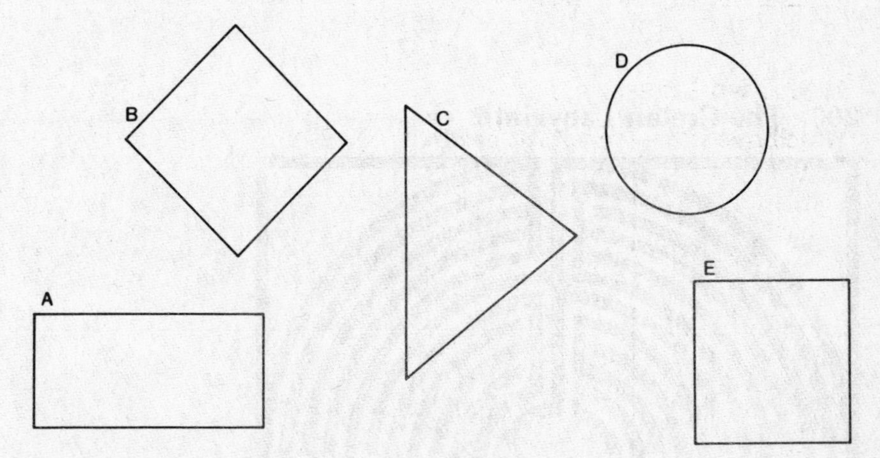

201. Two Circles ☆☆

Which of the two circles is the larger?

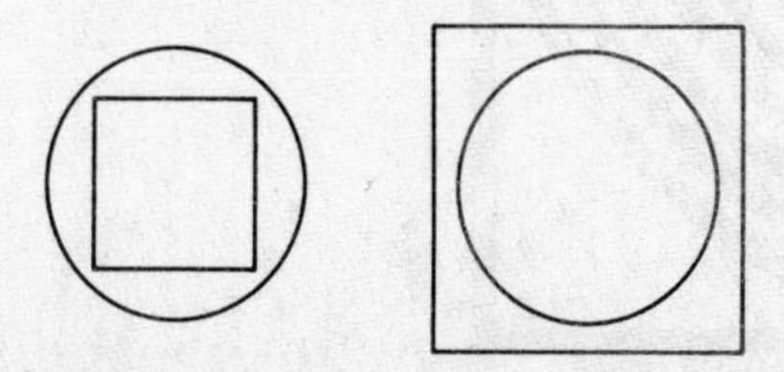

202. Horizontals ☆☆

Which of the two horizontal lines is longer, the top one of the bottom one?

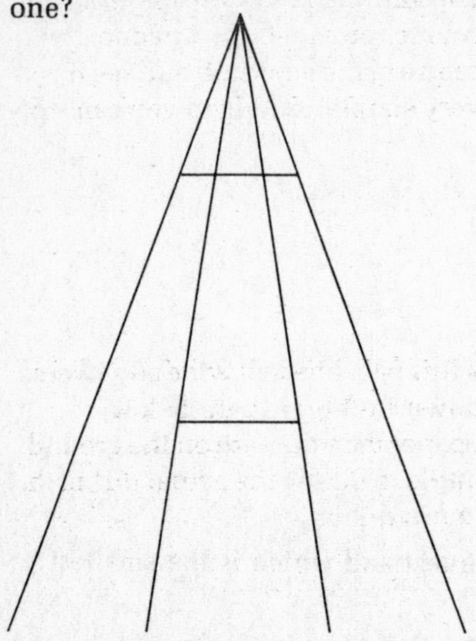

203. The Cretan Labyrinth ☆☆

The first and the best-known of all the ancient mazes was the Cretan Labyrinth designed by Daedalus as a devilish den for the famous Minotaur. Theseus slew the Minotaur and made his escape from the labyrinth. He used some thread of course, provided by Ariadne.

You're not so lucky. Start at the centre of the labyrinth and see if you can find your way out. This maze is very simple, as long as you can stop your eyes playing tricks with you.

204. The Somerton Maze ☆☆

At Somerton in Oxfordshire, there is a turf path one foot wide and twelve hundred feet long, constructed as shown in the diagram below.

Most mazes are easier to trace on paper than they are on the ground. But in this case, although it is very simple to follow the actual turf path, tracing the route on paper is rather more difficult.

It is the *dark* line you have to follow. See if you can trace it to the centre.

205. Crossings ☆☆☆

You cannot get to the centre of this maze without crossing some lines. What are the least number of lines you need to cross to get from B to A?

206. The Philadelphia Maze ☆☆☆☆

This maze is the creation of H. E. Dudeney, who posed the question: how many ways are there to the centre?

(CAUTION: It is reported that one person who tried to solve this puzzle drove himself to the point of insanity and took his own life!)

207. Trick Donkeys ☆☆☆

This is one of the most famous puzzles of Sam Loyd.

If the puzzle is cut along the dotted lines, how can the three pieces

be arranged – without folding – so that the two jockeys ride the two donkeys?

TANGRAM PUZZLES

Tangrams are an ancient form of puzzle from China. A tangram set consists of seven pieces, formed by dissecting a square as shown in the diagram.

The object of a tangram puzzle is to arrange the seven pieces to form a specified shape. All the pieces must be used, and no piece may overlap another.

208. Tangram Teasers ☆☆☆

See if you can make each of these shapes with the seven tangram pieces.

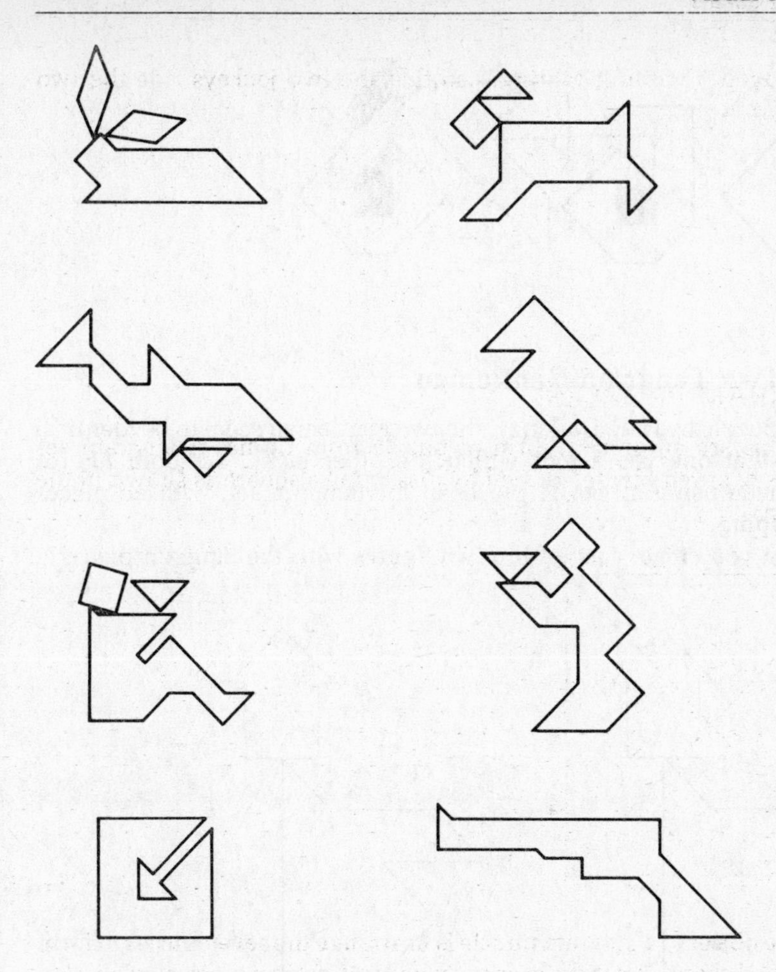

209. Tangram Digits ☆☆☆

Arrange the tangram pieces to make each of the digits from 1 to 8, as shown.

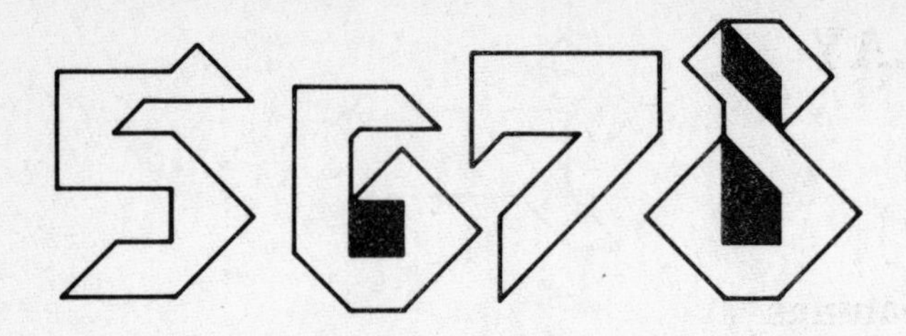

210. Two Tangram Gentlemen ☆☆☆

In this puzzle by H. E. Dudeney, the two gentlemen seem to be identical except that one has a foot which the other lacks. Yet both figures were made using all seven pieces of the tangram set, with no pieces overlapping.

Can you create each of the two figures with the tangram pieces?

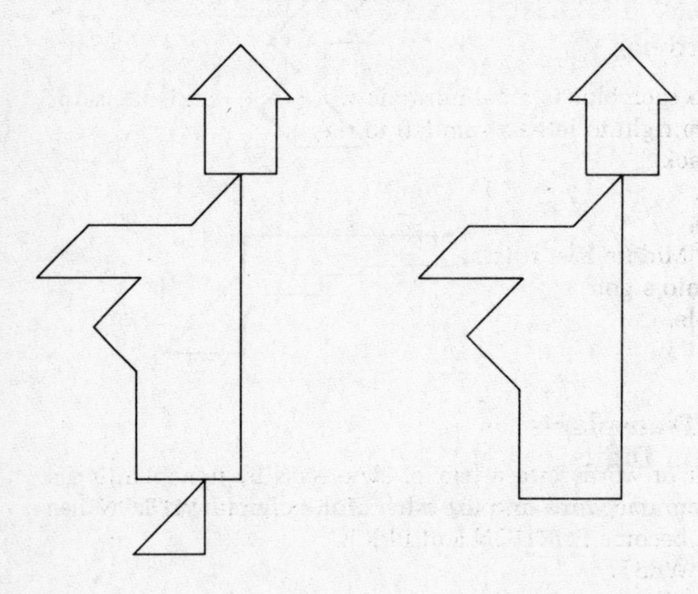

8. WORDPLAY

211. Double Meanings ☆☆

Find a single word which may mean the same as either word in the pair. For example, the answer to THROW ACTORS would be CAST.

1. Clever pain.
2. Produce whip.
3. Support couple.
4. Contrary talk.
5. Impartial goal.
6. Absolute state.

212. Palindromes ☆☆

The solution to each clue is a palindromic word (one that is the same when read from right to left as from left to right).

1. Wisecrack.
2. Action.
3. Twelve.
4. Former Middle-East rulers.
5. Made into a god.
6. Principle.

213. Letter Transplants ☆☆

Form each pair of words into a pair of synonyms by transplanting a single letter from one word into the other. For example, POTION and PIERCE would become PORTION and PIECE.

1. OAK & WEST.
2. TINE & BID.
3. FOG & BLEAT.
4. AGE & RANGER.
5. SHEAR & CAR.
6. AID & SCOUR.
7. RAVER & ASSET.
8. LAVE & QUITE.
9. SPINY & GRATE.
10. FLIT & CROQUET.

214. A Common Property ☆☆

The verbs BRING, BUY, CATCH, FIGHT, FREIGHT, SEEK, TEACH and THINK share a common property that no other common verbs in the English language possess. What is it?

215. Double Letters ☆☆☆

There are several letters which frequently occur as doubles in English words. Double L, double T, and double S are all very common. But can you find words containing the following doubled letters?

HH II KK UU VV WW

Your answers might be very obscure words, but they need not be – our answers are all perfectly common words in everyday use.

216. Words of Note ☆☆☆

Using the musical notes C, D, E, F, G, A, and B, what is the longest word that can be played on a piano? That is, using any of these letters, as many or as few times you like, but using no other letters, what is the longest word you can find? No foreign or hyphenated words, please.

217. Triple Word Squares ☆☆☆

A word square is an arrangement of words one below another in the form of a square so that they read the same horizontally and vertically.

Below are the clues for three such word squares. There's just one snag – the three sets of clues have been shuffled together, and you have to work out which clue belongs to which word square. To help you the central letters have already been inserted.

1. Group of eight; Delight; Striped quadruped.
2. Illegal activity; Mistake; Midday meal
3. Bury; Weary; Fetch.
4. Musical composition; View; Correct.
5. Termagant; Inert gas; Toy bear.

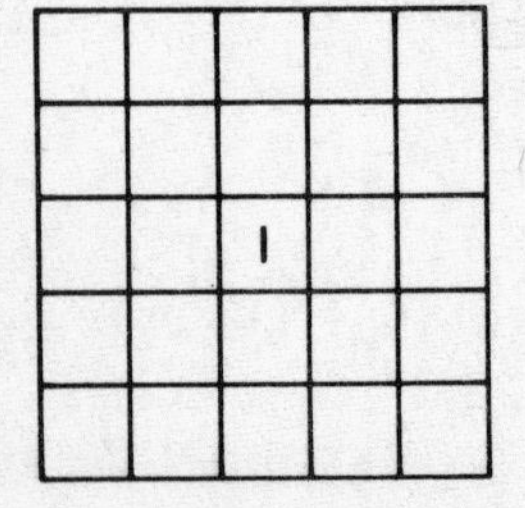

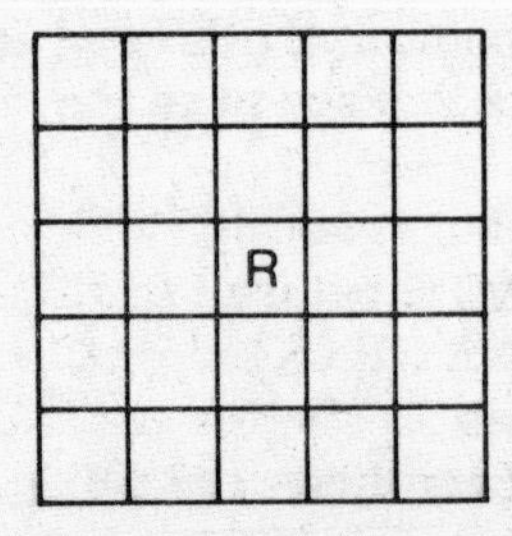

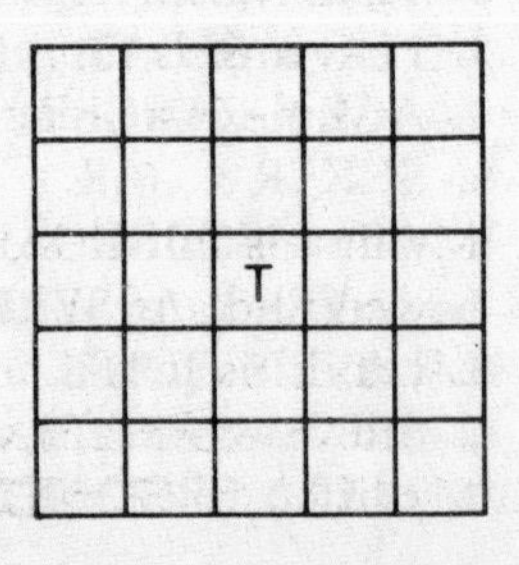

218. Rhyme Time ☆☆☆

The ten words and expressions given here (some of which are French) all rhyme with NO, and yet each ends with a different letter of the alphabet:

DOUGH	WOE	OHO
WHOA	DE TROP	APROPOS
SOL	ROW	BON MOT
GATEAU		

Now, can you find as many words and expressions as possible, ending with different letters of the alphabet, that rhyme with the word SAY? You may use the French language, and you should be able to find ten or more.

219. Anagrams Plus C ☆☆

By adding a C to each of the words below, then shuffling the letters, it is possible to form a new word. Add another C, shuffle again, and a third word appears. For example, by adding C to ESAU, you can create CAUSE. Add another C, and you have ACCUSE.

See how many you can solve, avoiding plurals and verbs ending in S.

OIL	TAPE	HERE	LEAN	LOUT
HAT	OUST	NEAR	HATE	SPITE
ARK	OAST	SEAR	HEAD	NOSE
IRK	ROSE	SOUR	RILE	NEAT

220. Three Riddles ☆☆☆

(a) My first is in BORDER and also in BED;
My second's in ROLL but never in BREAD;
My third is in MILE but isn't in METRE;
My fourth's found in PINT but not found in LITRE;
My fifth's not in PAIN but always in ACHE;
My sixth is in PIE but never in CAKE;
My seventh is found both in ANKLE and KNEE;
My whole is a creature that swims in the sea.

(b) My first is in SUGAR but is not in SWEET;
My second's in WARMTH but isn't in HEAT;
My third is found not in HILLS but in DALES;
While my fourth is seen in RIVETS not NAILS;
My fifth's in FIANCEE and also in WIFE;

And my sixth appears both in TROUBLE and STRIFE;
My seventh's in LADY but never in LORD;
My whole is a force that can't be ignored.

(c) My first is in LADY but isn't in MAN;
My second's in TIN but is not in CAN;
My third is found both in SCOTLAND and WALES;
My fourth is in HILLS as well as in DALES;
My fifth is in BLUE but is not in BLACK;
My sixth is in PARCEL and also in PACK;
My seventh's in SHOUT but isn't in SHREIKING;
My whole may be heard, in a manner of speaking.

221. Two Double Riddles ☆☆☆

Each of these riddles has two equally correct answers – you have to find both.

(a) My first is in SPLIT but is not in TEAR;
My second's in APPLE and also in PEAR;
My third is in BITTER but is not in SOUR;
My fourth is in MOMENT but is not in HOUR;
My fifth is in QUADRANT as well as in SQUARE;
My sixth is in CIRCUS but is not in FAIR;
My seventh's in SHINE and also in SHEEN;
My whole, you will see, has leaves that are green.

(b) My first is in RABBIT but is not in HARE;
My second's in BRACE but is not in PAIR;
My third is in LADDER but is not in CLIMB;
My fourth is in LEMON and also in LIME;
My fifth is in AUNT but is not in NIECE;
My sixth is in GANDER but is not in GEESE;
My seventh is seen both in GRANDMA and DAUGHTER;
My whole is an island surrounded by water.

222. American Names ☆☆☆

Which state of the USA does TINA come from? Well, it could be either norTh carolINA or wesT virgINiA, because both these states contain the letters of her name in the correct sequence.

Here are ten more names. See if you can find their states of origin.

(a) EVA (f) RHODA
(b) MAE (g) DIANA
(c) ALAN (h) SYLVIA
(d) ANTON (i) DEAN
(e) NESTA (j) SHARON

223. Linkwords ☆☆☆

The clues, which are in random sequence, define eight five-letter words. Solve the clues, and then insert the answers one below another in the diagram in the correct sequence so that each word differs from the preceding word by only one letter.

The first and last letters have been inserted to guide you.

(a) Depart
Animal
Weighty
Brag
Hire
Shore
Hoist
Minimum

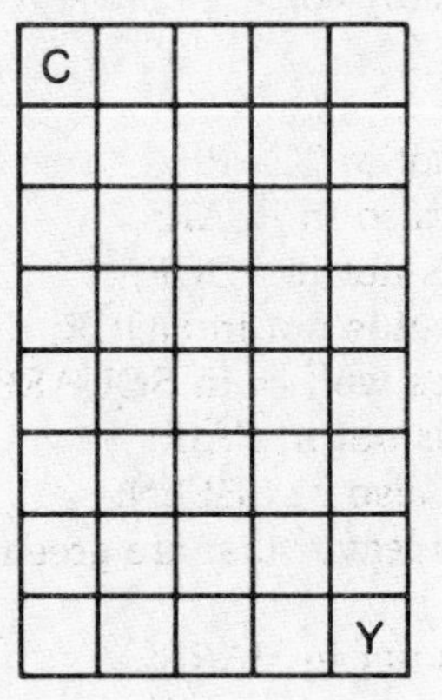

(b)					
Chest	B				
Fetch					
Dense					
Inebriated					
Lorry					
Edge					
Ruse					
Beverage					K

224. Confusibles ☆☆☆

This puzzle consists of pairs of words which are quite different in meaning but are frequently confused with each other. For example, FLAUNT and FLOUT, LUXURIANT and LUXURIOUS. See how many of the ten pairs you can identify.

(a) A hospital for the treatment of chronic diseases
An institution for the promotion of health
(b) To reveal
To depreciate
(c) Beggary
Dishonesty
(d) To command solemnly
To renounce
(e) To irritate or scrape
To censure or reprimand
(f) To rout
To make uneasy
(g) Corrupt
Pardonable
(h) To write or compose
To charge with a crime
(i) Self-pleased
Pleasing to others
(j) Occurring every two years
Occurring twice a year

225. Consecutive Letters ☆☆☆

The word ABSCOND contains the four consecutive letters ABCD, in the correct order. Indeed the word ABSCONDED contains the letters ABCDE. See if you can find words that contain the following groups of letters in the correct order.

DEFG FGHI HIJK MNOP QRST RSTU XYZ

226. Alphabetical Shifts ☆☆☆

Consider the word COLD. If you shift each letter forward three positions in the alphabet, C becomes F, O becomes R, L becomes O, and D becomes G – so you end up with a new word, FROG.

Similarly, BALK can be turned into ONYX by shifting each letter forward 13 positions in the alphabet.

We have performed a similar process on 10 five-letter words. How rapidly can you work backwards from the words given here, and determine what words we started with?

(a) BEEFS	(f) FERNS
(b) INGOT	(g) JOLLY
(c) LORRY	(h) TOFFS
(d) SORRY	(i) TIFFS
(e) FREUD	(j) TIGER

227. Word Patterns ☆☆☆

(a) There are 52 distinct patterns which can be displayed by five-letter words. For example, SATIN, with no repeated letters, has the pattern 12345; TRUTH, having the first and fourth letters the same, has the pattern 12314; RACER, having the first and fifth letters the same, has the pattern 12341; and LEVEL, having the first and fifth letters the same, as well as the second and fourth, has the pattern 12321.

See if you can find examples for the following patterns:

12344	12213	12323	12131
11232	12231	12331	12311
12123	12233	12332	12232
12132	12312	11231	12322
12133	12313	12113	12112

(b) Examples of patterns of six-letter words are:

SENSES = 123121	TITBIT = 121321
HUBBUB = 123323	MAMMAL = 121123
SETTEE = 123322	ACACIA = 121231

Now see if you can find words displaying the following patterns:

123232	122323	121133	123123
123321	122131	122321	123212
122132	121223	123443	123344

228. Typewriter Words ☆☆☆

(a) Q W E R T Y U I O P
A S D F G H J K L
Z X C V B N M

This is the order in which letters appear on a standard typewriter keyboard. ASH, RUG and TUG are three words whose letters occur in 'typewriter order'. Can you find longer examples? What is the longest such word you can find? Doubled letters (as in TOO) are acceptable.

(b) What is the longest word that can be typed using just the letters on the top row of the typewriter keyboard – Q, W, E, R, T, Y, U, I, O, P? QUIRE and PEPPER are two examples, but no doubt you will be able to find longer words than these.
(c) What is the longest word that can be typed using just the letters on the second row of the typewriter keyboard – A, S, D, F, G, H, J, K and L?

229. A,E,I,O,U ☆☆☆☆

(a) FACETIOUS is one English word which contains the five vowels A,E,I,O,U in the correct sequence, each vowel occurring once and only once. Can you think of another common English word which shares this property?
(b) There are, of course, many other words containing one occurrence of each of the five vowels, but in a different order. See if you can think of a word containing the five vowels in each of the sequences shown below:

AIEOU	OEAUI	AUIOE	AIOUE	EOUAI
IOUAE	EUOIA	EUAIO	OAUIE	OUEAI
UAIOE	UOIAE			

230. Headliner ☆☆☆

There are many words which form another word when the initial letter is removed. The pairs of clues for the columns in this puzzle refer to such words.

One clue defines the whole word; the other clue defines the word that is formed when the initial letter of the first word is removed. Either clue may come first in the pair.

For example, if the clue was 'Correct; shining' the answer would be B-RIGHT.

If you complete all the columns correctly, the headline formed by the initial letters will spell out the name of a famous person.

Column 1. SUFFER; PRISON.
Column 2. ASSENTED; AVARICE.
Column 3. IN GOOD TIME; ALMOST.
Column 4. MOVEMENT; FEELING.
Column 5. AFT; SEVERE.
Column 6. MORE CERTAIN; MONEY-LENDER.
Column 7. WITHOUT DIFFICULTY; SUGGEST.
Column 8. DIFFICULTIES; FOREIGN CURRENCY.
Column 9. ODD; ALIENATE.
Column 10. TIDY; DINE.

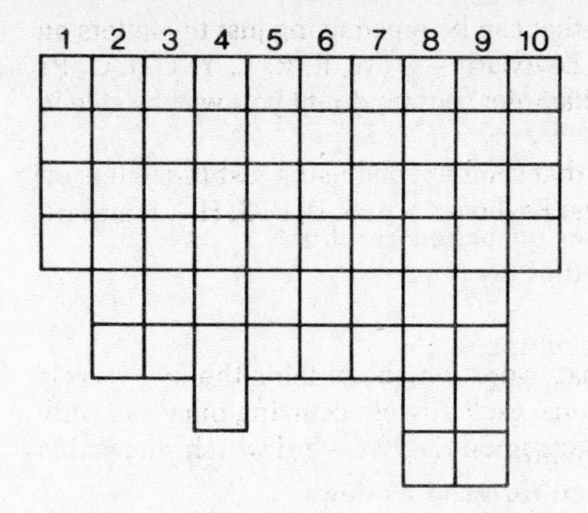

231. Single-Word Anagrams ☆☆☆

If you were asked to provide a single-word anagram of PARTISAN, it should not take you too long to find the answer ASPIRANT. See how long it takes you to find a single-word anagram for each of the following words:

(a) TREASON
(b) OBEYING
(c) BESTIARY
(d) ASSAYING
(e) MASCULINE
(f) DICTIONARY
(g) BARGAINED
(h) CATECHISM
(i) ESTIMATING
(j) CONSIDERATE
(k) EXCITATION
(l) LEGISLATOR
(m) CENTRALISE
(n) INCONSIDERATE
(o) CEPHALOMETRIC
(p) VICEPRESIDENTS

CHARADES

If you have ever played the party game of Charades (or seen it played as a panel game on TV) you will know what to expect here. A piece of verse defines a word – firstly syllable by syllable ('my first', 'my second', etc.) and then the whole word ('my whole'). You have to guess the word being thus defined.

Here are two examples of the genre, which reached the height of its popularity in the late Victorian period.

232. Beside the Brook ☆☆

Beside the brook one summer day
  When Nature all was merry,
I saw a gypsy maiden stray,
  As brown as any berry;
She with the limpid waters quenched her thirst,
And picked a simple salad of my *first*.

The woodbine and the eglantine,
  The woodruff and the mallow,
Delight to twine and intertwine
  Beside that streamlet shallow;
And kissed by sunlight and caressed by dews,
My *second* in the air around diffuse.

The sun went down, the twilight fell,
  Outshone the stars unnumbered;
Each floweret closed its honeyed cell,
  And nature softly slumbered.
While pale and cold across the heavens stole,
In modest maiden majesty, my *whole*.

233. Rifle Practice ☆☆

It was a gallant Volunteer,
  And he went forth to shoot;
He always went the bull's-eye near,
  And hit thrice to boot;
And he was clearly not the worst
  Who aimed his rifle at my *first*.

And while the yards they fired were few,
  Upon his feet stood he;
But when the distance greater grew,
  He knelt upon his knee;
And when the widest space was reckoned,
  He lay down flat upon my *second*.

Within the hut the marker stood,
  To score down every shot;
He signalled those whose aim was good,
  And those whose aim was not;

When to the bull's-eye bullets whirred,
He bade the red flag do my *third*.

Awakened by the early spring,
And taking little heed,
A poor unhappy giddy thing
Went straying o'er the mead,
And so got shot! Your tears control,
'Twas not a child – 'twas but my *whole*.

234. An Enigma ☆☆

A word there is of plural number,
Foe to ease and tranquil slumber;
Any other word you take
And add an S will plural make.
But if you add an S to this,
So strange the metamorphosis;
Plural is plural now no more,
And sweet what bitter was before.

This enigma was composed by the British Prime Minister George Canning (1770–1827).

235. Queen Victoria's Acrostic ☆☆☆

This puzzle is said to have been composed by Queen Victoria to entertain the royal children – presumably, on this occasion she *was* amused.

If you solve the clues correctly, the initial letters will be found to spell out the name of a town in England, and the final letters, read upwards, will spell out what that town is famous for.

1. A city in Italy
2. A river in Germany
3. A town in the United States
4. A town in the United States
5. A town in Holland
6. The Turkish name for Constantinople
7. A town in Bothnia
8. A city in Greece
9. A circle on the globe

236. Doublets ☆☆☆

This type of puzzle was invented by Lewis Carroll. Here he describes the puzzle in his own words:

'The rules of the puzzle are simple enough. Two words are proposed, of the same length; and the puzzle consists in linking these together by interposing other words, each of which shall differ from the next word *in one letter only*. That is to say, one letter may be changed in one of the given words, then one letter in the word so obtained, and so on, till we arrive at the other given word. The letters must not be interchanged among themselves, but each must keep its own place. As an example the word "head" may be changed into "tail" by interposing the words "heal, teal, tell, tall". I call the two given words "a Doublet", the interposed words "Links", and the entire series "a Chain", of which I here append an example:

HEAD
heal
teal
tell
tall
TAIL

'It is, perhaps, needless to state that it is *de rigueur* that the links should be English words, such as might be used in good society.'

You should now be ready to tackle the following Doublets.

3 Links
(a) Change WET to DRY
(b) Cover EYE with LID
(c) Make EEL into PIE
(d) Prove RAVEN to be MISER
(e) Change OAT to RYE
(f) Make TEA HOT

4 Links
(g) Drive PIG into STY
(h) Change FISH to BIRD
(i) REST on SOFA

5 Links
(j) Dip PEN into INK
(k) Touch CHIN with NOSE
(l) Change TEARS into SMILE
(m) PITCH TENTS

(n) Turn POOR into RICH
(o) Evolve MAN from APE
(p) Make FLOUR into BREAD
(q) Get COAL from MINE
(r) Stow FURIES in BARREL

6 Links

(s) Make WHEAT into BREAD
(t) Raise FOUR to FIVE
(u) Make HARE into SOUP
(v) Prove PITY to be GOOD
(w) Make BLACK WHITE
(x) Run COMB into HAIR
(y) WHIP LASH
(z) Sell SHOES for CRUST
(aa) Make BREAD into TOAST

7 Links

(bb) STEAL COINS
(cc) Get WOOD from TREE
(dd) Prove GRASS to be GREEN
(ee) Change ELM into OAK
(ff) Combine ARMY and NAVY
(gg) Place BEANS on SHELF
(hh) BUY an ASS
(ii) Raise ONE to TWO

8 Links

(jj) Change CAIN into ABEL
(kk) Change BLUE to PINK

9 Links

(ll) Pay COSTS in PENCE
(mm) Put LOAF into OVEN
(nn) Make KETTLE HOLDER

10 Links

(oo) Prove ROGUE to be BEAST
(pp) QUELL a BRAVO
(qq) Trace RIVER to SHORE

12 Links

(rr) Turn WITCH into FAIRY

237. Find the States ☆☆☆

Enter the answers to the cryptic clues (all five-letter words) in the diagram. The columns containing the first and last letters of the answers will then spell out the names of two American states. Then rearrange the letters contained in the shaded squares to give the name of a third American state.

1. Now his tricks include a game of cards.
2. Is little Susan having children?
3. It's an odd mark.
4. Fowl with headdress on.
5. The weight of a wild cat.
6. Fasteners at one's fingertips.
7. Mistakes with underwear.
8. Harden in river.
9. Scandinavian boatmen or seafarers take part.

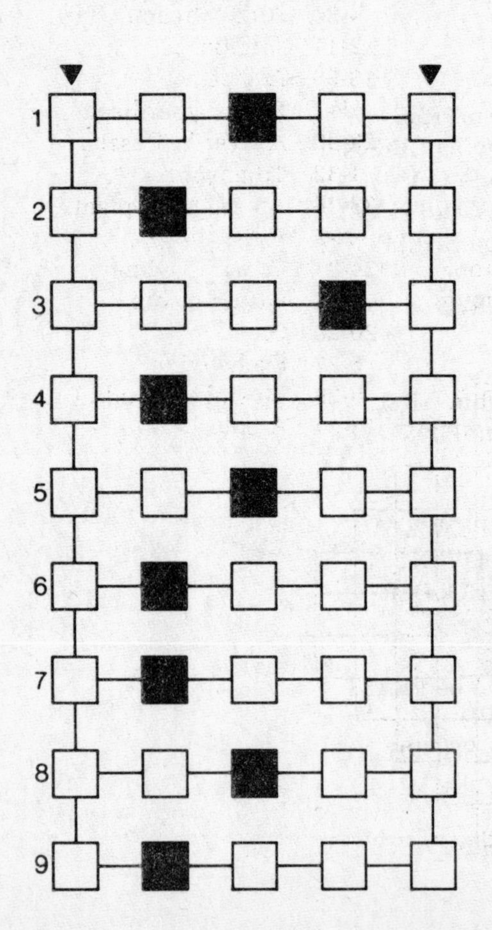

9. CROSSWORDS AND FRIENDS

(the spellings in the answers to the clues that follow are American or English according to the nationality of the compiler)

238. The Original Crossword ☆☆☆

The world's first crossword was published in the newspaper *The New York World* in December 1913. It was the work of Arthur Wynne, an expatriate Liverpudlian. Here it is:

2-3 What bargain hunters enjoy.
4-5 A written acknowledgement.
6-7 Such and nothing more.
10-11 A bird.
14-15 Opposed to less.
18-19 What this puzzle is.
22-23 An animal of prey.
26-27 The close of a day.
28-29 To elude.
30-31 The plural of is.
8-9 To cultivate.
12-13 A bar of wood or iron.
16-17 What artists learn to do.
20-21 Fastened.
24-25 Found on the seashore.
10-18 The fibre of the gomuti palm.
6-22 What we all should be.
4-26 A day dream.
2-11 A talon.
19-28 A pigeon.
F-7 Part of your head.
23-30 A river in Russia.
1-32 To govern.
33-34 An aromatic plant.
N-8 A fist.
24-31 To agree with.
3-12 Part of a ship.
20-29 One.
5-27 Exchanging.
9-25 To sink in mud.
13-21 A boy.

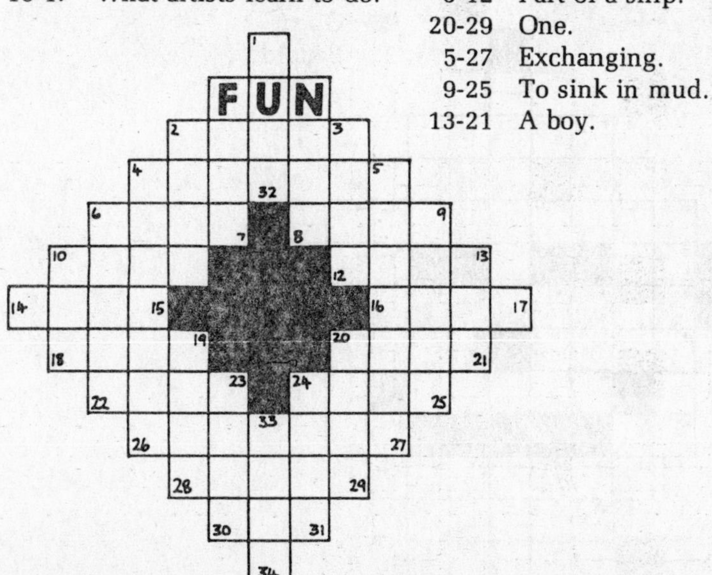

239. The Crossword Clown ☆☆☆

This crossword was published by H. E. Dudeney in 1925.

We give a portrait of our old friend, the Clown. The words defined begin at the numbers and go horizontally or vertically, as the case may be, and stop at the blacked-out squares. Every blank square has to be filled with a letter.

HORIZONTAL

1 A fruit.
4 A boat.
6 Conflict.
8 'An excellent substitute for butter'.
10 For example.
11 A drink beheaded.
12 Answers.
17 A knot.
18 A throw.
19 A sail.
20 Therefore.
22 Either.
23 An English county.
29 A well-known boxer.
30 A poet.

VERTICAL

1 To cultivate.
2 A youngster.
3 The mark.
4 A conveyance.
5 A period.
6 A conveyance.
7 Ideal gardens.
8 Military dinners.
9 A season of the Church.
13 'The' in foreign language.
14 Exclamation of disgust.
15 A congealed liquid.
16 A grain.
21 Surmounts.
22 Slang for all correct.
24 Belongs to.
25 A tear.
26 From.
27 Open.
28 Behold.

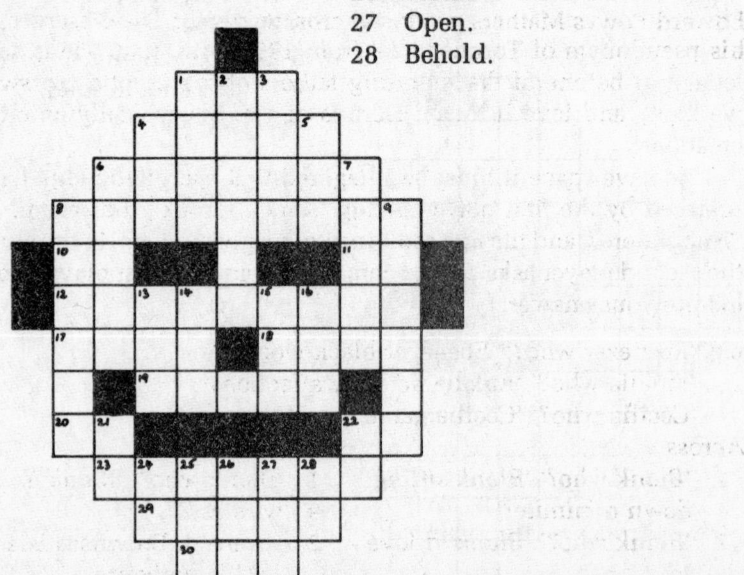

240. The Alphabet ☆☆☆

Here is another unusual crossword by H. E. Dudeney.

The point of this crossword is that every one of the twenty-six letters of the alphabet is used once and only once. We give the definitions, but do not indicate the locations of the words or their direction, horizontal or vertical.

DEFINITIONS

A metal. Parts of trees. To annoy. Whim or imagination. A sign, example. What person or persons. A man's shortened Christian name. To puzzle or make sport of.

241. Knock Knock ☆☆☆☆

Edward Powys Mathers produced crosswords for *The Observer*, under his pseudonym of Torquemada, from 1926 until 1939. He is acknowledged to be one of the founding fathers of the cryptic crossword as we know and love it today. Here is one of his typically entertaining creations.

To save space it must be imagined that each italic clue has been prefaced by the first player saying 'Knock Knock', the second saying 'Who's there?' and the first replying with a given-name. In the clue itself the second player asks 'Given-name who?' and the first player amplifies his previous answer,

e.g. 'Ebenezer who?' 'Ebenezer black wood'
'Eulalia who?' 'Eulalia nate my affections'
'Cecilia who?' 'Cecilia game than I thought'

Across

1 *'Blank who?' 'Blank sitting down a minute?'*

7 *'Blank who?' 'Blank 'd love to'.*

Down

1 } 9 } *'Blank who?' 'Blank a wireless?'*

2 reversed. Brownsea Island is in this harbour.

Across

14 *'Blank who?' 'Blank no-how'.*
15 reversed. Lear had a runcible one.
16 Mulde contributes to me.
17 It's awkward to find the Lord Chancellor upside down in the street on a rainy day.
19 Plant obtainable from high ground overlooking a river valley.
22 reversed. A theocracy.
23 Wore a russet mantle in Shakespeare.
25 Out of the eater came forth meat.
26 'Food for his . . . , repasture for his den'.
28 A peep into taste.
29 See 33.
30 *'Blank who?' 'Blank terrible state of affairs'.*
31 reversed. 54.
32 *'Blank who?' 'Blank fool and caught a cold'.*
35 } 42 } *'Blank who?' 'Blank the bounds of possibility'.*
37 *'Blank who?' 'Blank out and do it again'.*
39 Vowels of 53.
40 *'Blank who?' 'Blank by a tiger'.*
44 } 48 } Make a song about it.
46 *'Blank who?' 'Blank ute ickle sing'.*
49 *'Blank who?' 'Blank, where is fancy bred?'*
53 Creeper formed of Edmund and his son Charles.
55 *'Blank who?' 'Blank pants, I make-a you another pair'.*
56 reversed. Better in character than sugar.

Down

3 } 9 } *'Blank who?' 'Blank note of it'.*
4 *'Blank who?' 'Blank attack of itch'.*
6 *'Blank who?' 'Blank fool, aren't you?'*
7 reversed } 5 } Volume of a particle of dust.
8 *'Blank who?' 'Blank I haven't had a drink all day'.*
10 Room for a dislocated 25.
12 } 11 } *'Blank who?' 'Blank and a small stout'.*
13 } 9 } *'Blank who?' 'Blank ropodist called about my corns?'*
18 My small brother goes round the meadow.
20 reversed. 27.
21 I'm in from the sign.
23 reversed. *'Blank who?' 'Blanks pictures'.*
24 reversed. Impetus.
26 *'Blank who?' 'Blank mow the lawn'.*
27 'On Ararat there grew a vine; When . . . from her bathing rose'.
33 Gets into a 26 ac. with 29.
34 *'Blank who?' 'Blank elephant never forgets'.*
36 With or may say without if you are slow to learn.
38 *'Blank who?' 'Blank who waits'.*
39 My first is unchecked in 28, and my second in 13, 21, 23 dn., 52 and 55.
40 } 52 } *'Blank who?' 'Blank did me wrong'.*
41 More than the reverse of negative colours.
43 '. . . dim . . . red, like God's own head'.

Down

45 reversed. There can be a chick before and a hen behind.

50 }
47 } Almost poached rat.

51 reversed. First half of 41.

52 reversed. 39 do.

54 reversed. 31.

242. A Crossword by Afrit ☆☆☆

While Torquemada's crosswords were appearing in the *Observer*, another English master of the crossword, A. F. Ritchie, better known as Afrit, was entertaining readers of the magazine *The Listener*. Here is an Afrit puzzle which is rather easier than most of his crosswords but every bit as entertaining.

Across

1 He may be a 'richt in the heid, but he's aye wandering (5).

4 Curious fellow: he usually has to pay sixpence (6).

8 The fragrance of an old *amour*. It seems to have gone off a bit! (8).

9 Pat says he made all the running, and of course things have to be to run smoothly (5).

Down

1 You can't say *he* hasn't got a shilling to his name (5).

2 He'll keep you in order, and the motor, too. There's something in that (7).

3 A laying down of the law. Still it doesn't tell you to follow Father (5).

4 Do as the doctor does, and the praise will be equally divided (8).

Across

11 The sum I do here has chemical results (6).

12 They have ends, but they're really beginnings – twelve a year (7).

13 Summary way of making a cab start (8).

14 Stop! – or proceed slowly if the road is (5).

15 To make these you begin with leaves, and end with roots – even if they end in smoke (8).

19 Is it his unnatural need and baffled rage which makes him so false, the rat? (8).

22 Men go like this, little man (5).

24 Truly rural, he is, though not till he's had his beer! (8).

27 It takes two on 'em to do it properly (7).

28 Not experienced, so if you haven't got the right 'un try the left 'un (6).

29 It's dear and old when you sing about it, but it sings for the camper when it's new and cheap (5).

30 Hides away, but shows that the island lies between the South and South-east (8).

31 You may safely do so to the baby; otherwise you might get landed! (6).

32 Lots and lots, though they may be reduced to a shred (5).

Down

5 There's a hindrance *en route*, and that makes the game merely one of chance (8).

6 It really is a moving spectacle to see Mother after the cows!

7 'Tear asunder a broken reed' is one account of it, but it's another kind of account which usually is (8).

8 A design which is revealed in the name of the Law (6).

10 An untidy study is naturally bound to be (5).

16 She doesn't sound as if she were mass-produced, so she should render good service (8).

17 Considerably abashed, as Vera would be by a proposal like this! (8).

18 To get across, let art go one way and poetry the other (8).

20 You can't approve his way of getting money, especially as he's got enough under his head to keep a roof over his head (7).

21 Foxes had them long before the wireless was thought of (6).

22 This is desire in an immoderate degree, so the degree should be modified and diminished (5).

23 Spoil a good drink? Why, it's the outside edge! (6).

25 Pitch and toss. If you're right in this you won't be left in this (5).

26 They make an end of themselves, being mere creatures of fancy (5).

243. A Crossword by Ximenes ☆☆☆☆

Ximenes, whose real name was Derrick Somerset MacNutt, was the successor of Torquemada in the *Observer*, and was probably the greatest crossword compiler of all time. Here is one of his difficult puzzles.

Across

1 Dam chilly in Scotland (5).
5 Rush needed here – it could be prussic (7).
11 This fruit will be nearly made into jelly if you turn the gas out (10).
12 Audibly masticate a pie and thin cake (8).
14 In black I win – more often than not (4).
15 Almost a stink about a cap that's red (7).
16 Sat working with hardened felon in prison (6).

Down

1 Strutter, and what he isn't, seen at a fair (7).
2 Pitch with a hole, spoilt – I was cautious (10).
3 Bits of lava envelop unfortunate one (7).
4 Tipple before a series of excitements (5).
6 Irish tenant has a small boat and a row (7).
7 Antelope occupying a den got up (6).
8 Pages and pages make a big bore – skim (4).

Across

18 See where a river runs with broad branches (5).
19 Old Soldier afire in anticipation (7).
24 Car tire has become unpredictable (7).
25 I'm rapid: if unfinished, I show impatience (5).
26 Yearly split – so will one shock the kids? (6)
28 About to sprout: those that don't will die (7).
30 It's an advantage to move like a crab (4).
31 Indian farmer in daze, mind arrested (8).
32 Film presentations, big bits to be scrapped (10).
33 Modern poet seems to be extravagant (7).
34 Rude men, baffled by aitches (5).

Down

9 Salt, a small portion found in feathers (8).
10 Lester's first in a race – no longer rare (5).
13 Tiny nail to cut into a pendulous tree (10).
17 A soft sheen in a sheaf of volutes (8).
20 Pains once taken about sin of the world (7).
21 Rout of German – nought; should be Austrian (7).
22 Nasty disease – its cure is complicated (7).
23 Jammed and stuck about right-hand side (6).
25 Confront angry mongrel (5).
27 In flight – it's terrible (5).
29 What Jock hoes, upwards – its edge is sharp (4).

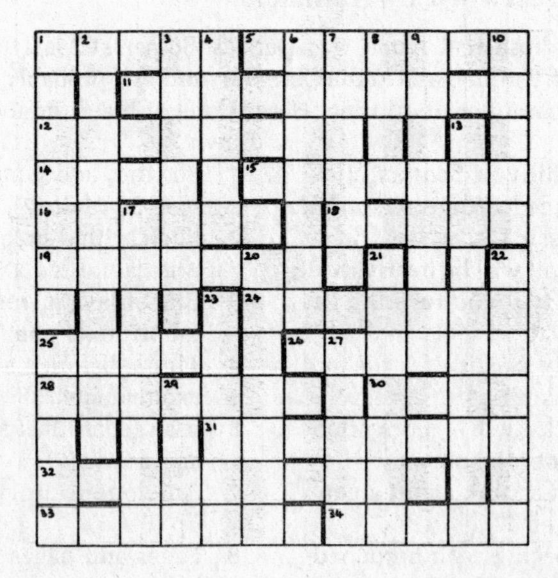

244. Contrary Crossword ☆☆☆

The answers are words opposite in meanings to the clues. For example if the clue is FINISH the answer might be START or BEGIN.

Also, the answers are inserted not from left to right (ACROSS) and from top to bottom (DOWN) as in a normal crossword, but from right to left (BACK) and from bottom to top (UP).

BACK

1 Affluent (5).
2 Helps (7).
3 Figurative (7).
4 Adorned (5).
6 Takes (5).
8 Concentrated (7).
12 Worked (6).
14 Multiply (6).
15 Health (7).
16 Sour (5).
17 Equatorial (5).
18 Success (7).
22 Lax (7).
25 Sluggish (5).

UP

5 Prose (5).
7 Relaxed (5).
8 Shallowness (5).
9 Children (6).
10 Conceal (7).
11 Darken (7).
13 Hero (7).
19 Commons (5).
20 Truly (7).
21 Attract (5).
22 Debit (6).
23 Believed (7).
24 Humility (5).
25 Accepted (7).

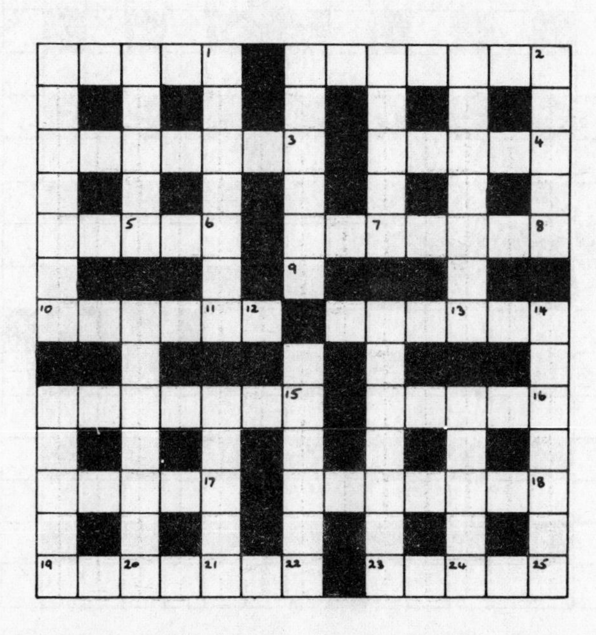

245. An Anagram Crossword ☆☆☆

This puzzle is by Michael Curl, who creates crosswords for a number of British newspapers and magazines.

In this crossword the clues are simply anagrams.

Across

1 Centaurs.
5 Rested.
9 Sceptres.
10 Recipe.
11 Shingled.
12 Strait.
14 Undressing.
18 Impression.
22 Dagger.
23 Salesmen.
24 Routed.
25 Presides.
26 Trance.
27 Gantries.

Down

1 Hearty.
2 Enters.
3 Tassel.
4 Stagnation.
6 Resisted.
7 Engrains.
8 Treaties.
13 Coordinate.
15 Picadors.
16 Berthing.
17 Insecure.
19 Peered.
20 Recede.
21 Stares.

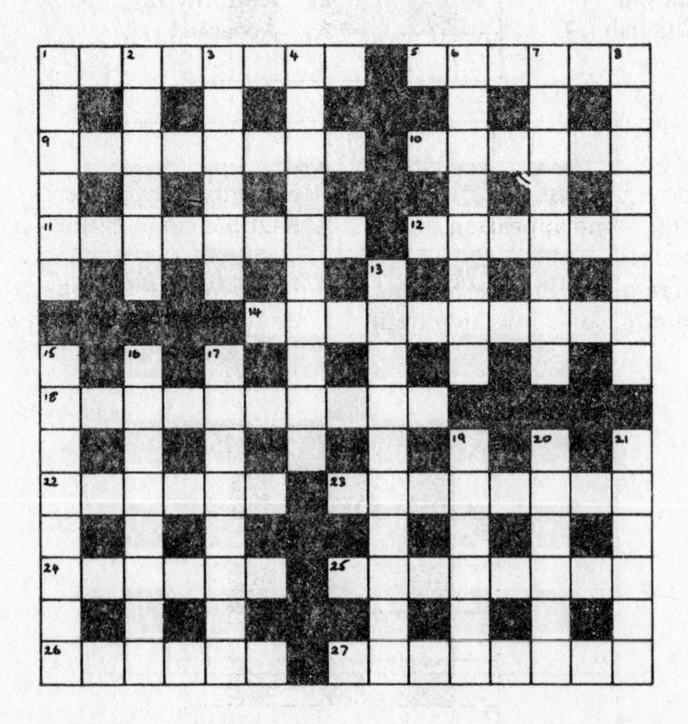

246. Two Miniature Crosswords ☆☆☆

These two crosswords by Michael Curl are small but perfectly formed.

(a)

Across

1 Greek horseman.
5 Some epic adored by a bullfighter.
6 Dante is translated in lieu.
7 Confused as sleep slips away.

Down

1 Overturn? It's a measure of one's bigheadedness!
2 A coin is collected as capital.
3 A speech – and where it should be delivered?
4 Sort of red rose found in church.

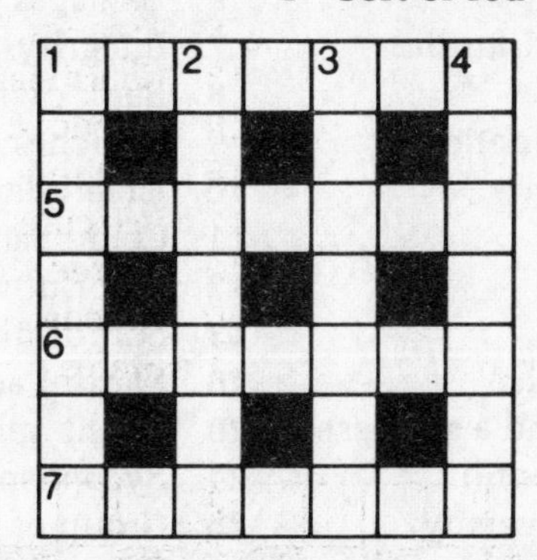

(b)

Across

1 House in open land?
5 Actor – one appearing in musical.
6 Asian queen in New Spain.
7 Reunite, somehow, in a train.

Down

1 Fall from a harvester?
2 Ragtime composition for a sleuth.
3 If you want a personal view, there's nothing to a cogwheel.
4 It's unusual for a saint to wander.

1		2		3		4
	■		■		■	
5						
	■		■		■	
6						
	■		■		■	
7						

247. A Crossword by Luzzatto ☆☆☆

The modern American crossword has evolved in quite a different way from its British counterpart. Here is an example by Jack Luzzatto, one of the most popular crossword compilers in America.

Across

1 Criticize for error.
6 —— kebab.
11 Epoch.
14 Steel shielding.
15 Made a bridge of boats to cross a river.
17 White oak of California.
18 A time between.
19 Eggs with imagination.
21 Hurts and disables.
22 Hindu dress.
23 Quiet periods.
25 Overrule.
27 Magician's word.
29 Icy pinnacle amid a crevasse.
30 Hot dry desert wind.
33 Boola-boola university.
35 Superb craftsmanship.
36 Device to change function.
38 Dining alcove.
40 Central: Abbr.
41 Waterless.
43 Wooded area.
44 Fine threads.
46 Categories of plants or animals.
48 Letter A, in communications.
49 A well-planned crime.
50 Heroic tale.
54 Submarine detector.
56 Spaces for stowing cargo.
58 Of atomic particles.
60 Shame.
61 Weaken the foundation.
62 Chosen few.
63 Manuscripts: Abbr.
64 Waned.
65 Consonants said softly.

Down

1 Western card game.
2 Cooking fragrance.
3 Brown oil paint.
4 Sop for a tot.
5 Coatrack.
6 Damages out of malice.
7 Integrity.
8 Bank dividend: Abbr.
9 Stanches.
10 Israeli dance.
11 Count each one.
12 Colorful warblers.
13 Soft drink.
16 Martini additive.
20 Slight quake.
24 Sycophant.
26 Group of eight.
28 Rolls of names, for duty.
29 Spanish title.
30 —— Guitry, French actor.
31 Boy paragons: 2 wds.
32 Makes many copies.
34 Long-term convicts.
37 Latvian seaport capital.
39 Delible.
42 Step out onto the landing strip.
45 Rajah's wife.
47 Approached.
49 Morse
51 Repeatedly.
52 Beau ——.
53 Partner of sackcloth.
55 Land measure.
57 Chinese money of account.
58 Not talking.
59 Movement for freedom, for short.

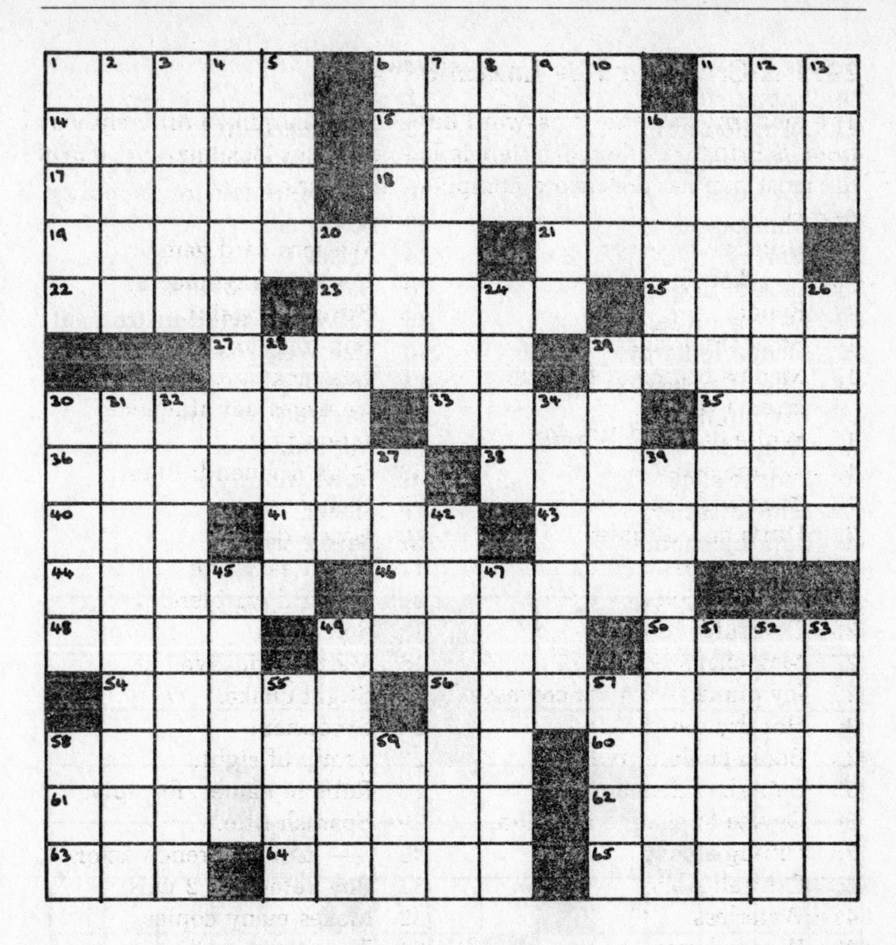

248. Another Crossword by Luzzatto ☆☆☆

Here is another crossword by Jack Luzzatto.

Across

1 Drank.
8 Intimidator.
14 Experience.
15 Poison gas from antimony.
16 Wins affection.
17 Four-element vacuum tube.
18 Former Brazilian money.
19 Breakout.
21 Flee.
22 U.S. tax service.
23 Ship ends.

Down

1 Questioned to clear up doubt.
2 Rattle.
3 Steele's literary partner.
4 Professional charges.
5 Monk's title.
6 Fine-plumed heron.
7 Bedded down in a flophouse.
8 Paces.
9 Mention.
10 Hebrew patriarch: Abbr.
11 Broadway girl of the past.

Across

24 Encircled.
25 Summon forth.
27 Acted so.
28 Dwindle.
29 Abnegation.
31 Martial.
33 Lack of originality.
35 Frill or ruffle.
38 Mental lethargy.
42 Tale of a classic siege.
43 Used to be.
45 Think so.
46 Ladder step.
47 Mine disaster.
49 Run the engine.

Down

12 Sufferer.
13 Return to earth.
15 Substitute actor.
20 Lots of trouble for the police.
23 Scorched.
24 Arises.
26 Handy travel sack.
28 Valve in a wind instrument.
30 Mae West role.
32 French plural article.
34 Haulable by rope.
35 Andiron.
36 Howl weirdly.
37 Skater.
39 Bayou canoe.

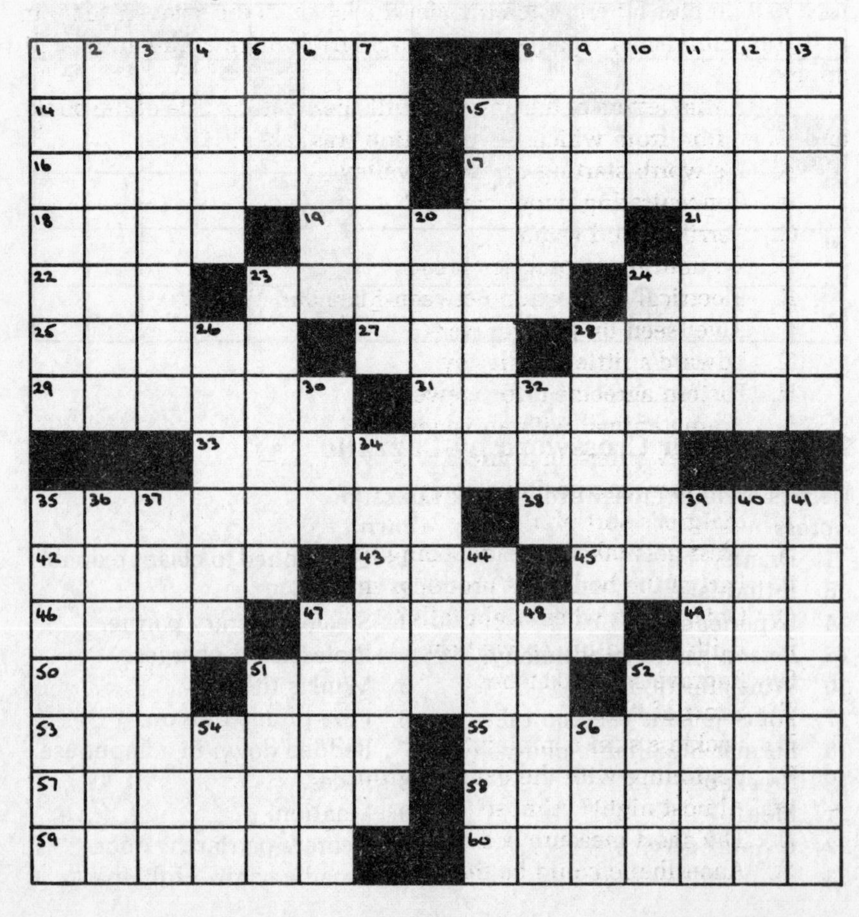

Across

50 Large deer.
51 Threads for cloth.
52 Sun hat.
53 Doggone stupid.
55 Outside the law.
57 Of the eared seals.
58 Main movie on program.
59 Slaves of the lamp.
60 City roads.

Down

40 Single installment in a magazine: 2 wds.
41 Heaps abuse upon.
44 Strokes on typefaces.
47 Twigs or shoots for grafting.
48 Small island.
51 Pâté de —— gras.
52 Head: Fr.
54 Last workday for most: Abbr.
56 Household god.

249. Cryptic Acrostic 1 ☆☆☆

Solve the clues and place the answers into one of the two smaller grids next to their clue letters. Then transfer the letters of the answers to their matching numbered squares in the large grid where a quotation will appear.

The initial letters of the answers will spell out the title of the book, and its author, from which the quotation was taken.

A. It's worth starting up in the valley
B. Concentrating under canvas?
C. Terribly loud game
D. Do nothing to produce bread
E. Electrical connection between Mars and Venus?
F. River seen on golf-course?
G. Edward's little cuddly toy
H. Eastern agreement for viewers
J. Young animal with an islander
K. Do they entertain armies?
L. The man composing a song
M. Maigret's sort of music?
N. West gets taken outside, being obscene
P. Part of the body that produces music?
Q. Object seen when night falls?
R. Faith is tied up, so we hear
S. Engrave some sketches
T. Short of fibre
U. Reckless skin complaint
V. Beginning with the exterior group?
W. Almost night? Almost!
X. The short measure is a crime!
Y. Anaesthetic could be there

A	51	23	88	9	100		
B	95	45	38	3	81	17	
C	78	93	112	57			
D	12	108	33	74			
E	21	48	65	1	104		
F	87	36	71	6			
G	19	61	107	82	69		
H	99	106	5	41			
J	29	85	53	64	101		
K	2	111	90	59	14		
L	27	96	66	18	52	67	
M	84	31	10	103	16	73	40
N	28	79	15	102			
P	110	43	11	68	22		
Q	24	98	50	55	109		
R	49	8	25	91	76		
S	13	97	34	60			
T	92	37	77	63	83		
U	26	80	4	62			
V	44	75	56	70	89	35	
W	47	86	46	30			
X	94	39	54	58	7		
Y	105	42	20	72	32		

1E	2K	3B	4U	5H		6F	7X	8R	9A	10M	11P	12D	13S
14K		15N	16M	17B	18L		19G	20Y	21E		22P	23A	24Q
25R	26U	27L	28N		29J	30W	31M	32Y	33D	34S	35V	36F	37T
	38B	39X	40M		41H	42Y	43P	44V	45B	46W		47W	48E
49R	50Q	51A	52L		53J	54X	55Q	56V		57C	58X		59K
60S	61G		62U	63T	64J	65E	66L		67L	68P	69G		70V
71F	72Y	73M		74D	75V	76R	77T	78C	79N		80U	81B	82G
	83T	84M	85J	86W	87F	88A	89V	90K	91R		92T	93C	94X
	95B	96L		97S	98Q	99H		100A	101J	102N		103M	104E
105Y	106H		107G	108D		109Q	110P	111K	112C				

250. Cryptic Acrostic 2 ☆☆☆

Solve the clues and place the answers into one of the two smaller grids next to their clue letters. Then transfer the letters of the answers to their matching numbered squares in the large grid where a quotation will appear.

A	9	127	32	106	87	51	72	
B	100	55	28	109	70	58	42	
C	126	8	63	25	57	105	41	92
D	82	65	103	97	77	69	43	
E	107	35	50	128	108	90		
F	49	2	38	24	34	104	68	
G	118	40	71	125	20	91	27	
H	31	6	59	21	124	1	86	119
J	74	132	67	96	85	16	56	
K	22	88	120	79	12	46	5	
L	84	29	61	122	99			
M	23	102	7	53	80	33		
N	45	95	116	66	4	39		
P	115	44	52	36	121	15	10	83
Q	94	11	13	48	130	64		
R	54	101	30	81	117	98		
S	89	47	131	76				
T	37	123	14	110	60	111	75	
U	114	73	113	3	26	18		
V	112	62	78	93	17	129	19	

The initial letters of the answers will spell out the title of the book, and its author, from which the quotation was taken.

A. Turner is a cheat! (7)
B. A fish had a weed (7)
C. Charm one's way in (8)
D. Several new shows! (7)
E. Making a request like a ruler (6)
F. He does not believe in Castro (7)
G. Now present – but not in any place (7)
H. But rings may be splitting (8)
J. Rhetoric – or standing beside a politician (7)
K. Lash pet dog (7)
L. Study, perhaps, requiring a sweep? (5)
M. Basket that may be an impediment? (6)
N. Learner, terrible but legal (6)
P. Sailors in the drink (8)
Q. Break the law to obtain riches (6)
R. Royal Engineers have two to mend (6)
S. Employ sound sheep (4)
T. Ron goes back to people in the county (7)
U. Chicken or cow on a road (6)
V. Observing eastern espionage (7)

1H	2F		3U	4N	5K	6H	7M	8C		9A	10P	11Q		12K	13Q
14T	15P	16J	17V	18U	19V	20G	21H		22K	23M	24F	25C	26U	27G	28B
	29L	30R		31H	32A	33M	34F	35E		36P	37T		38F	39N	40G
41C	42B	43D		44P	45N	46K	47S		48Q	49F	50E	51A		52P	53M
54R	55B	56J		57C	58B	59H	60T	61L	62V		63C	64Q	65D		66N
67J	68F	69D	70B	71G		72A	73U	74J	75T	76S		77D	78V	79K	80M
81R	82D	83P	84L		85J	86H		87A	88K	89S		90E	91G	92C	93V
	94Q	95N	96J	97D	98R	99L		100B	101R	102M	103D	104F	105C	106A	
107E	108E	109B		110T	111T	112V	113U		114U	115P	116N	117R	118G	119H	
120K	121P	122L	123T		124H	125G	126C		127A	128E	129V	130Q	131S	132J	

251. Spiralword ☆☆☆

The answers are to be entered spirally into the diagram, the last two or more letters of each answer forming the beginning of the next one.

1 Unassuming.
2 Warship.
3 Fur.
4 Planet.
5 Notwithstanding.
6 Absolutely necessary.
7 Height.
8 Flood.
9 Japanese entertainer.
10 Disadvantage.
11 Competent.
12 Young hare.
13 Game dog.
14 Word for word.
15 Huge.
16 Signalling system.
17 American state.
18 Burdensome.
19 Person seizing power.
20 Ground that's always frozen.
21 Salary.
22 Strive.
23 Suave.
24 The drink of the gods.
25 Craftsman.
26 Firedog.
27 Wild ass.
28 Scholarly.
29 Storm.
30 Dagger.
31 Poison.
32 Blue dye.
33 Giant champion of the Philistines.

1		2							3			
	10					11					12	4
			18					19				
				24				25				
9	17			29						20		
		23					33	30			13	
				32								5
								26				
8			28		31							
						27						
	16			22				21				
					15						14	
		7							6			

252. Codeword ☆☆☆

In this crossword each letter of the alphabet is represented by a number. The problem is to work out which letter each number represents. We have given you three letters to start you off. If you fill in these letters wherever the corresponding number occurs in the diagram, it should not take you too long to determine the other letters.

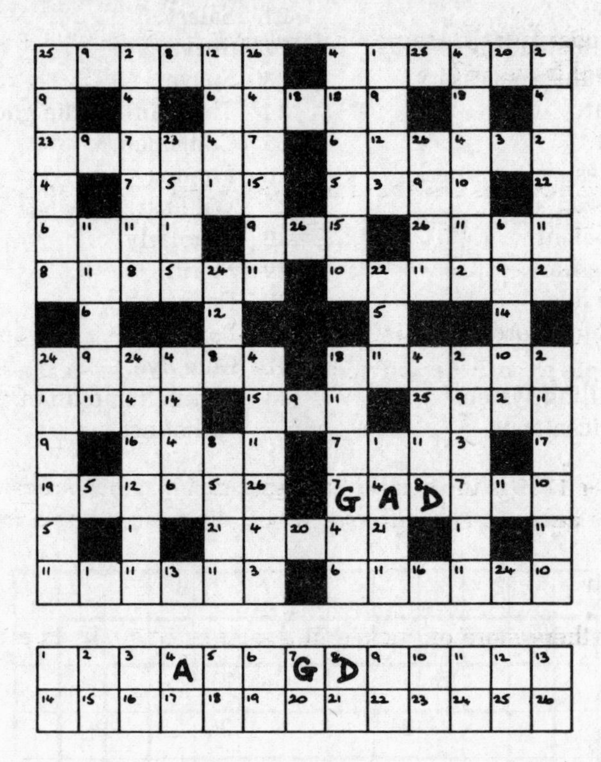

10. QUICK THINKING

253. ☆☆

Which number gives the same result when it is divided by -6 as when it is subtracted from -6?

254. ☆☆

Which three numbers give the same result when they are added as when they are multiplied together.

255. ☆

There are five apples in a basket and five people in a room. How can you give an apple to each person and still leave an apple in the basket?

256. ☆☆☆

The number 1729 is the smallest number that may be expressed as the sum of two cubes in two different ways. What are the two ways?

257. ☆☆

Which are there more of: inches in a mile or Sundays in a thousand years?

258. ☆☆

Which are there more of: seconds in a week or feet in 100 miles?

259. ☆☆

Which is heavier: 1000 kilograms or 1 ton?

260. ☆☆

Which is longer: 250 centimetres or 8 feet?

261. ☆☆

Which is colder: minus 40 degrees Centigrade or minus 40 degrees Fahrenheit?

262. ☆☆

Which is longer:

(a) 666 days or 95 weeks?
(b) 666 inches or 55 feet?
(c) 666 hours or 28 days?
(d) 666 millimetres or 2 feet?
(e) 666 minutes or one-fourteenth of a week?

263. ☆☆

A driver goes once round a 5-mile circular track at 30 miles per hour. How fast must he travel on the second lap in order to average 60 miles per hour for the two laps?

264. ☆☆

What is the value of one-half of two-thirds of three-quarters of four-fifths of five-sixths of six-sevenths of seven-eighths of eight-ninths of nine-tenths of 1000?

265. ☆☆

In a race, the runner who came three places in front of the runner who finished last came two places ahead of the runner who came seventh.

How many finished the race?

266. ☆☆

A man smoked 100 cigarettes in five days, each day smoking six more than on the previous day.

How many cigarettes did he smoke on the first day?

267. ☆☆

If you put a coin into an empty bottle and then insert a cork into the neck of the bottle, how can you get the coin out of the bottle without taking out the cork or breaking the bottle?

268. ☆☆

A man had a square swimming pool in his garden with a tree growing at each corner, like this:

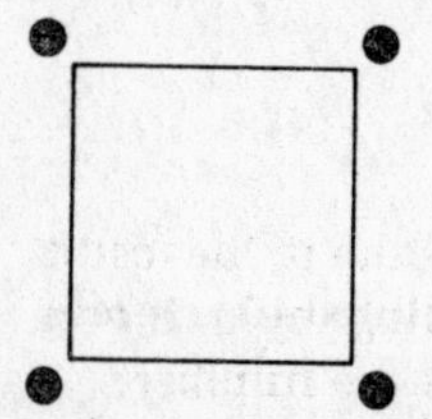

How could he double the size of his swimming pool, keeping it square, without cutting down or moving any of the trees?

269. ☆☆

Can you draw four straight lines through these nine dots without lifting your pen from the paper?

● ● ●

● ● ●

● ● ●

270. ☆☆

If I said to you 'I will bet you £1 that if you gave me £2 I will give you £3 in return' would that be a good bet for you to accept?

271. ☆☆

A's watch is 5 minutes fast but he thinks it is 10 minutes slow. B's watch is 10 minutes slow but he thinks it is 5 minutes fast. They both plan to catch the 12 o'clock train. Who gets to the station first?

272. ☆☆

A boy has as many sisters as brothers, but each sister has only half as many sisters as brothers.

How many boys and how many girls are there in the family?

273. ☆☆

How many triangles are there in this diagram?

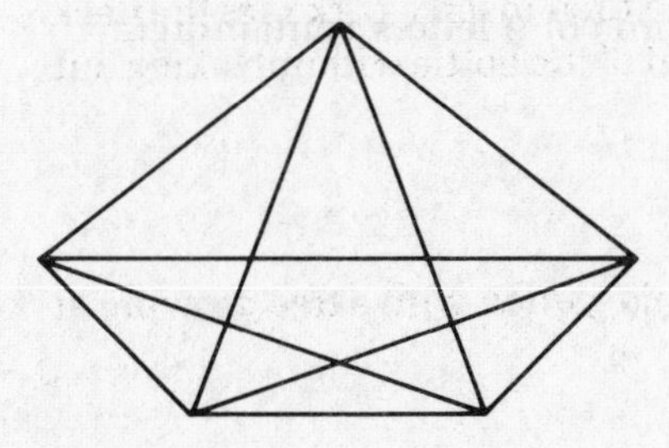

274. ☆☆

I am thinking of a three-digit number. If you subtract 8 from it, the result is divisible by 8. If you add 9 to it, the result is divisible by 9. If you subtract 7 from it, the result is divisible by 7. What is the number?

275. ☆☆☆

What is the sum of all the integers from 1 to 2000?

276. ☆☆☆

How many times on average must an ordinary six-sided die be tossed before every number from one to six comes up at least once?

277. ☆☆

A traveller in a strange country, with no map, comes to a crossroads where a signpost has been knocked down. How can he find his way without asking anyone for directions?

278. ☆☆☆

If twenty people, on parting, all shake hands with each other once, how many handshakes will there be altogether?

279. ☆☆

Show how six sixes can equal a gross.

280. ☆☆

Can you think of common English words containing:

(a) two double E's?
(b) two double O's?
(c) two double S's?
(d) two double F's?

281. ☆☆☆

Can you think of common English words of 9 letters containing:

(a) five E's?
(b) five S's?

11. MODERN MASTERS

HUBERT PHILLIPS

Hubert Phillips has had thousands of puzzles published both under his own name and his pseudonym of 'Caliban' – in publications such as the *Daily Telegraph*, the *Evening Standard*, the *New Statesman*, the *Law Journal* and countless others.

282. Good Eggs ☆☆☆☆

'You don't like arithmetic, child?' said Humpty Dumpty. 'I don't very much.'

'But I thought you were good at sums,' said Alice.

'So I am,' said Humpty Dumpty. 'Good at sums; oh, certainly. But what has that to do with liking them? When I qualified as a Good Egg – many, many years ago, that was – I got a better mark in arithmetic than any of the others who qualified. Not that that's saying a lot. None of us did as well in arithmetic as in any other subject.'

'How many subjects were there?' said Alice, interested.

'Ah!' said Humpty Dumpty, 'I must think. The number of subjects was one-third of the number of marks obtainable in any one subject. And I ought to mention that in no two subjects did I get the same mark, and that is also true of the other Good Eggs who qualified.'

'But you haven't told me —' began Alice.

'I know I haven't,' said Humpty Dumpty. 'I haven't told you how many marks in all one had to obtain to qualify. Well, I'll tell you now. It was a number equal to four times the maximum obtainable in one subject. And we all just managed to qualify.'

'But how many —' said Alice.

'I'm coming to that,' said Humpty Dumpty. 'How many of us were there? Well, when I tell you that no two of us obtained the same assortment of marks – a thing which was only just possible – you'll be well on the way to the answer. But to make it as easy as I can for you, I'll put it another way. The number of other Good Eggs who qualified when I did, multiplied by the number of subjects (I've told you about that already), gives a product equal to half the total number of marks obtained by each Good Egg. And now you can find out all you want to know.' He composed himself for a nap.

Alice was almost in tears. 'I can't,' she said, 'do any of it. Isn't it differential equations, or something I've never learned?'

Humpty Dumpty opened one eye. 'Don't be a fool, child,' he said crossly. 'Anyone ought to be able to do it, who is able to count on five fingers.'

What was Humpty Dumpty's mark in arithmetic?

283. Helpuselph ☆☆☆

A settler in the island of Helpuselph applied to the Governor for some land. 'How much would you like?' asked the Governor.

'About 100 square miles.'

'Okay,' said the Governor. 'You may choose a rectangular parcel of land in the township of Little Rainfall. Its dimensions must be such that, if one side of the rectangle were 5 miles longer, and the other 4 miles longer, the area of the rectangle would be twice as great; and its perimeter must be exactly 46 miles.'

The applicant duly selected and fenced his land in accordance with these conditions. But he got away with six square miles more than the Governor had anticipated.

What was the area of the selected rectangle?

284. Dodecahedra ☆☆☆☆

I have an indefinite number of regular dodecahedra, indistinguishable in appearance from one another. I have pots of red and blue paint. If each face of each dodecahedron is to be painted red or blue, how many dodecahedra which are distinguishable from one another shall I be able to produce?

DAVID WELLS

Here are three puzzles from David Wells, professional puzzler and games inventor, and former editor of the magazine *Games and Puzzles*.

285. Behind the Scenes ☆☆☆

The results were about to be announced in the annual Ruritanian song festival, but there was apparently some delay. Gradually the word was passed round that one of the four finalists, instead of giving three marks to the other finalist he rated highest, and two marks for the next best finalist and one mark for the third best (naturally no finalist was asked to rate his own song), had reversed the marks given, hoping to improve his own chances. He had given one mark to his best choice, two marks to his middle choice and three marks to the finalist he actually thought worst.

The commotion was of course tremendous and it only increased when it was revealed that two of the other finalists had taken exactly the same dishonest step in the hope, so they thought, of improving *their* chances.

Before these revelations were made all four finalists had been tied on six points. When the judges eventually reversed the marking orders of the three dishonest finalists, in what place did the honest singer find himself?

286. Electronic Lullaby ☆☆

Our small neighbour was given an electronics set for Christmas and we have had no peace since. His latest model is an electronic organ. Unfortunately, it only plays three notes: a high note, *ping*, a middle note, *mmmmmm*, and a low note, *boing*. He has wired these up so that the same note repeated, for example *ping-ping*, is immediately followed by an *mmmmmm*. A note followed by a lower note is followed in turn by *ping*, and a note following a lower note is then followed by a *boing*.

Really quite impressive for a twelve-year-old, but the contraption is getting on our nerves. Can you explain why?

287. Trigger Happy ☆☆☆

'So how much do we know?' asked Patterson, doodling with his pencil on the desk.

'It's a five-figure number and it's a perfect square,' replied Gerson, 'but don't forget that if we get the wrong number the mechanism will jam and we'll lose all chance of detonating it.' He drummed his fingers. The phone rang. He picked it up.

'Good heavens! Yes!' He looked at Patterson. 'The first two figures are 69, and it reads the same either way! That must fix it, surely? The number is palindromic.' Patterson scribbled quickly on his pad. '26 . . . 265 . . . 264, ah, 264 squared is 69696, just a moment . . . mmmm, that's it.' He looked up at Gerson and grinned. Gerson picked up the phone and spoke quickly, then sat back and said nothing. After several minutes, the phone rang again and he picked it up confidently . 'Yes? It's . . . jammed?' Beads of sweat appeared on his forehead and Patterson felt sick. What had gone wrong?

PIERRE BERLOQUIN

The puzzles of Pierre Berloquin are tremendously popular in his native France. He has published several books of puzzles, as well as many other books about indoor games, and has regular columns in the magazine *Science et Vie* and in the Paris newspaper *Le Monde*. Here are two puzzles selected from his works.

288. Cross-Country ☆☆☆

Every month Timothy, Urban and Vincent run cross-country before breakfast.

After a month they realize that Timothy has finished before Urban more often than after him and that Urban has finished before Vincent more often than after him.

Is it possible that Vincent has finished before Timothy more often than after him?

289. Five Friends ☆☆☆

Five friends, Andrew, Bernard, Claude, Donald and Eugene, each have a son and a daughter. Their families are so close that each has married his daughter to the son of one of his friends, and as a result the daughter-in-law of the father of Andrew's son-in-law is the sister-in-law of Bernard's son, and the son-in-law of the father of Claude's daughter-in-law is the brother-in-law of Donald's daughter.

But although the daughter-in-law of the father of Bernard's daughter-in-law has the same mother-in-law as the son-in-law of the father of Donald's son-in-law, the situation is simplified by the fact that no daughter-in-law is the sister-in-law of the daughter of her father-in-law.

Who married Eugene's daughter?

BORIS KORDEMSKY

Boris Kordemsky, who was born in 1907, is a retired secondary school mathematics teacher living in Moscow. He has produced several books on mathematics and on mathematical recreations. But it is for his collection of puzzles, *Mathematical Know-how*, first published in 1956, that he is famous. This work has been translated from the original Russian into Ukrainian, Estonian, Lettish and Lithuanian. Outside the USSR translations of the book have appeared in Bulgaria, Hungary, Rumania, Poland, Czechoslovakia, France, Germany, China, Japan and Korea. The following four puzzles are taken from this collection.

290. Down and Up ☆☆☆

A boy presses a side of a blue pencil to a side of a yellow pencil, holding both pencils vertically. One inch of the pressed side of the blue pencil, measuring from its lower end, is smeared with paint. The yellow pencil is held steady while the boy slides the blue pencil down 1 inch, continuing to press it against the yellow one. He returns the blue pencil to its former position, then slides it down 1 inch. He continues until he has lowered the blue pencil 5 times and raised it 5 times – 10 moves in all.

Suppose that during this time the paint neither dries nor diminishes in quantity. How many inches of each pencil will be smeared with paint after the tenth move?

This problem was thought up by the mathematician Leonid Mikhailovitch Rybakov while on his way home after a successful duck hunt. What led him to make up this puzzle is explained in the answer, but don't read it until you have solved the problem.

291. Large Segments Instead of Small ☆☆☆

In the Soviet machine industry a marker is a man who draws lines on a metal blank. The blank is cut along the lines to produce the desired shape.

A marker was asked to distribute 7 equal-sized sheets of metal among 12 workers, each worker to get the same amount of metal. He could not use the simple solution of dividing each sheet into 12 equal parts, for this would result in too many tiny pieces. What was he to do?

He thought awhile and found a more convenient method.

Later he easily divided 5 sheets for 6 workers, 13 for 12, 13 for 36, 26 for 21, and so on.

What was his method?

292. A Jar with Lead Shot ☆☆

The builders of an irrigation canal needed a lead plate of a certain size, but had no lead in stock. They decided to melt some lead shot. But how could they find its volume beforehand?

One suggestion was to measure a ball, apply the formula for the volume of a sphere, and multiply by the number of balls. But this would take too long, and anyway the shot wasn't all the same size.

Another was to weigh all the shot and divide by the specific gravity of lead. Unfortunately, no one could remember this ratio, and there was no manual in the field shop.

Another was to pour the shot into a gallon jug. But the volume of the jug is greater than the volume of the shot by an undetermined amount, since the shot cannot be packed solid and part of the jug contains air.

Do you have a suggestion?

293. A Singular Trip ☆☆☆☆

Two boys go on a bicycle trip. En route one of the bicycles breaks down and has to be left behind for repairs. They decide to share the remaining bicycle. They start simultaneously, one on bicycle, one on foot. At a certain point the cyclist dismounts, leaves the bicycle behind, and continues on foot. His friend, when he reaches the waiting bicycle, mounts it and rides until he catches up with his friend, who takes the bicycle, and so on.

How far from their destination should the bicycle be left behind the last time so they reach the destination simultaneously? The distance from breakdown to destination is 60 miles, and they each walk 5 miles per hour and bicycle 15 miles per hour.

MARTIN GARDNER

Martin Gardner, born 1914, is well known for his recreational mathematics columns in *Scientific American*, which ran for over two decades, and for the numerous collections of puzzles and mathematical diversions that he has had published. Here are three examples.

294. The Circle on the Chessboard ☆☆☆

A chess board has squares that are two inches on the side. What is the radius of the largest circle that can be drawn on the board in such a way that the circle's circumference is entirely on black squares?

295. Dividing the Cake ☆☆☆☆

There is a simple procedure by which two people can divide a cake so that each is satisfied he has at least half: One cuts and the other chooses. Devise a general procedure so that *n* persons can cut a cake into *n* portions in such a way that everyone is satisfied he has at least 1/*n* of the cake.

296. Three Prisoners ☆☆☆☆

Three men – A, B and C – were in separate cells under sentence of death when the state governor decided to pardon one of them. He wrote their names on three slips of paper, shook the slips in a hat, drew out one of them, and telephoned the prisoner governor, requesting that the name of the lucky man be kept secret for several days. Rumour of this reached prisoner A. When the governor made his morning rounds, A tried to persuade the governor to tell him who had been pardoned. The governor refused.

'Then tell me,' said A, 'the name of one of the others who will be executed. If B is to be pardoned, give me C's name. If C is to be pardoned, give me B's name. And if I'm to be pardoned, toss a coin to decide whether to name B or C.'

'But if you see me toss the coin,' replied the wary governor, 'you'll know that you're the one pardoned. And if you see that I don't toss a coin, you'll know it's either you or the person I don't name.'

'Then don't tell me now,' said A. 'Tell me tomorrow morning.'

The governor, who knew nothing about probability theory, thought it over that night and decided that if he followed the procedure suggested by A, it would give A no help whatever in estimating his survival chances. So next morning he told A that B was going to be executed.

After the governor left, A smiled to himself at the governor's stupidity. There were now only two equally probable elements in what mathematicians like to call the 'sample space' of the problem. Either C would be pardoned or himself, so by all the laws of conditional probability, his chances of survival had gone up from ⅓ to ½.

The governor did not know that A could communicate with C, in an adjacent cell, by tapping in code on a water pipe. This A proceeded to do, explaining to C exactly what he had said to the governor and what the governor had said to him. C was equally overjoyed with the news because he figures, by the same reasoning used by A, that his own survival chances had also risen to ½.

Did the two men reason correctly? If not, how should each have calculated his chances of being pardoned?

DAVID SILVERMAN

David Silverman, a resident of Los Angeles, established his reputation on the basis of one incredible book called *Your Move* as a brilliant creator of original puzzles. The following three puzzles are taken from that book.

297. The Truel ☆☆☆☆

After a mutual and irreconcilable dispute among Red, Black and Blue, the three parties have agreed to a three-way duel. Each man is provided a pistol and an unlimited supply of ammunition. Instead of simultaneous volleys, a firing order is to be established and followed until only one survivor remains.

Blue is a 100 per cent marksman, never having missed a bull's-eye in his shooting career. Black is successful two out of three times on the average, and you, Red, are only a 1/3 marksman. Recognizing the disparate degrees of marksmanship, the seconds have decided that you will be the first and Black second in the firing order.

Your pistol is loaded and cocked. At whom do you fire?

298. Yes or No? ☆☆☆

This is a variation of the game *Twenty Questions*, with a bit of *What's My Line?* thrown in to make it more interesting.

Red and Black each covertly write down an integer from 1 to 100. The objective is to guess the other player's number first. Questions may be asked concerning the opponent's number provided that they can be answered truthfully with a 'yes' or 'no'. A player is permitted to continue asking questions so long as he receives 'yes' answers. 'The first 'no' transfers the role of questioner to the opponent.

The conservative *Twenty Questions* strategy of questioning in such a manner as most nearly to equalise the chance of 'yes' and 'no' answers is most effective in that game. Using it, you can, in only twenty questions, invariably pinpoint any number in the range of 1 to 500,000. But in the game *Yes or No?* this may not be the best way to proceed.

Suppose you are the first player. What will your questioning strategy be, and how much of an advantage do you feel you have over your opponent?

299. Modified Russian Roulette ☆☆☆☆

In this harmless version of Russian Roulette, two players alternately shoot a six-shot revolver, only one chamber of which contains a cartridge, at a target. The player who first gets a 'bang' rather than a 'click' is the loser.

There is an option, however. At any turn, instead of shooting the next chamber, a player may randomly spin the magazine before shooting. Once either player elects to spin before shooting, all successive shots, if any, must be preceded by a spin.

You have first shot. Do you spin first and shoot, or shoot without spinning?

After you have worked this one out, decided what you would do as the first player in the *misère* version (first player to get a 'bang' wins).

12. TOMORROW'S CLASSICS

RUBIK'S CUBE

Rubik's Cube was a major world-wide sensation in 1980–1. Although the craze has now abated, the cube still continues to generate interest. It is used by teachers of mathematics as a teaching aid when dealing with group theory and the mathematics of symmetry. It has been given a permanent place in the New York Museum of Modern Art. But more importantly, as far as we are concerned, it continues to be the basis for new puzzles.

The three puzzles included here all involve producing a pattern from a 'plain' cube – that is, you start with a cube on which all nine squares on each face are similarly coloured.

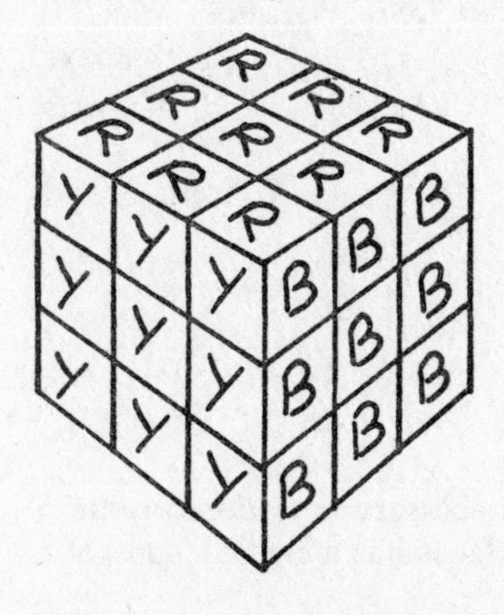

(In the diagram, the faces you can see are yellow, blue and red; the faces you cannot see are green, white and orange. It may be that the cube you use for these puzzles has a different colour arrangement – don't worry, the patterns produced will be the same even if the colours vary).

300. Cross-Check ☆☆☆

Starting with a plain cube, find the moves necessary to produce a cross-check pattern on all the six faces, as shown in the diagram.

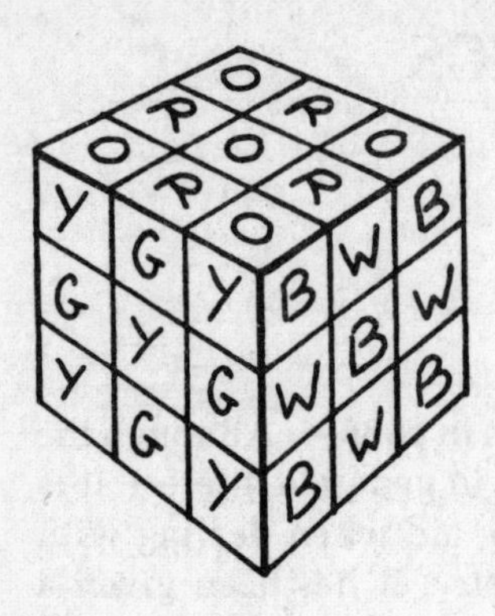

301. Stripes ☆☆☆

Starting with a plain cube, find the moves necessary to produce a stripe on four of the faces, as shown in the diagram.

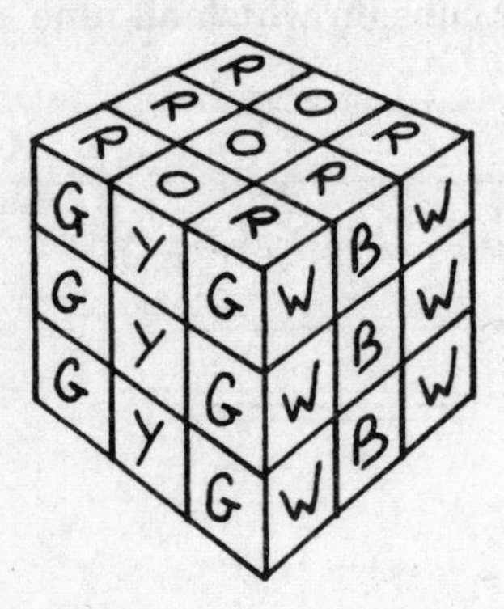

302. Dots ☆☆☆☆

Starting with a plain cube, find the moves necessary to produce a pattern like that shown, in which each of the six faces has a central 'spot' of a different colour from the rest of the face.

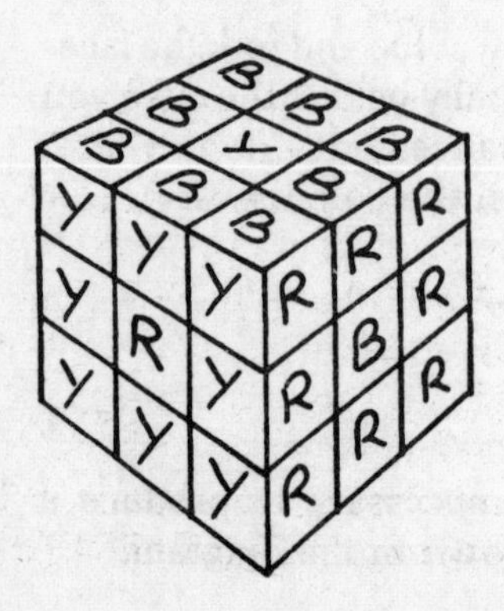

POCKET CALCULATOR PUZZLES

303. A Common Factor ☆☆☆

Perform these calculations:

$8 \times 473 =$
$9 \times 351 =$
$15 \times 93 =$
$21 \times 87 =$
$27 \times 81 =$
$35 \times 41 =$

What is the common factor?

304. Another Common Factor ☆☆☆

Perform these calculations:

$483 \times 12 =$
$297 \times 18 =$
$198 \times 27 =$
$186 \times 39 =$
$138 \times 42 =$
$154 \times 48 =$

What is the common factor?

305. Hidden Significance ☆☆

Perform the following calculations on your calculator. Each answer has some literal significance. If you don't see it at first, try looking at the answer from a different perspective.

(a) $(366 \times 10) + (4 \times 11)$
(b) $(366 \times 15) + (4 \times 55)$
(c) $(366 \times 16) - (3 \times 41)$
(d) $(366 \times 19) + (3 \times 17) + 100$
(e) $(366 \times 20) + (9 \times 44)$
(f) $(366 \times 21) + (4 \times 37)$
(g) $(366 \times 2) + 230^2 + 119$
(h) $(366 \times 867) + (5 \times 43)$

SCIENCE FICTION AND SCIENCE FACT

The next two puzzles are Science Fiction Puzzle Tales by Martin Gardner – but today's science fiction is tomorrow's science fact.

306. Tube Through the Earth ☆☆☆☆

In the twenty-third century an enormous gravity transport tube, with a diameter of 20 metres, was constructed straight along the earth's axis to join the metropolises of North Polaris and South Polaris. Through this tunnel cylindrical cars carrying both supplies and people were dropped from one city to the other. All friction was eliminated by maintaining a vacuum inside the tube, and by using magnetic fields to keep the cars away from the tube's side. The trip from pole to pole took only slightly longer than 42 minutes.

How many of the following questions about the transport tube can you answer?

(1) As the car travels from North Polaris to the earth's centre, does its velocity increase, decrease, or stay the same?
(2) Does the car's *acceleration* increase, decrease, or remain the same?
(3) If you are riding in a car and it stops halfway down to the earth's centre, would you weigh less or more on a spring scale than on the earth's surface?
(4) At what point during the trip would you experience zero gravity?
(5) At what spot does the car reach maximum speed, and how fast is it going?
(6) If a car fell down a similar tube through the centre of the moon, would the time for a one-way trip be shorter or longer than 42 minutes?
(7) A famous SF story was written about an attempt to dig a deep hole below the earth's crust. It turns out that the earth is a living organism, and when its epidermis is punctured the earth lets out a mighty yell of pain. What is the story's title and who wrote it?

307. Vacation on the Moon ☆☆☆☆

Edgar D. Twitchell, a New Jersey plumber, was on his way to the moon for a three-week holiday. The rocket ship was too small to generate artificial gravity by spinning, so Twitchell had the strange sensation of feeling his weight steadily diminish as the ship sped towards its destination. When it reached the spot where earth's stronger gravity field was exactly balanced by the moon's weaker field, zero g prevailed inside the ship. All passengers were kept fastened to their seats, but Twitchell enjoyed the floating feeling nonetheless as he twiddled his thumbs and contentedly puffed a cigar.

Many hours later the ship slowly settled next to one of the huge domes that house the US moon colony, its descent cushioned by rocket brakes. Through the thick glass window by his seat Twitchell caught his first glimpse of the spectacular lunar landscape. Several large seagulls, with tiny oxygen tanks strapped to their backs, were flying near the dome. Above the dome an American flag fluttered in the breeze.

Although it was daylight, the sky was inky black and splattered with twinkling stars. Low on the horizon a rising 'New Earth' showed a thin bluish crescent of light with several faint stars shining between the crescent's arms. As Twitchell later learned, the moon makes one rotation during each revolution around the earth. Because a rotation takes about twenty-eight days, it takes the earth about fourteen days to rise and set on the moon.

On the sixth day of his vacation, Twitchell was allowed to put on a space suit and hike around the crater in which the dome had been built. After bounding along for a while he came upon a group of children, in pink space suits, playing with boomerangs. One girl tossed a boomerang that made a wide circle and Twitchell had to duck as it whirled past his helmet. Behind him he heard it thud against a large boulder. He turned to look, but the curved stick had fallen into the rock's ebony shadow where it instantly seemed to vanish. Since there is no atmospheric scattering of light on the moon, objects cannot be seen in shadows without a flashlight.

The sun was low in the sky when Twitchell began his walk. Now it was sinking out of sight. The 'terminator', that sharp line separating the lunar day from night, was gliding across the gray terrain toward the brightly lit dome at a speed of about 40 miles an hour – much too fast for Twitchell to keep up with it by vigorous hopping. Overhead a meteor left a fiery trail as it fell to the moon's surface.

Twitchell was so exhausted when he returned to his quarters that he fell asleep on his bed, fully clothed, and did not awake until the rising sun flooded his room with brilliant sunlight.

How many scientific mistakes can you find in the above narrative?

COMPUTER-GENERATED PUZZLES

Perhaps the puzzles of the future will all be created (and solved?) by computers. Here, as a harbinger of things to come, are three puzzle-generating programs by Michael and David Curl, which are designed to be run on home micro-computers. Each of these programs generates puzzles of a particular format but, by using random variables, is able to produce a large number of different puzzles within that format. The programs will ask for your answers and will tell you whether you are right or wrong.

If you have a Spectrum computer, you can type in and run the programs just as they are shown here. If you own a different type of home computer, you will probably have to make one or two slight amendments to the programs before you can use them.

308. 'Age Puzzle' Program

```
10 RANDOMIZE
20 CLS
30 LET ted=5+INT (10*RND)
40 LET diff=2+INT (8*RND)
50 PRINT AT 3,10
60 PRINT TAB 10;"AGE PUZZLE"
70 PRINT AT 7,0
80 PRINT INK 3;" Dave is ";
90 PRINT INK 2;diff
100 PRINT INK 3;"years older than Ted"
110 PRINT AT 9,0
120 PRINT TAB 2;INK 3;"The sum of their age is ";
130 PRINT INK 2;diff+(2*ted)
140 PRINT AT 13,0
150 PRINT TAB 8;INK 3;"How old is Ted?"
160 INPUT TAB 12;INK 3;"Age??";INK 2;answer
170 IF answer=ted THEN GO TO 500
180 PRINT AT 17,10
190 PRINT INK 1;TAB 5;FLASH 1;" Sorry, that's wrong "
200 PRINT INK 1;TAB 5;FLASH 1;"The correct answer is "
210 PRINT INK 1;FLASH 1;ted;"  "
220 PAUSE 300
230 GO TO 20
500 PRINT AT 17,10
510 PRINT TAB 5;INK 1;FLASH 1;" CORRECT! Well done! "
520 FOR n=1 to 5:BEEP .15,n:NEXT n
530 PAUSE 200
540 GO TO 20
```

309. 'Integer Product' Program

```
10 RANDOMIZE
20 CLS
30 LET x=5+INT (15*RND)
40 PRINT AT 4,0;INK 4;"xxxxxxxxxxxxxxxxxxxxxxxxxxxxxxxx"
50 PRINT AT 4,7;INK 3;" PRODUCT PUZZLE "
60 PRINT AT 7,0
70 PRINT INK 1;" Three consecutive integers   are multiplied together"
80 PRINT AT 10,0
90 PRINT TAB 2;INK 2;"The product is ";
100 PRINT INK 2;x*(x+1)*(x+2)
110 PRINT AT 12,0
120 PRINT INK 1;" What is the lowest of the 3   integers?"
130 INPUT answer
140 IF answer=x THEN GO TO 500
150 PRINT AT 16,0
160 PRINT TAB 8;INK 3;FLASH 1;" You're wrong! "
170 PRINT AT 18,0
180 PRINT TAB 2;INK 3;FLASH 1; "The correct answer is "
190 PRINT INK 3;FLASH 1;x;"  "
200 PAUSE 300
210 GO TO 20
500 PRINT AT 16,0
510 PRINT TAB 2;INK 3;FLASH 1;"Sure looks right to me! "
520 For n=-10 TO 30:BEEP .005,n:NEXT n
530 PAUSE 100
540 GO TO 20
```

310. 'Rectangle Puzzle' Program

```
10 RANDOMIZE
20 CLS
30 LET x=1+INT (10*RND)
40 LET y=x+1+INT (10*RND)
50 PRINT AT 3,7;
60 PRINT "RECTANGLE PUZZLE"
70 PRINT AT 7,0;
80 PRINT INK 1;"The perimeter of a rectangle is "
90 PRINT TAB 3;INK 3;2*(x+y)
100 PRINT AT 9,0
110 PRINT INK 1; "The area is "
120 PRINT TAB 3;INK 3;x*y
```

```
130 PRINT AT 13,5
140 PRINT INK 2;"What's the length of the shorter sides?"
150 INPUT answer1
160 PRINT AT 13,5
170 PRINT INK 2;"What's the length of the longer sides? "
180 INPUT answer2
190 IF answer1=x AND answer2=y THEN GO TO 500
200 PRINT AT 16,10
210 PRINT INK 3;TAB 4;FLASH 1;" Sorry – you're wrong "
220 PRINT AT 17,0
230 PRINT INK 3;TAB 4;FLASH1;"The CORRECT answers are "
240 PRINT INK 2;TAB 12;x;' & ';y
250 PAUSE 300
260 GO TO 20
500 PRINT AT 15,10
510 PRINT
520 PRINT TAB 10;INK 1;FLASH 1;" Well done! "
530 FOR n=1 TO 30
540 BORDER INT (RND*8)
550 BEEP .01,(INT (RND*80))-40
560 NEXT n
570 BORDER 7
580 GO TO 20
```

13. SOLUTIONS

OLD MASTERS

1. 40 talents.

2. The donkey had five and the mule seven sacks.

3. 28 scholars.

4. The minimum number of apples per basket is 4, but any multiple of 4 provides any equally valid solution.

5. 60 years old.

6. The 'obvious' solution, 3 piastres and 5 piastres, is wrong. The 8 piastres was in payment for 2⅔ loaves. Therefore one loaf is worth 3 piastres. Since each ate 2⅔ loaves, the first shepherd gave ⅓ of a loaf to the hunter, and the other shepherd gave 2⅓. Therefore 1 piastre should go to the first shepherd, and 7 piastres to the second shepherd.

7. 27.

8. 19.2 yards.

9. 54 ducats.

10. 92 ducats.

11. 29 ducats.

12. The value of a barrel is 110 francs, and the duty payable is 10 francs.

13.
In Shylock's bargain for the flesh was found
No mention of the blood that flowed around:
So when the stick was sawed in pieces eight,
The sawdust lost diminished from the weight.

14. One. In this genealogy, which demonstrates the relationships, males are denoted by capitals, and females by small letters. The governor is E and his guest is C

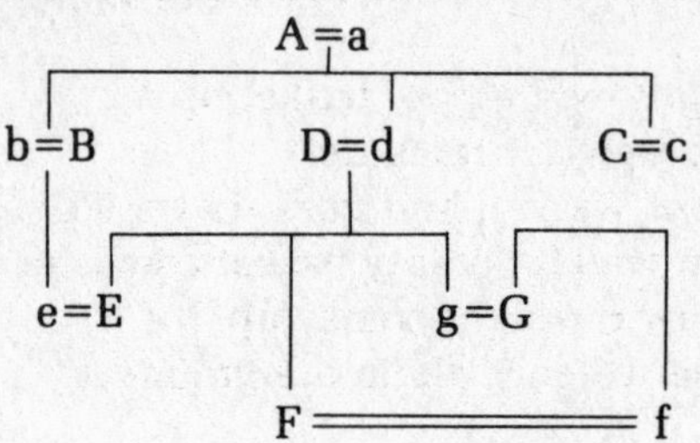

15.
24 miles; half past six.

A level mile takes quarter of an hour, up hill one third, down hill one sixth. Hence to go and return over the same mile, whether on the level or on the hill-side, takes half an hour. Hence in six hours they went 12 miles out and 12 back. If the 12 miles out had been nearly all level, they would have taken a little over 3 hours; if nearly all up hill, a little under 4. Hence 3½ hours must be within half an hour of the time taken in reaching the peak; thus, as they started at 3, they got there with half an hour of half past six.

16. (**a**) 19 (**b**) The easterly traveller met 12, the other 8.

17.
5½, 6½, 7, 4½, 3½.

The sum of all the weighings, 61 lbs, includes sack 3 thrice and each of the others twice. Deducting twice the sum of the first and fourth weighings, i.e. 21 lbs for thrice 3 – i.e. 7 lbs for sack 3. The rest follows.

18. The order is M, L, Z.

19. 60 yards by 60½ yards.

20. 10 per cent.

21. 15 and 18.

22. As the monkey climbs, the weight will rise by the same amount.

23.
(a) The weight is sent down; the empty basket comes up.
(b) The son goes down; the weight comes up.
(c) The weight is taken out; the daughter goes down; the son up.

(d) The son gets out; the weight goes down; the empty basket up.
(e) The queen goes down; daughter and weight come up; daughter gets out.
(f) The weight goes down; empty basket up.
(g) Son goes down; weight comes up.
(h) Daughter removes weight, and goes down; son comes up.
(i) Son sends down weight; empty basket comes up.
(j) The son goes down; weight comes up.
(k) Son gets out; the weight falls to the ground.

24.

In the puzzle of the young stenographer's salary, she gains $12.50 the first year, but after that loses steadily. Some puzzlists fall into the error of adding the whole of each raise in a lump sum at the end of every six months, whereas the salary was raised each time to a yearly basis of $25 better, which is only an improvement of $12.50 every six months. Of course a raise of $100 per year would give the stenographer in five years, $600 plus $700 plus $800 plus $900 plus $1,000, equalling $4,000. Instead of which the stenographer loses $437.50 by her own plan, as follows:

		Yearly basis
First six months	$300.00	$600
Second six months	312.50	625
Third six months	325.00	650
Fourth six months	337.50	675
Fifth six months	350.00	700
Sixth six months	362.50	725
Seventh six months	375.00	750
Eighth six months	387.50	775
Ninth six months	400.00	800
Tenth six months	412.50	825

25.

Out of the 216 equally probable ways the dice may be thrown, you will win on only 91 of them, lose on 125. So your chance of winning at least as much as you bet is 91/216, your chance of losing 125/216.

If the dice always showed different numbers, the game would be a fair one. Suppose each square is covered with a dollar. The operator would, on each roll that showed three different numbers, take in three dollers and pay out three. But on doubles he makes a dollar and on triples he makes two dollars. In the long run, for every dollar wagered by a player, regardless of how he places the money and in what amounts, he can expect to lose about 7.8 cents. This gives the operator a profit of 7.8 per cent on each dollar bet.

26.
Hank had 11 animals, Jim 7, and Duke 21, making 39 animals altogether.

27.
From the facts given we can conclude that Jack eats lean pork at the rate of 1 barrel in 10 weeks, therefore he would finish the half-barrel of lean in 5 weeks. During this same period, his wife (who eats fat at a rate of 1 barrel in 12 weeks) would consume 5/12 of a barrel of fat. This would leave 1/12 of a barrel of fat for both of them to eat at a rate of 1 barrel in 60 days. They would finish the fat in 5 days, so the total amount of time would be 35 days plus 5 days, or 40 days altogether.

28.
The ball would travel a distance of 218.7777.... feet, or 218 feet, 9⅓ inches.

29.
Susie paid five cents for silk, four cents for worsted.

30.
The number of children on the carousel, including Sammy himself, was thirteen.

31.
Last year Mrs Wiggs raised 11,025 cabbages on a square with 105 patches on the side. This year she will raise 11,236 cabbages on a square with 106 patches on the side.

32.
In that interesting problem of the reapers who cut a swath around a rectangular field until half the crop was gathered, I find that they had a simple rule. They said: 'One-quarter the difference between a short cut cross lots, and round by the road.' Mathematicians will understand it better if we say: from the sum of the two sides subtract the diagonal of the field and divide the remainder by four.

The field was 2,000 yards long by 1,000 yards wide. Using a tape line, those honest farmers found that the diagonal from one corner to the opposite one was a little over 2,236 yards. To go 'round by the road', of course, was 3,000 yards, so the difference was a little less than 764 yards. One-quarter of this is just a bit shy of 191 yards (190.983), which is the width the border strip should be.

33. The land was divided into 18 lots.

34. Sam Loyd's Boxes

1. Sam Loyd writes: 'The original problem is impossible to solve except by such skullduggery as turning the 6 and 9 blocks upside down. One of the puzzle's peculiarities is that any such interchange involving two blocks immediately converts the puzzle to a solvable one. In fact, any odd number of interchanges has the same effect, whereas an even number leaves the puzzle unsolvable as before.'

2. 44 moves are required to get the vacant square in the top left-hand corner: 14, 11, 12, 8, 7, 6, 10, 12, 8, 7, 4, 3, 6, 4, 7, 14, 11, 15, 13, 9, 12, 8, 4, 10, 8, 4, 14, 11, 15, 13, 9, 12, 4, 8, 5, 4, 8, 9, 13, 14, 10, 6, 2, 1.

3. 39 moves are required to solve the third problem: 14, 15, 10, 6, 7, 11, 15, 10, 13, 9, 5, 1, 2, 3, 4, 8, 12, 15, 10, 13, 9, 5, 1, 2, 3, 4, 8, 12, 15, 14, 13, 9, 5, 1, 2, 3, 4, 8, 12.

4. The magic square can be produced in fifty moves: 12, 8, 4, 3, 2, 6, 10, 9, 13, 15, 14, 12, 8, 4, 7, 10, 9, 14, 12, 8, 4, 7, 10, 9, 6, 2, 3, 10, 9, 6, 5, 1, 2, 3, 6, 5, 3, 2, 1, 13, 14, 3, 2, 1, 13, 14, 3, 12, 15, 3.

5. This puzzle can be solved in 23 moves – the fewest possible. Move the blocks in the following order: A, B, F, E, C, A, B, F, E, C, A, B, D, H, G, A, B, D, H, G, D, E, F.

35. The time must have been $5\frac{5}{11}$ minutes past two o'clock.

36.

The correct and only answer is that 11,616 ladies made proposals of marriage. Here are all the details, which the reader can check for himself with the original statements. Of 10,164 spinsters, 8,085 married bachelors, 627 married widowers, 1,221 were declined by bachelors, and 231 declined by widowers. Of the 1,452 widows, 1,155 married bachelors, and 297 married widowers. No widows were declined. The problem is not difficult, by algebra, when once we have succeeded in correctly stating it.

37.

The nine men, A, B, C, D, E, F, G, H, J, all go 40 miles together on the one gallon in their engine tanks, when A transfers 1 gallon to each of the other eight and has 1 gallon left to return home. The eight go another 40 miles, when B transfers 1 gallon to each of the other seven and has 2 gallons to take him home. The seven go another 40 miles, when C transfers 1 gallon to each of the six others and returns home on the remaining 3 gallons. The six go another 40 miles, when D gives each of five 1 gallon and returns home. The five go 40 miles, when E gives each of four 1 gallon and returns home. The four go another 40 miles, when F gives each of three 1 gallon and returns home. The three go 40 miles, when G gives each of two 1 gallon and returns home. The two go 40 miles, when H gives 1 gallon to J and returns home. Finally, the last man, J, goes another 40 miles and then has 9 gallons to take him home. Thus J has gone 360 miles out and home, the greatest distance in a straight line that could be reached under the conditions.

38.
The man said, 'I am going twice as deep' not 'as deep again'. That is to say, he was still going twice as deep as he had gone already, so that when he had finished, the hole would be three times its present depth. Then the answer is that at present the hole is 3 ft 6 ins deep and the man 2 ft 4 ins above ground. When completed the hole will be 10 ft 6 ins deep, and therefore the man will be 4 ft 8 ins below the surface, or twice the distance that he is now above ground.

39.
The candles must have burnt for 3¾ hours. One candle had one-sixteenth of its total length left and the other four-sixteenths.

40. The time must have been $43\frac{7}{11}$ past two o'clock.

41.
The ordinary schoolboy would correctly treat this as a quadratic equation. Here is the actual arithmetic. Double the product of the two distances from the walls. This gives us 144, which is the square of 12. The sum of the two distances is 17. If we add these two numbers, 12 and 17, together, and also subtract one from the other, we get the two answers that 29 or 5 was the radius. Consequently the diameter was 58 inches or 10 inches. But a table of the latter dimensions would be absurd. Therefore the table must have been 58 inches in diameter.

42.
The number must be the least common multiple of 1, 2, 3, etc., up to 15, that, when divided by 7, leaves the remainder 1, by 9 leaves 3, by 11 leaves 10, by 13 leaves 3, and by 14 leaves 8. Such a number is 120. The next number is 360,480, but as we have no record of a tree – especially a very young one – bearing anything like such a large number of apples, we may take 120 to be the only answer that is acceptable.

CHILD'S PLAY

43. 27 lbs.

44. JUST ONE WORD.

45. I have built my house at the North Pole.

46. Smith, where Jones had had 'had', had had 'had had'. 'Had had' had had the examiners' approval.

47. The speaker was looking at a portrait of his son.

48. Sunday.

49.
Too wise you are,
Too wise you be;
I see you are
Too wise for me.

50. Eighteen days (on the eighteenth day he would reach the top and not slip back).

51. You can't dig half a hole!

52. UNDERGROUND.

53. E (the letters in the series are the initial letters of: one, two, three, four . . . and so on).

54.

6	7	2
1	5	9
8	3	4

55.

16	2	3	13
5	11	10	8
9	7	6	12
4	14	15	1

56. Four years ago.

57. 17 dogs and 26 chickens.

58. 15.

59. 3 animals.

60. The word TOBACCO.

61. It will take 7 days – each day the squirrel carries out one ear of corn and the two ears on his head.

62. 80 years.

63. 3 minutes.

64. N and T, these being the next letters of the alphabet composed solely of straight lines.

65. Water, the chemical formula being H_2O (H to O).

66. None – the longest river is the Nile.

67. 3.

68. Once – after that you'll be subtracting from 23, then from 21, and so on.

69. Father.

70. 300 miles.

71. East.

72. The nursery rhyme has been rewritten so that it does not contain a single occurrence of the letter E – usually the commonest letter in the English language.

73. 15 miles.

74. The Ten of Diamonds, the King of Hearts and the Eight of Spades.

75. One.

76. Eight – he makes seven cigarettes, smokes them, and makes another cigarette from those ends.

77. A missionary and a cannibal cross. The missionary returns. Two cannibals cross. One cannibal returns. Two missionaries cross. One missionary and one cannibal return. Two missionaries cross. One cannibal returns. The remaining two cannibals cross.

78. Bill.

79. 3.

80. 16.

81. CAR.

82. Mary (or Myra), Kate, Amy (or May), Enid, Lisa, Ruth, Cathy, Delia, Marian (or Marina).

73. Eric, Lee, Stan, Neil, Silas, Steven, Cyril, Daniel, Andrew.

84. Polo, Pool, Onion, Oboe, Ukelele, Cello, Canoe, Ease.

NUMBER PUZZLES

85. The father distributed £39. The first child received £15, the second £8, the third £10, and the fourth £6.

86. First boat – 15 minutes 45 seconds; second boat – 16 minutes.

87. 23 and 24.

88. 76, 24.

89. 10, 22, 26.

90. $55^2 = 3025$. $99^2 = 9801$.

91. Man 69 years 12 weeks; Woman 30 years 40 weeks.

92. Jim 18 hours; Bill 22½ hours.

93. The contents of the ten bags should be $1, $2, $4, $8, $16, $32, $64, $128, $256 and $489.

94. 30 (16, 8, 4, 2).

95. Potato 11 ounces, orange 7 ounces, apple 5 ounces, tomato 3 ounces, banana 2 ounces.

96. A 3240. B 2916. C 1944. D 2052. E 1728. Electors 6480.

97. 324.

98. 9 feet 2 inches.

99.
The third and fourth powers must contain 10 digits between them, so the number sought can only be 18, 19, 20 or 21. Of these, 20 and 21 are bound to duplicate zeros and ones, respectively. Testing 18 and 19 reveals that 18 is the answer. The third and fourth powers of 18 are 5832 and 104,976.

100. 1, 4, 16, 64.

101. £24, £20, £8, £28.

102. 18.

103. Abe $65, Bert $35, Cal $20.

104.
If I walk 26 steps, I need 30 seconds; and if I walk 34 steps, I need only 18 seconds. Multiply 30 by 34 and 26 by 18, and we get 1020 and 468. Divide the difference (552) by the difference between 30 seconds and 18 seconds (12 seconds). The answer is 46, the number of steps in the stairway, which descends at the rate of 1 step in 1½ seconds. The speed at which I walk on the stairs does not affect the question, as the step from which I alight will reach the bottom at a given moment, whatever I do in the meantime.

105.
The smallest such number is 35,641,667,749. Other numbers with the same properties may be found by adding multiples of 46,895,573,610 to the aforementioned number.

106.
The car, when Alex met it, would have reached the station in another six minutes. So Alex had been walking for 30 minutes. Hence, had his wife met Alex at the station, he would have arrived 24 minutes earlier at the point where he actually met the car. So he would have arrived home at 5.36.

107.
The camel lives 75 years, the carp 150, the cat 15, the dog 17, the elephant 300, the chicken 18, the horse 30, the ox 21, the guinea pig 15, the stork 100, the whale 400 years.

108. David 13 times, Jonathan 8 times.

109.
Multiply 273863 by 365 and the product is 99959995.

Working the problem backwards, any number whatever that consists of eight digits with the first four repeated is divisible by 73 (and by 137), because 73 times 137 is 10001. If it ends with 5 or 0, it is divisible by 365 (5 times 73). Taking all this into account, the highest possible product can be written down at once.

110. 40 coaches.

111. 3½ minutes.

112. Eight marks are required – at the 1, 3, 6, 13, 20, 27, 31 and 35 inch positions.

113. The second way is really the same as the first in reverse – either way it takes 40 minutes (⅔ of an hour) to burn the candle out.

114. The river is 1760 yards wide. The time that the boats stayed at their slips is of no relevance.

115. 3 and 2.

116. 20 gallons.

117.
$13 \times 62 = 26 \times 31$
$13 \times 93 = 39 \times 31$
$14 \times 82 = 28 \times 41$
$23 \times 64 = 46 \times 32$
$34 \times 86 = 68 \times 43$
$36 \times 84 = 48 \times 63$

118.
Call the children A, B, C, D and E in order of their weights, A being the lightest and E the heaviest. A and B together weigh 114 pounds, D and E together weigh 129 pounds. These four together weigh 243. The total

weight of all five is 303 pounds (add all the pairs together and divide by 4, since each child was weighed four times). Hence, C weighs 60 pounds. The lightest and next lightest but one weighed 115 pounds – hence A must be 55 pounds. The rest is straightforward. The individual weights are 55, 59, 60, 63 and 66 pounds.

119. $123 - 45 - 67 + 89 = 100$ (using three signs).

120. $98 - 76 + 54 + 3 + 21 = 100$ (using four signs).

121. The father and mother were both 36. The three children – triplets – were all 6 years old.

122. Joe's share was 264, Jack's 198, and Jim's 308. Their ages are 6, 4½ and 7 years, respectively.

123. $32{,}547{,}891 \times 6 = 195{,}287{,}346$.

124.

1,680 (1681 is the square of 41, 841 is the square of 29).
57,120 (57,121 is the square of 239, 28,461 is the square of 169).
1,940,448 (1,940,449 is the square of 1,393, 970,225 is the square of 985).

125.

If a square number ends in identical digits, those digits must be 4. But it is not possible for there to be more than three identical digits, so the solution is 1444 (the square of 38).

126.

There are many possible solutions for each fraction. Here are some representative solutions:

(a) $\dfrac{5832}{17496}$ (b) $\dfrac{3942}{15768}$ (c) $\dfrac{2769}{13845}$ (d) $\dfrac{2943}{17658}$

(e) $\dfrac{2394}{16758}$ (f) $\dfrac{3187}{25496}$ (g) $\dfrac{6381}{57429}$

127.

Since each letter is a final digit, they must be 1, 3, 7 and 9. A and C must be 1 or 7, otherwise the numbers ADDD and AACA would be divisible by 3. Thus B and D must be 3 or 9.

BCDB, thus, may be 3193, 3793, 9139 or 9739. But 3193 is divisible by 31 and 9139 is divisible by 13. So BCDB may be 3793 or 9739 – in both cases, C = 7 and hence A = 1.

BDAC must be 9317 or 3917, but 9317 is divisible by 7, so BDAC = 3917. Therefore A = 1, B = 3, C = 7, D = 9.

128. The four primes are 1483, 4813, 4831 and 8431.

129.

$$\begin{array}{r} 9567 \\ \underline{1085} \\ \underline{10652} \end{array}$$

130.

$$\begin{array}{r} 850 \\ 850 \\ \underline{29786} \\ \underline{31486} \end{array}$$

131.

$$\begin{array}{r} 7088062 \\ \underline{17531908} \\ \underline{24619970} \end{array}$$

132. $\frac{219}{3} = 73$ $\frac{438}{6} = 73$ $\frac{657}{9} = 73$

133.

$$\begin{array}{r} 570140 \\ \underline{6} \\ \underline{3420840} \end{array}$$

134.

$$\begin{array}{r} 97809 \\ 124 \overline{)12128316} \\ \underline{1116} \\ 968 \\ \underline{868} \\ 1003 \\ \underline{992} \\ 1116 \\ \underline{1116} \end{array}$$

CIRCLES, SQUARES AND ANGLES

135.

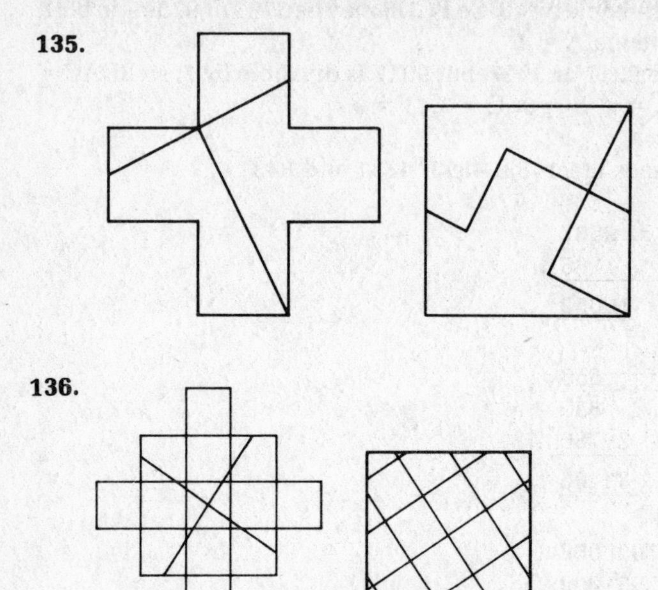

136.

137. As shown in the diagram, eleven non-overlapping triangles can be produced by seven lines.

138.
Fold the square in half and make the crease FE. Fold the side AB so that the point B lies on FE, and you will get the points G and H, from which you can fold HGJ. While B is on G, fold AB back on AH, and you will have the line AK. You can now fold the triangle AJK, which is the largest equilateral triangle obtainable.

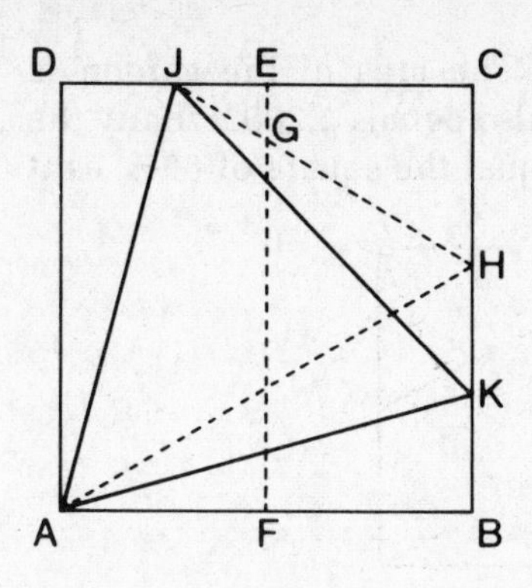

139.

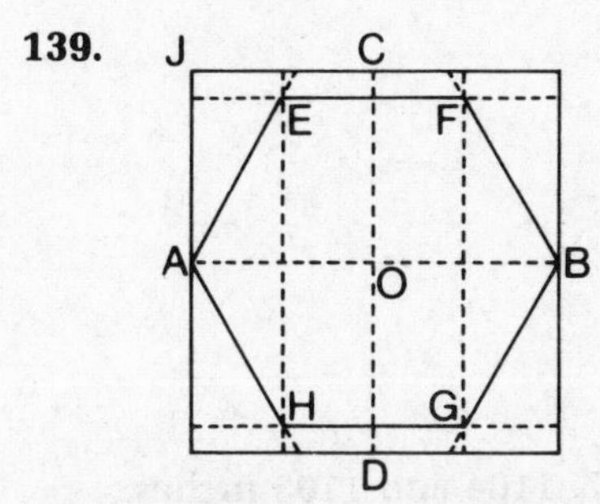

Folding the paper in half horizontally and vertically we obtain the lines AOB and COD. We then get EH and FG by folding the edges over to the centre line COD, thus bisecting AO and OB.

We fold over AJ so that J lies on the line EH – at the point E. We do the same at the other three corners to obtain the points F, G and H.

Then it is a simple matter to fold AE, EF, FB, BG, GH and HA to give the hexagon AEFBGH.

140. 8.

141. 157⅐ square miles approximately.

142.
Referring to the original diagram, let AC be x, let CD be x−9, and let EC be x−5. Then x−5 is a mean proportional between x−9 and x, from which we find that x=25. Therefore the diameters are 50 ins. and 41 ins. respectively.

143. 2513.28 square yards, approximately.

144.
The area of the path is exactly 66⅔ square yards, which is clearly seen if you imagine a little triangular piece cut off at the bottom and removed to

the top right corner. Here is the proof. The area of the garden is 55 × 40 = 2,200. And (55⅓ × 40) + 66⅔ also equals 2,200. Finally the sum of the squares of 53⅓ and 40 must equal the square of 66⅔, as it does.

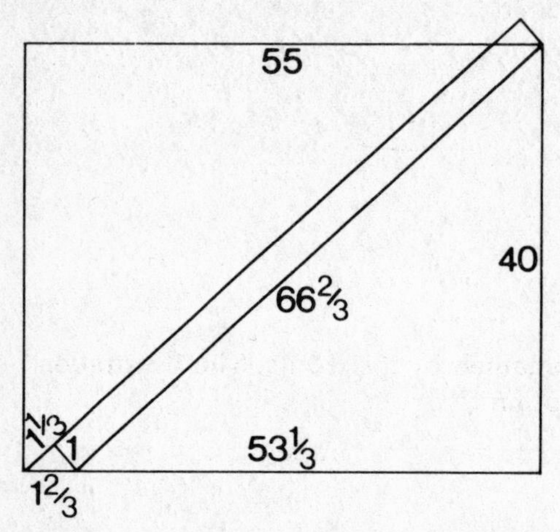

145. The triangle has integral sides of 47, 1104 and 1105 inches.

146.
The distance from the top of the ladder to the ground was ⅘ of the length of the ladder. Multiply the distance from the wall – 4 yards – by the denominator of this fraction – 5 – and you get 20. Now deduct the square of the numerator from the square of the denominator of ⅘, and you have 9, which is the square of 3. Finally, divide 20 by 3, and there is the answer: 6⅔ yards.

147. The bell rope must have been 32 feet 1½ inches in length from ceiling to floor.

148. 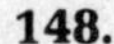

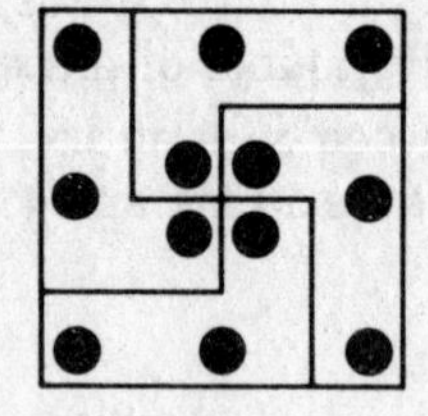

149.
Divide the diameter of the circle into four equal parts. Then describe semicircles on each side of the diameter as shown.

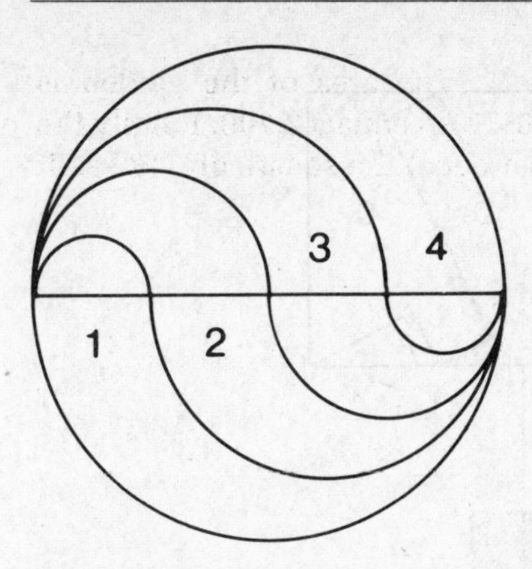

150.
As many as 22 pieces may be obtained by the 6 cuts. The illustration shows a pretty symmetrical solution.

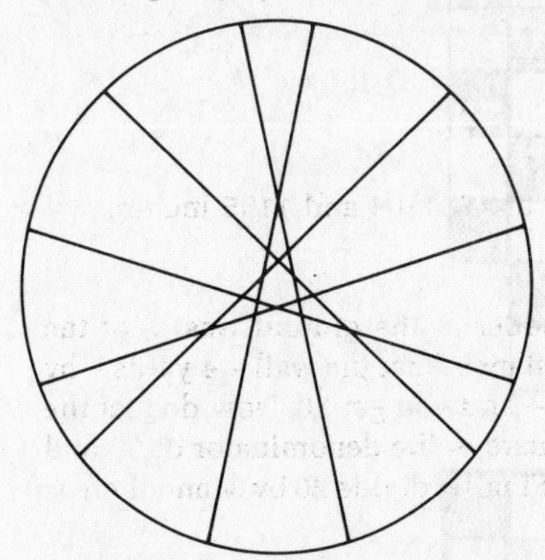

The rule in such cases is that every cut shall intersect every other cut and no two intersections coincide; that is to say, every line passes through every other line, but more than two lines do not cross at the same point anywhere. There are other ways of making the cuts, but this rule must always be observed if we are to get the full number of pieces.

151.

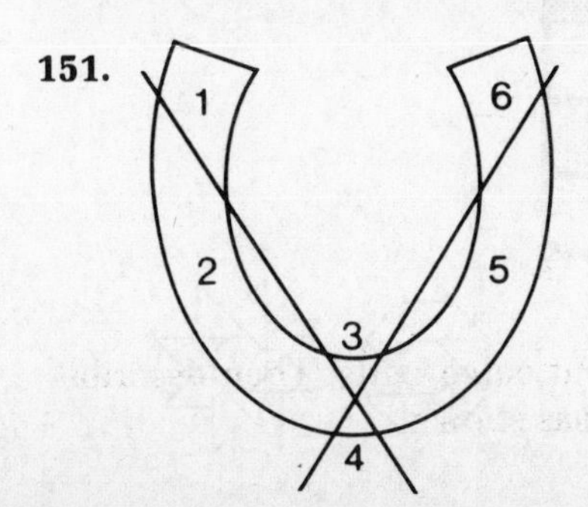

152.

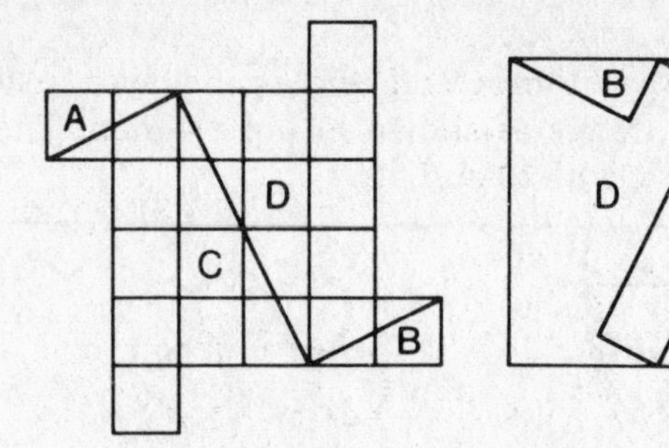

153.

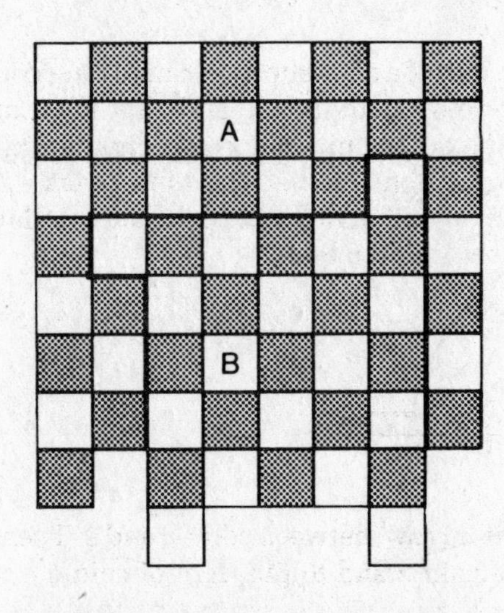

154.

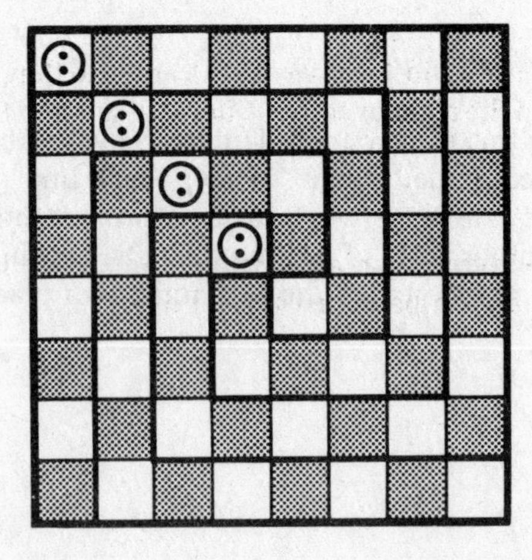

155. The diagram shows how it is done.

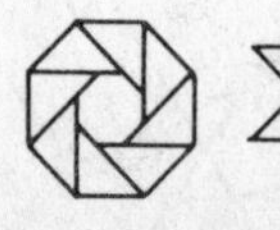

156.
We place 20 cigarettes in the bottom layer. In the second layer, instead of having 20, we place 19, arrange as shown in the diagram. Then we continue with alternate layers of 20 and 19.

Original method

New method

Let us suppose the diameter of a cigarette is 2 units. The second and subsequent layers, using our new method, will add only 1.732 units to the height. The depth of the box is 16 units, since it originally contained eight layers. With our new method we shall get nine layers – 2 plus 8 × 1.732 is equal to 15.856. So with five layers of 20 and four layers of 19 we shall get 176 cigarettes into the box.

THREE-DIMENSIONAL PUZZLES

157.
Move coin 1 to below the bottom row, between coins 8 and 9. Then move coins 7 and 10 to the left of coin 2 and to the right of coin 3.

158.
Move coins 6 and 7 to the left of coin 1. Move coins 3 and 4 to the right of coin 5. Move coins 7 and 1 to the right of coin 2. Move coins 4 and 8 to the right of coin 6.

159.
Each time, after turning over a coin, start again from the coin that is three further on from the coin that you have just turned over.

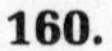
160.

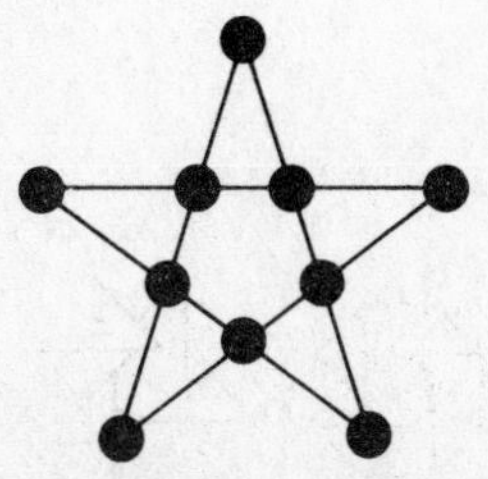

161.

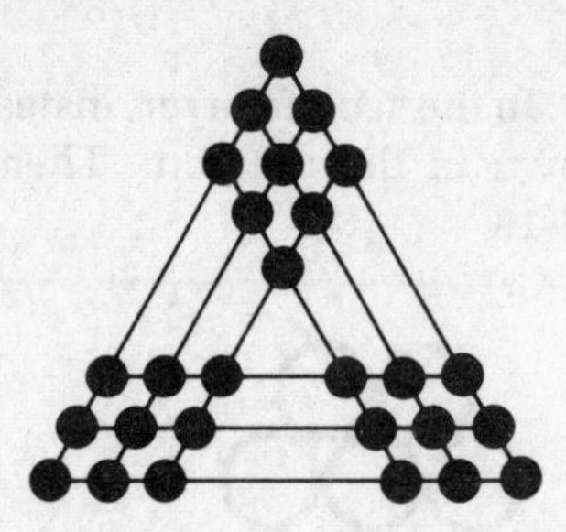

162.

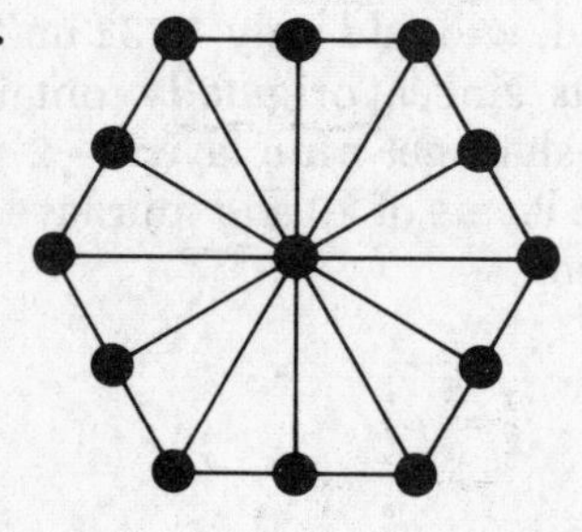

163.

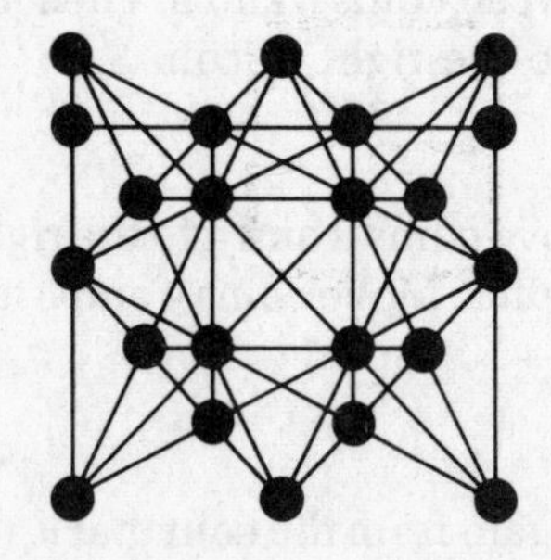

164. (1) Move from 1 to 5.
(2) Move from 3 to 7 to 1.
(3) Move from 8 to 4 to 3 to 7.
(4) Move from 6 to 2 to 8 to 4 to 3.
(5) Move from 5 to 6 to 2 to 8.
(6) Move from 1 to 5 to 6.
(7) Move from 7 to 1.

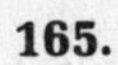

165.

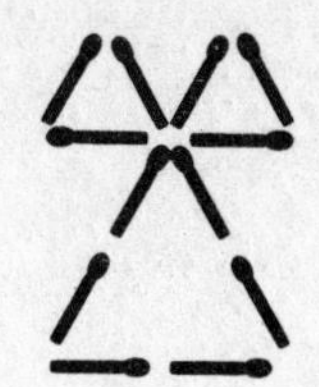

166. (a)

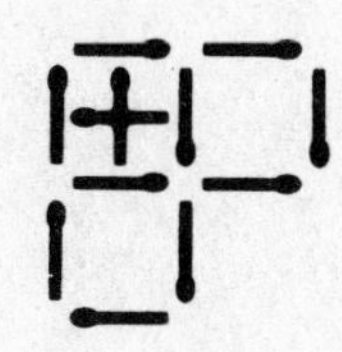

(d)

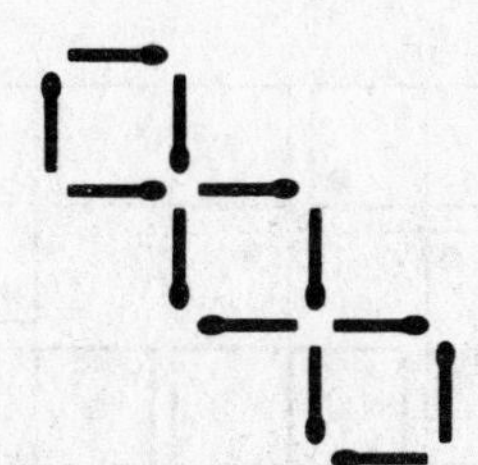

(b)

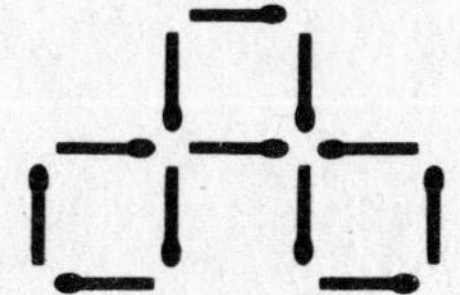

(e)

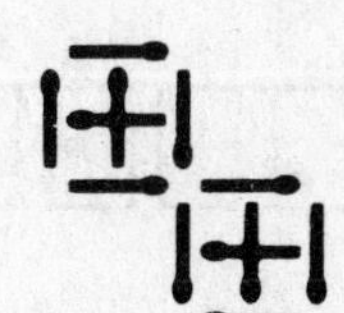

(c)

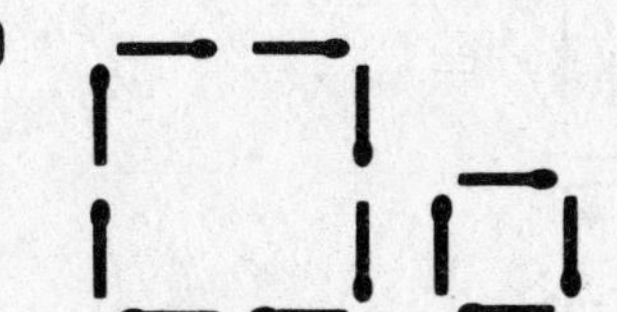

(f)

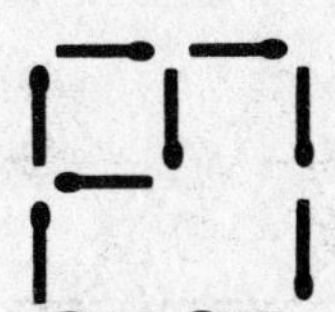

167.

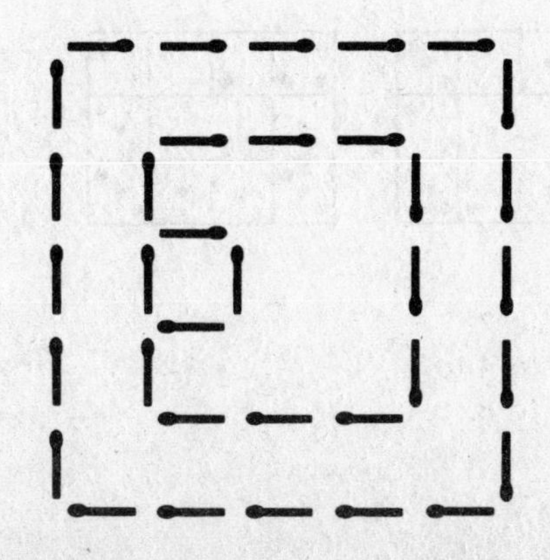

168.

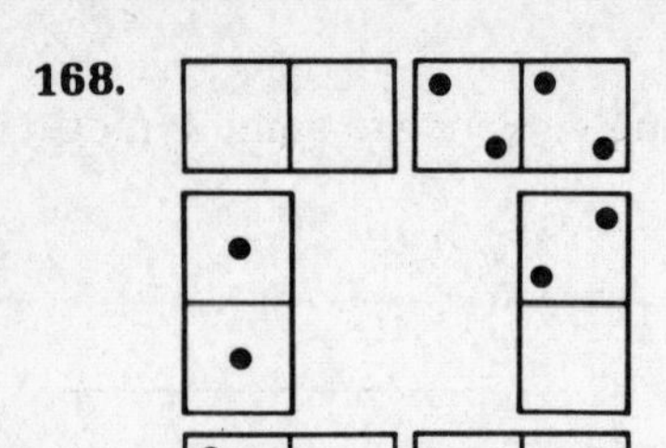

169.

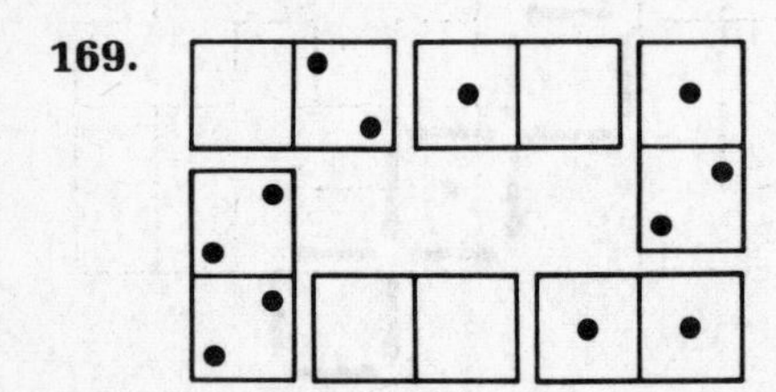

170.

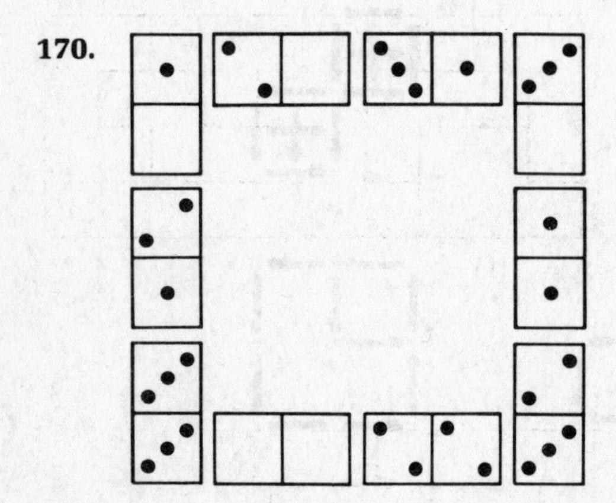

171.

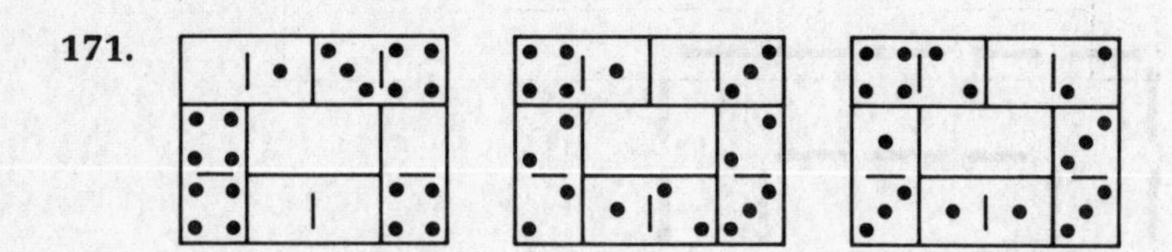

172. 0/0 – 0/4 – 4/4
0/1 – 1/4 – 4/2
1/1 – 1/3 – 3/3
1/2 – 2/2 – 2/3
2/0 – 0/3 – 3/4

173.
There are several solutions for each rectangle. Here are some typical solutions.

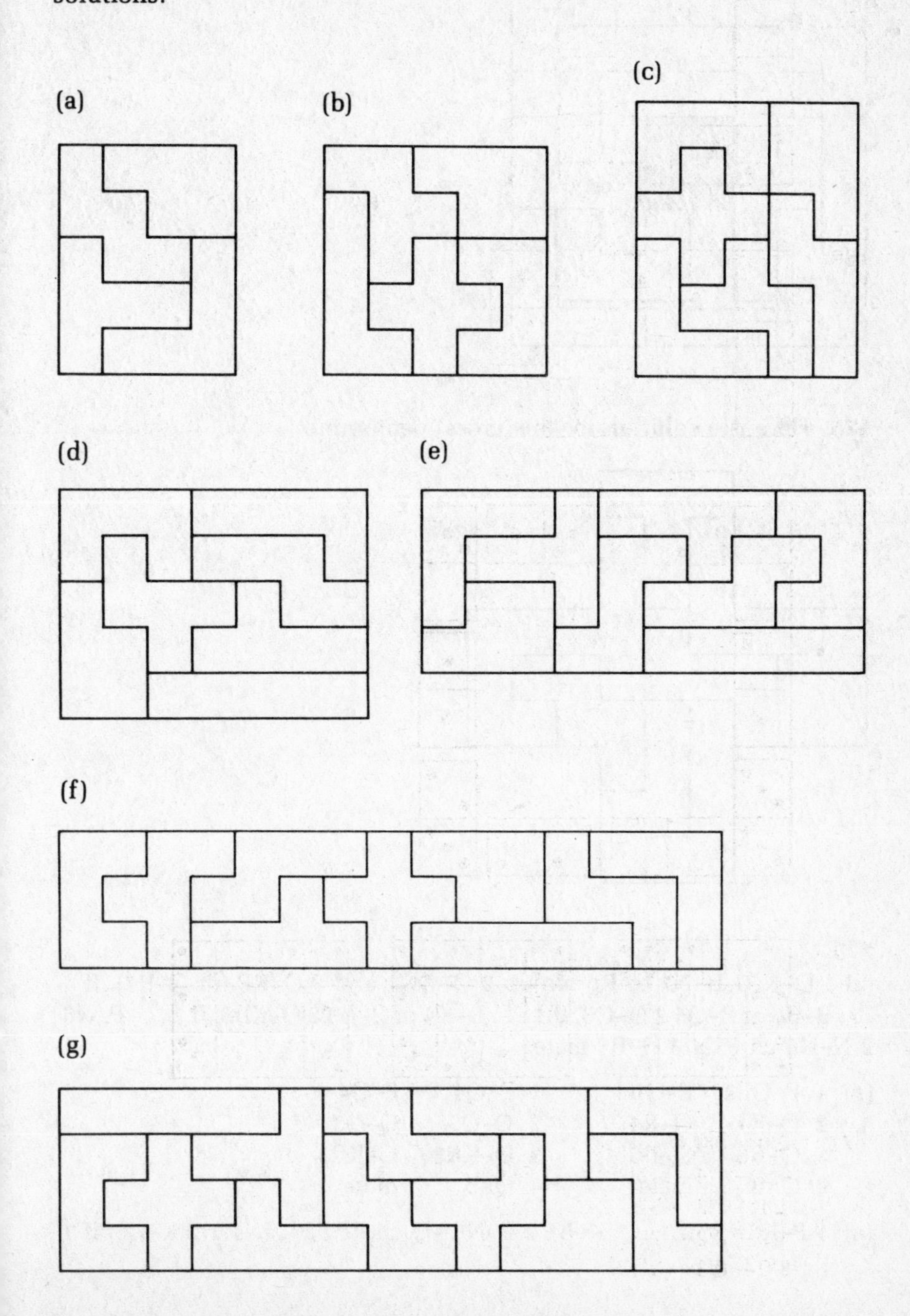

174. Here is one possible solution:

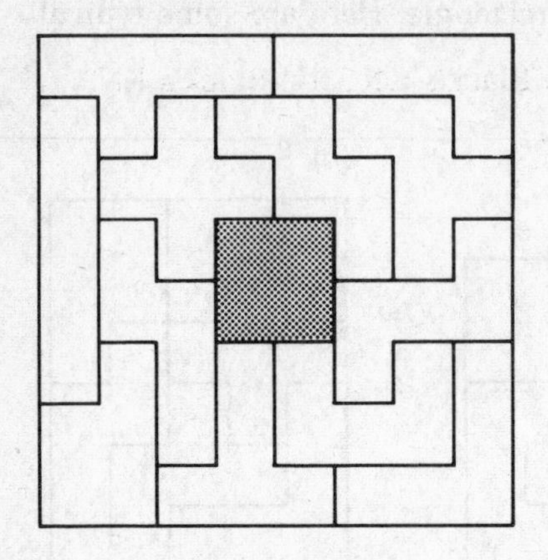

175. Here is a solution for the 'cross' pentomino.

176.

(a) 1 Q–KB1 B–N7 or Rp moves 2 Q–QN1 and 3 QxRP (or Q–R7). If 1 . . . B–B6 or B–Q5 2 Q–Q3. If 1 . . . B–K4 or B–B3 2 Q–KB5. If 1 . . . P–N6 2 N–N6 ch PxN 3 Q–R3 mate.

(b)

1 P–QB4	P–QB4		1 P–Q4	P–Q4
2 Q–R4	Q–R4		2 Q–Q3	Q–Q3
3 Q–B6	Q–B6		3 Q–KR3	Q–KR3
4 QxB	mate		4 QxB	mate

(c) 1 P–R8=B. If 1 . . . K–B1 2 P–N8=Q ch. If 1 . . . K–K1 2 K–K6. If 1 . . . K–N1 2 K–N6.

(d) 1 B–B5 NxB 2 Q–QR7 any 3 Q–N1 mate. If 1 . . . any other move 2 Q–Q7 and 3 Q–Q1 mate.

(e) (i) Black's KR8 (ii) Black's K6 (iii) Black's QR1 (iv) Black's KN2.

177. 43 – 23
45 – 43
53 – 33
23 – 43
42 – 44

178. 45 – 47
43 – 45
64 – 44 – 46
24 – 44
47 – 45 – 43
42 – 44

179. 54 – 74
43 – 63
44 – 46
34 – 36 – 56 – 54
15 – 35
75 – 73 – 53 – 55
65 – 45 – 25 – 23 – 43
42 – 44

180. 42 – 44
23 – 43
31 – 33
34 – 32
51 – 31 – 33
43 – 23
45 – 43
64 – 44
52 – 54
44 – 64
25 – 45
37 – 35
45 – 25
65 – 45
57 – 55
45 – 65
47 – 45
13 – 33
14 – 34
15 – 35
73 – 53
74 – 54
75 – 55

LOGIC PUZZLES

181.
Either man should be asked the following question: 'If I were to ask you if this is the way I should go, would you say yes?' While asking the question, the hiker should be pointing at either of the directions going from the fork.

182.
The clerk gave back 5 dollars and kept 25 dollars. The boy gave each man 1 dollar and kept 2 dollars. Each man paid 9 dollars which, less the 2 dollars kept by the boy, makes the 25 dollars given to the clerk.

183.
On the second evening King Arthur arranged the knights and himself in the following order round the table: A, F, B, D, G, E, C. On the third evening they sat thus: A, E, B, G, C, F, D.

He thus had B next but one to him (the nearest possible) on both occasions, and G was the third from him (the furthest possible) on both occasions. No other way of seating the knights would have been so satisfactory.

184.
The age of Mary to that of Ann must be in the ratio of 5 to 3. As the sum of their ages was 44, Mary was 27½ and Ann 16½.

185.
The locomotive pushes truck 1 up to the points, then returns to the opposite siding and pushes truck 2 up to truck 1 at the points. The two trucks are then pulled by the locomotive down the siding and pushed on to the main line to a position between the two sidings. Truck 1 is then uncoupled and left standing while the locomotive pulls truck 2 along the main line in order to push it up to the points where it is left. The locomotive returns to truck 1, pulls it along the main line and then pushes it up the siding to its required final position. The locomotive then proceeds up the other siding to the points to pull truck 2 to its required position, then uncouples and returns to the main line.

186.
The engine that has had its fire drawn and therefore cannot move is No. 5. Move the other engines in the following order: 7, 6, 3, 7, 6, 1, 2, 4, 1, 3, 8, 1, 3, 2, 4, 3, 2 – seventeen moves in all, leaving the engines in the required order.

187.
Jennifer, the blonde hairdresser, is the oldest; Jane, the brunette receptionist, comes next; and Judy, the red-headed typist, is the youngest.

188.
(c) Viktor can outlift Boris by more than he can outlift Tam.

189.
The musician is Bertram Fuller.

Here is an outline of the solution, giving only the successive conclusions: Dwight is Mr Hooper, Clint is the accountant, Bertram is the musician, Ambrose is the priest, Dwight Hooper is the doctor, Ambrose is not Mr Grimm, Mr Eastwood is Ambrose, Clint is not Mr Fuller, Clint is Mr Grimm (the accountant), and Bertram Fuller is the musician.

190.
Diana lives two miles from Ann, and Cathy Black is the oldest of the four girls.

191.
(a) John is an advertising man; Paul is an actor; George is an auditor.
(b) Harry the actor is older than Dick the auditor who is older than Tom the advertising man.
(c) George the actor earns more than David the advertising man who earns more than Lloyd the auditor.
(d) Freeman the auditor is the chairman; Hardy the actor is the treasurer; Willis the advertising man is the secretary.

192.
Cetri, 1 million, English, amethysts.
Auni, 2 million, French, coffee.
Equin, 3 million, Portuguese, dates.
Dequar, 4 million, Spanish, bananas.
Bebi, 5 million, Dutch, emeralds.

193.
Carpet Fitting by Matt Coates has a yellow cover and 170 pages.
Indoor Heating by Celia Holmes has a white cover and 190 pages.
Domestic Insulation by Anita Lawn has a red cover and 220 pages.
Painting and Decorating by Bernard Cole has a green cover and 240 pages.
Improve Your Garden by Walter Wall has a blue cover and 300 pages.

194.
1. No acrobatic feat which involves turning a quadruple somersault is ever attempted in a circus.
2. No bird in this aviary lives on mince-pies.
3. All your poems are uninteresting.
4. Rainy days are always cloudy.
5. No badger can guess a conundrum.
6. I always avoid a kangaroo.

VISUAL PUZZLES

195. The distance from A to B is the same as the distance from B to C.

196. They are all equal.

197.
(a) It is impossible to say whether the cube is viewed from above or below – it could be either.
(b) The line is perfectly straight.

198. AC and BD are the same length.

199. All three are the same length.

200. All five are equal in area.

201. The two circles are the same size.

202. Despite the evidence of your eyes, both horizontal lines are the same length.

203.

204. There is only one route to the centre.

205.

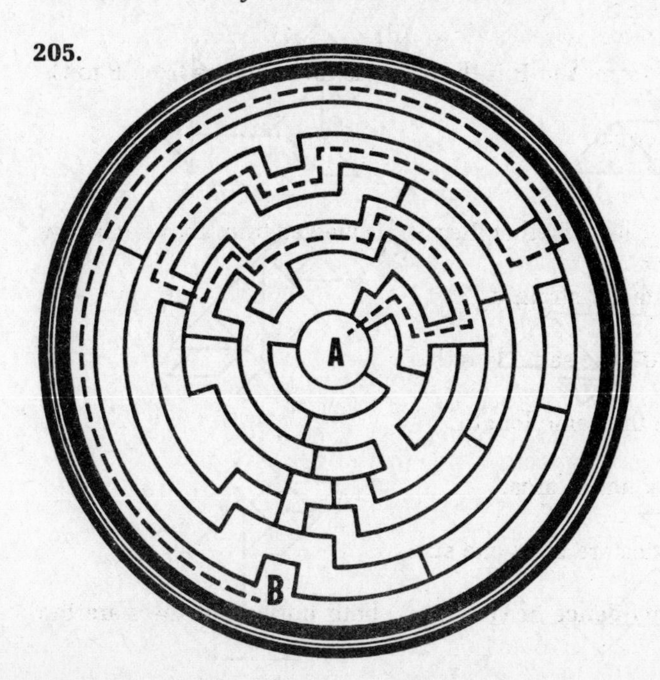

206. There are 640 routes to the centre.

207.

208. (a)

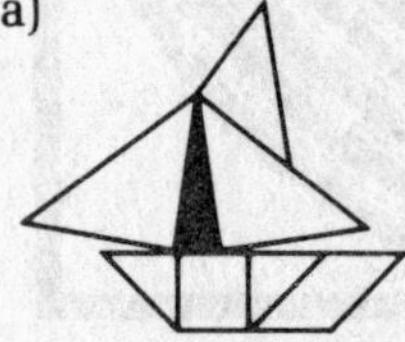

(b)

(c)

(d)

(e)

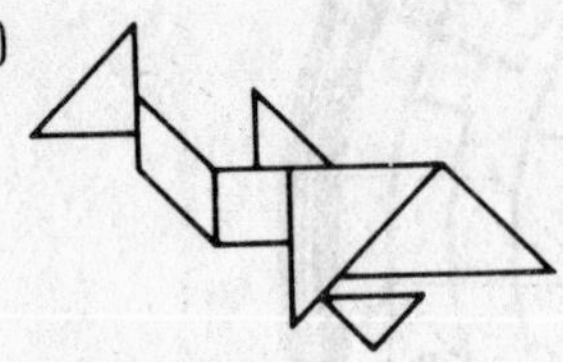

(f)

(g)

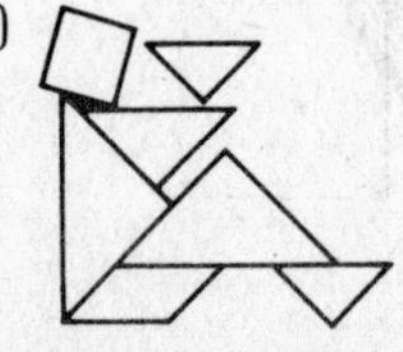

(h)

(i)

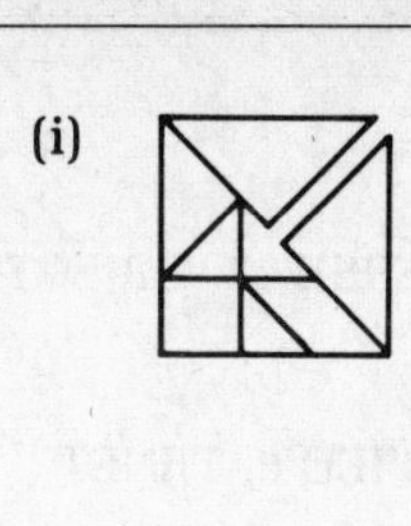

(j)

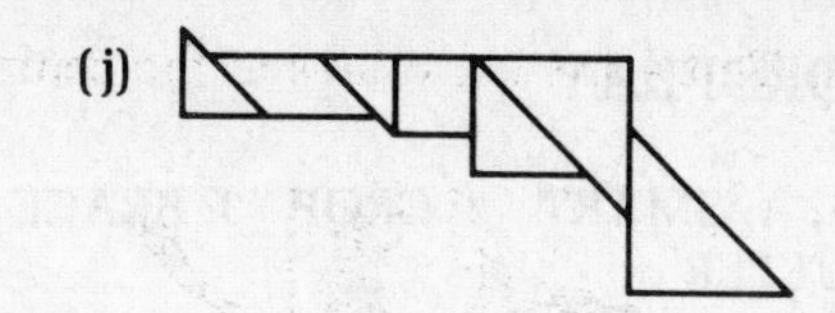

209.

210.

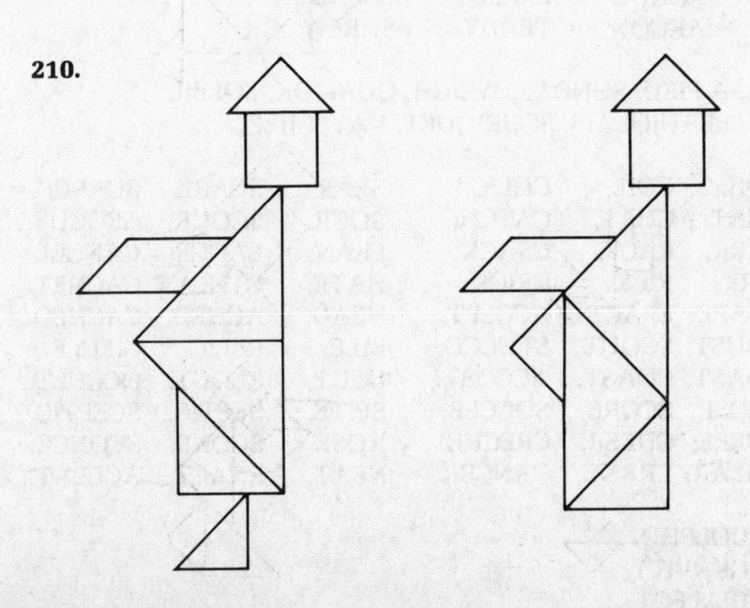

WORDPLAY

211. 1. SMART 2. CROP 3. BRACE 4. CONVERSE 5. OBJECTIVE 6. UTTER

212. 1. GAG 2. DEED 3. NOON 4. SHAHS 5. DEIFIED 6. TENET

213.
1. SOAK & WET 2. TIE & BIND 3. FLOG & BEAT 4. RAGE & ANGER 5. SEAR & CHAR 6. ACID & SOUR 7. AVER & ASSERT 8. LEAVE & QUIT 9. SPIN & GYRATE 10. FLIRT & COQUET.

214. The past tense of the eight verbs all rhyme with TAUT.

215. WITHHOLD, SKIING, BOOKKEEPER, VACUUM, NAVVY, POWWOW.

216.
There are several 7-letter words: ACCEDED, BAGGAGE, CABBAGE, DEFACED and EFFACED. There is also at least one 8-letter word: CABBAGED.

217.

ZEBRA	OCTET	BLISS
ERROR	CRIME	LUNCH
BRING	TIRED	INTER
RONDO	EMEND	SCENE
ARGON	TEDDY	SHREW

218. YEA, A PIED, SUNDAE, WEIGH, QUAI, OK, SOLEIL, DOSSIER, BEAUJOLAIS, SOBRIQUET, DAY, CHEZ.

219.

OIL,	COIL,	COLIC.	SEAR,	SCARE,	SCARCE.
HAT,	CHAT,	CATCH.	SOUR,	SCOUR,	CROCUS.
ARK,	RACK,	CRACK.	LEAN,	LANCE,	CANCEL.
IRK,	RICK,	CRICK.	HATE,	CHEAT,	CACHET.
TAPE,	EPACT,	ACCEPT.	HEAD,	ACHED,	CACHED.
OUST,	SCOUT,	STUCCO.	RILE,	RELIC,	CIRCLE.
OAST,	COAST,	ACCOST.	LOUT,	CLOUT,	OCCULT.
ROSE,	SCORE,	SOCCER.	SPITE,	SEPTIC,	SCEPTIC.
HERE,	CHEER,	CRECHE.	NOSE,	SCONE,	SCONCE.
NEAR,	CRANE,	CANCER.	NEAT,	ENACT,	ACCENT.

220. (a) DOLPHIN
(b) GRAVITY
(c) DIALECT

221. (a) LETTUCE, SPINACH
(b) BERMUDA, ICELAND

222.
(a) NEVADA (b) MAINE (c) MARYLAND (d) WASHINGTON
(e) MINNESOTA (f) RHODE ISLAND (g) INDIANA
(h) PENNSYLVANIA (i) RHODE ISLAND (j) SOUTH CAROLINA.

223.

(a)	(b)
COAST	BRING
BOAST	BRINK
BEAST	DRINK
LEAST	DRUNK
LEASE	TRUNK
LEAVE	TRUCK
HEAVE	TRICK
HEAVY	THICK

224. (a) SANATORIUM, SANITARIUM
(b) DESCRY, DECRY
(c) MENDICITY, MENDACITY
(d) ADJURE, ABJURE
(e) ABRADE, UPBRAID
(f) DISCOMFIT, DISCOMFORT
(g) VENAL, VENIAL
(h) INDITE, INDICT
(i) COMPLACENT, COMPLAISANT
(j) BIENNIAL, BIANNUAL

225. DEFYING, FIGHTING, HIJACK, MONOPOLY, QUERIST, UNDERSTUDY, OXYGENIZE.

226.
(a) ADDER (1 letter back) (b) CHAIN (6 letters back) (c) FILLS (6 letters back) (d) MILLS (6 letters back) (e) COBRA (3 letters back) (f) BANJO (4 letters back) (g) CHEER (7 letters back) (h) SNEER (1 letter back) (i) SHEER (1 letter back) (j) PECAN (4 letters back).

227.
There are many possible answers but here are mine: (a) 12344 – GLASS; 11232 – LLAMA; 12123 – COCOA; 12132 – MAMBA; 12133 – AMASS; 12213 – ALLAY; 12231 – SEEDS; 12233 – COOEE; 12312 – VERVE; 12313 – ENDED; 12323 – CEDED; 12331 – TWEET; 12332 – MANNA; 11231 – EERIE; 12113 – LULLS; 12131 – RARER; 12311 – FLUFF; 12232 – ERROR; 12322 – LEVEE; 12112 – MAMMA.

(b) 123232 – BANANA; 123321 – REDDER; 122132 – TEETHE; 122323 – NEEDED; 122131 – EFFETE; 121223 – COCOON; 121133 – TATTOO; 122321 – DEEMED; 123443 – GROTTO; 123123 – MURMUR; 123212 – REVERE; 123344 – TOFFEE.

228.
(a) 4-letter examples: RASH, RISK.
5-letter examples: TOPAZ, WEEPS.
7-letter example: WETTISH.
(b) TYPEWRITER is usually considered to be the longest word using the letters on the top row. There are several other 10-letter words though – REPERTOIRE, PROPRIETOR and PERPETUITY – and there are also a couple of 11-letter words – PROPRIETORY and RUPTUREWORT.
(c) The longest common word is FLASKS. Longer, though less common, words are HALAKAH, FLAGFALL and HAGGADAH.

229. (a) ABSTEMIOUS
(b) There are other possible solutions, but these are probably the most common words:

AIEOU – Ambidextrous
OEAUI – Overhauling
AUIOE – Cautioned
AIOUE – Anxiousness
EOUAI – Encouraging
IOUAE – Discourage
EUOIA – Pneumonia
EUAIO – Reputation
OAUIE – Consanguine
OUEAI – Housemaid
UAIOE – Ultraviolet
UOIAE – Unsociable

230.
1. J-AIL 2. A-GREED 3. N-EARLY 4. E-MOTION 5. A-STERN 6. U-SURER 7. S-IMPLY 8. T-ROUBLES 9. E-STRANGE 10. N-EAT. (JANE AUSTEN)

231.
(a) SENATOR (b) BIOGENY (c) SYBARITE (d) GAINSAYS (e) CALUMNIES (f) INDICATORY (g) GABARDINE (h) SCHEMATIC (i) ENIGMATIST (j) DESECRATION (k) INTOXICATE (l) ALLEGORIST (m) INTERLACES (n) CONTAINERISED (o) PETROCHEMICAL (p) PREDICTIVENESS.

232. CRESCENT (CRESS, SCENT).

233. BUTTERFLY (BUTT, TURF, FLY).

234. CARES, CARESS.

235.

1. NAPLES 2. ELBE 3. WASHINGTON 4. CINCINNATI 5. AMSTERDAM 6. STAMBOUL 7. TORNEA 8. LEPANTO 9. ECLIPTIC.
This gives NEWCASTLE and COALMINES.

236.

(a) WET, bet, bey, dey, DRY.
(b) EYE, dye, die, did, LID.
(c) EEL, e'en, pen, pin, PIE.
(d) RAVEN, riven, risen, riser, MISER.
(e) OAT, rat, rot, roe, RYE.
(f) TEA, sea, set, sot, HOT.

(g) PIG, wig, wag, way, say, STY.
(h) FISH, fist, gist, girt, gird, BIRD.
(i) REST, lest, lost, loft, soft, SOFA.

(j) PEN, e'en, eel, ell, ill, ilk, INK.
(k) NOSE, note, cote, core, corn, coin, CHIN.
(l) TEARS, sears, stars, stare, stale, stile, SMILE.
(m) PITCH, pinch, winch, wench, tench, tenth, TENTS.
(n) POOR, boor, book, rook, rock, rick, RICH.
(o) APE, are, ere, err, ear, mar, MAN.
(p) FLOUR, floor, flood, blood, brood, broad, BREAD.
(q) MINE, mint, mist, most, moat, coat, COAL.
(r) FURIES, buries, buried, burked, barked, barred, BARREL.

(s) WHEAT, cheat, cheap, cheep, creep, creed, breed, BREAD.
(t) FOUR, foul, fool, foot, fort, fore, fire, FIVE.
(u) HARE, hark, hack, sack, sock, soak, soap, SOUP.
(v) PITY, pits, pins, fins, find, fond, food, GOOD.
(w) BLACK, blank, blink, clink, chink, chine, whine, WHITE.
(x) COMB, come, home, hole, hale, hall, hail, HAIR.
(y) WHIP, whit, wait, want, cant, cast, last, LASH.
(z) SHOES, shops, chops, crops, cross, cress, crest, CRUST.
(aa) BREAD, break, bleak, bleat, blest, blast, boast, TOAST.

(bb) STEAL, steel, steer, sheer, shier, shies, shins, chins, COINS.
(cc) TREE, free, flee, fled, feed, weed, weld, wold, WOOD.
(dd) GRASS, crass, cress, tress, trees, frees, freed, greed, GREEN.
(ee) ELM, ell, all, ail, air, fir, far, oar, OAK.
(ff) ARMY, arms, aims, dims, dams, dame, name, nave, NAVY.
(gg) BEANS, beams, seams, shams, shame, shale, shall, shell, SHELF.
(hh) BUY, bud, bid, aid, aim, arm, ark, ask, ASS.
(ii) ONE, owe, ewe, eye, dye, doe, toe, too, TWO.

(jj) CAIN, chin, shin, spin, spun, spud, sped, aped, abed, ABEL.
(kk) BLUE, glue, glut, gout, pout, port, part, pant, pint, PINK.
(ll) COSTS, posts, pests, tests, tents, tenth, tench, teach, peach, peace, PENCE.
(mm) LOAF, leaf, deaf, dear, deer, dyer, dyes, eyes, eves, even, OVEN.
(nn) KETTLE, settle, settee, setter, better, betted, belted, bolted, bolter, bolder, HOLDER.
(oo) ROGUE, vogue, vague, value, valve, halve, helve, heave, leave, lease, least, BEAST.
(pp) QUELL, quill, quilt, guilt, guile, guide, glide, glade, grade, grave, brave, BRAVO.
(qq) RIVER, rover, cover, coves, cores, corns, coins, chins, shins, shine, shone, SHORE.
(rr) WITCH, winch, wench, tench, tenth, tents, tints, tilts, tills, fills, falls, fails, fairs, FAIRY.

237.
1. WHIST 2. ISSUE 3. STAIN 4. CAPON 5. OUNCE 6. NAILS 7. SLIPS 8. INURE 9. NORSE.
States: WISCONSIN, TENNESSEE, LOUISIANA.

CROSSWORDS AND FRIENDS

238.

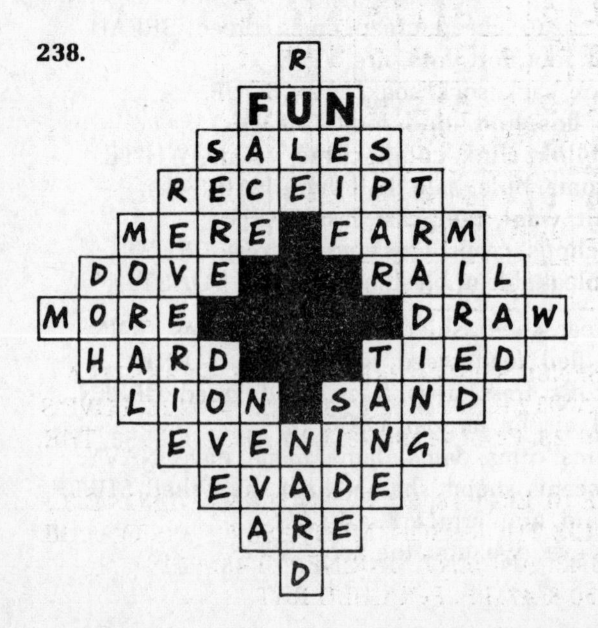

239.

Horizontal: 1. FIG 4. CANOE 6. WARFARE 8. MARMALADE 10. E.G. 11. EA 12. SOLUTION 17. SNAG 18. CAST 19. SHEET 20. SO 22. OR 23. NORFOLK 29. FIRPO 30. POE.

Vertical: 1. FARM 2. INFANT 3. GOAL 4. CAR 5. ERA 6. WAGON 7. EDENS 8. MESSES 9. EASTER 13. LAS 14. UGH 15. ICE 16. OAT 21. ON 22. O.K. 24. OF 25. RIP 26. FRO 27. OPE 28. LO.

240.

241.

J	E	M	I	M	A	O	B	A	D	I	A	H
O	L	I	V	E	R	T	A	H	E	L	B	E
N	O	C	A	B	N	A	R	D	N	O	I	Z
M	O	R	N	L	O	I	N	I	R	A	G	E
I	P	R	E	E	L	S	A	M	O	S	A	K
A	B	I	N	A	D	A	B	S	W	I	T	I
R	O	B	E	R	T	E	A	C	L	A	U	D
H	I	N	L	A	I	I	S	A	A	C	T	Y
P	T	O	L	E	M	Y	I	S	N	A	K	E
E	U	R	I	P	I	D	E	S	D	N	A	S

Notes

Across: 15. REV. NONSENSE SONGS, PREFACE, 'HE WEARETH A RUNCIBLE HAT'. 19. RAND 23. HAMLET I 1 166 25. LION 26. LOVE'S LABOUR'S LOST IV 1 79. 28. PEER 44 and 48. LAY ABOUT IT. 53. THE TWO KEANS.

Down: 7 REV. & 5. MOTE 10. LION 18. BR. ROUND LEA 21. I'M IN D.S., DAL SEGNO 27. FRANCIS THOMPSON, MISTRESS OF VISION, XIII 36. TUT(OR) 41. D-YES 43. ANCIENT MARINER, II 45. REV. CHICK-PEA, PEAHEN 50 & 47. I.E. POUCHED RAT.

242.
Across: 1. NOMAD 4. PARKER 8. MALODOUR 9. OILED 11. SODIUM 12. CALENDS 13. ABSTRACT 14. TARRY 15. CHEROOTS 19. RENEGADE 22. GNOME 24. VILLAGER 27. EMBRACE 28. UNFELT 29. DIXIE 30. SECRETS 31. DANDLE 32. HERDS.
Down: 1. NABOB 2. MONITOR 3. DOGMA 4. PRACTISE 5. ROULETTE 6. KINEMA 7. RENDERED 8. MOSAIC 10. DUSTY 16. HANDMAID 17. OVERAWED 18. TRAVERSE 20. GRAFTER 21. EARTHS 22. GREED 23. MARGIN 25. LURCH 26. ELVES.

243.
Across: 1. CAULD 5. SCIRPUS 11. JARGONELLE 12. CHUPATTY 14. KIWI 15. STAMMEL 16. STALAG 18. LOBED 19. HOPLITE 24. ERRATIC 25. CHUTE 26. PARENT 28. RESPIRE 30. EDGE 31. ZEMINDAR 32. SCREENINGS 33. SPENDER 34. GOTHS.
Down: 1. COCKSHY 2. ACHITOPHEL 3. LARPILLI 4. DRAMA 6. COTTIER 7. INYALA 8. REAM 9. PLUMBITE 10. SEELD 13. WEEPING ASH 17. APLUSTRE 20. TERRENE 21. MARENGO 22. ICTERUS 23. SEIZED 25. CROSS 27. AWING 29. PEEN.

244.
Back: 1. NEEDY 2. HINDERS 3. LITERAL 4. PLAIN 6. GIVES 8. DILUTED 12. PLAYED 14. DIVIDE 15. ILLNESS 16. SWEET 17. POLAR 18. FAILURE 22. CAREFUL 25. RAPID.
Up: 5. VERSE 7. TENSE 8. DEPTH 9. ADULTS 10. DISPLAY 11. LIGHTEN 13. VILLAIN 19. LORDS 20. FALSELY 21. REPEL 22. CREDIT 23. DOUBTED 24. PRIDE 25. REFUSED.

245.
Across: 1. ETRUSCAN 5. DESERT 9. RESPECTS 10. PIERCE 11. HINDLEGS 12. ARTIST 14. UNDERSIGNS 18. PERMISSION 22. RAGGED 23. NAMELESS 24. DETOUR 25. DISPERSE 26. CANTER 27. ANGRIEST.
Down: 1. EARTHY 2. RESENT 3. STEALS 4. ANTAGONIST 6. EDITRESS 7. EARNINGS 8. TREATISE 13. DECORATION 15. SPORADIC 16. BRIGHTEN 17. SINECURE 19. DEEPER 20. DECREE 21. ASSERT.

246.
(a) **Across:** 1. CENTAUR 5. PICADOR 6. INSTEAD 7. ELAPSES
Down: 1. CAPSIZE 2. NICOSIA 3. ADDRESS 4. REREDOS
(b) **Across:** 1. COMMONS 5. OLIVIER 6. PERSIAN 7. RETINUE
Down: 1. CROPPER 2. MAIGRET 3. OPINION 4. STRANGE

247.

F	A	U	L	T	■	S	H	I	S	H	■	E	R	A
A	R	M	O	R	■	P	O	N	T	O	O	N	E	D
R	O	B	L	E	■	I	N	T	E	R	L	U	D	E
O	M	E	L	E	T	T	E	■	M	A	I	M	S	■
S	A	R	I	■	R	E	S	T	S	■	V	E	T	O
■	■	■	P	R	E	S	T	O	■	S	E	R	A	C
S	I	M	O	O	M	■	V	A	L	E	■	A	R	T
A	D	A	P	T	O	R	■	D	I	N	E	T	T	E
C	E	N	■	A	R	I	D	■	F	O	R	E	S	T
H	A	I	R	S	■	G	E	N	E	R	A	■	■	■
A	L	F	A	■	C	A	P	E	R	■	S	A	G	A
■	S	O	N	A	R	■	L	A	S	T	A	G	E	S
M	O	L	E	C	U	L	A	R	■	A	B	A	S	H
U	N	D	E	R	M	I	N	E	■	E	L	I	T	E
M	S	S	■	E	B	B	E	D	■	L	E	N	E	S

248.

Q	U	A	F	F	E	D	■	■	S	C	A	R	E	R
U	N	D	E	R	G	O	■	S	T	I	B	I	N	E
E	N	D	E	A	R	S	■	T	E	T	R	O	D	E
R	E	I	S	■	E	S	C	A	P	E	■	R	U	N
I	R	S	■	S	T	E	R	N	S	■	G	I	R	T
E	V	O	K	E	■	D	I	D	■	P	E	T	E	R
D	E	N	I	A	L	■	M	I	L	I	T	A	R	Y
■	■	■	T	R	I	T	E	N	E	S	S	■	■	■
F	U	R	B	E	L	O	W	■	S	T	U	P	O	R
I	L	I	A	D	■	W	A	S	■	O	P	I	N	E
R	U	N	G	■	C	A	V	E	I	N	■	R	E	V
E	L	K	■	F	I	B	E	R	S	■	T	O	P	I
D	A	M	F	O	O	L	■	I	L	L	E	G	A	L
O	T	A	R	I	N	E	■	F	E	A	T	U	R	E
G	E	N	I	E	S	■	■	S	T	R	E	E	T	S

249.
A. Value B. Intent C. Ludo D. Loaf E. Earth F. Tees G. Teddy H. Eyes J. Cuban K. Hosts L. Anthem M. Ragtime N. Lewd P. Organ Q. Thing R. Trust S. Etch T. Brief U. Rash V. Outset W. Nigh X. Theft Y. Ether.

Quotation: 'These struggles with the natural character, the strong native bent of the heart, may seem futile and fruitless but in the end they do good.'
Villette, Charlotte Brontë.

250.
A. Twister B. Haddock C. Entrance D. Reveals E. Asking F. Infidel G. Nowhere H. Bursting J. Oratory K. Whippet L. Dusty M. Hamper N. Lawful P. Absinthe Q. Wealth R. Repair S. Ewes T. Norfolk U. Coward V. Espying.
Quotation: 'In Autumn the partridges whirred up, birds in flocks blew like spray across the fallow, rooks appeared on the grey watery heavens and flew cawing into the winter.'
The Rainbow, D. H. Lawrence.

251.
1. Modest 2. Destroyer 3. Ermine 4. Neptune 5. Nevertheless 6. Essential 7. Altitude 8. Deluge 9. Geisha 10. Handicap 11. Capable 12. Leveret 13. Retriever 14. Verbatim 15. Immense 16. Semaphore 17. Oregon 18. Onerous 19. Usurper 20. Permafrost 21. Stipend 22. Endeavour 23. Urbane 24. Nectar 25. Artisan 26. Andiron 27. Onager 28. Erudite 29. Tempest 30. Stiletto 31. Toxin 32. Indigo 33. Goliath.

252.

QUICK THINKING

253. −7.2.

254. 1, 2, 3.

255. Give the fifth person the basket with the apple still in it.

256. $1^3 + 12^3$. $9^3 + 10^3$.

257. Inches in a mile (63,360 to about 52,000).

258. Seconds in a week (604,800 to 528,000).

259. 1 ton.

260. 250 centimetres.

261. They are both the same.

262. (a) 666 days.
(b) 666 inches.
(c) 28 days.
(d) 666 millimetres.
(e) One-fourteenth of a week.

263. He cannot average 60 miles per hour for the two laps – unless he covers the second lap in no time at all!

264. 100. The fractions cancel out to leave one-tenth of 1000.

265. 8.

266. 8.

267. Push the cork *into* the bottle, then shake out the coin.

268.

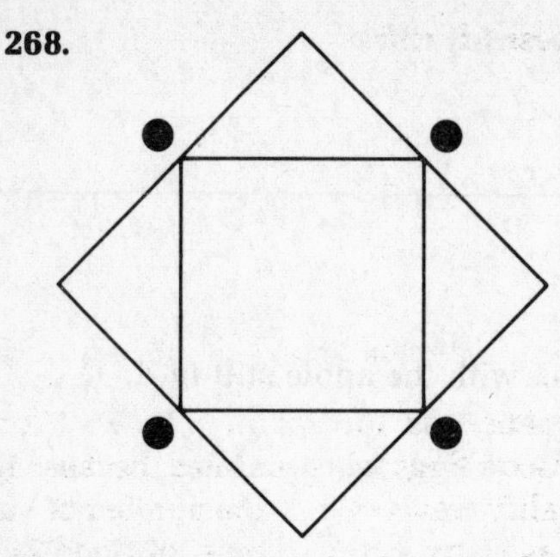

The diagram shows how it may be done.

269.

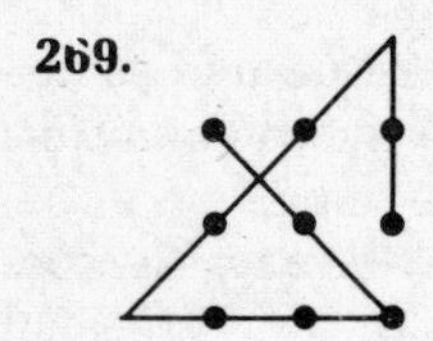

270. No. I would take your £2, say 'I lose', and give you £1. You would have won the bet but lost £1.

271. A gets to the station first. B probably misses the train.

272. Four boys and three girls.

273. Thirty-five.

274. 504.

275. 2,001,000.

276. 14.7 times. (This is found by taking the sum of 1 + 6/5 + 6/4 + 6/3 + 6/2 + 6/1).

277. He stands the signpost up so that the arm indicating the place he has come from is pointing in the correct direction. The other arms will then point correctly too.

278. 190.

279. 66 + 66 + 6 + 6.

280. (a) teepee (b) voodoo (c) assess (d) riffraff

281. (a) beekeeper (b) assessors.

MODERN MASTERS

282.

Humpty Dumpty's mark in arithmetic was 10.

There were altogether seven Good Eggs who qualified, because the number of marks necessary to qualify was 4 × 3 × the number of subjects, and at the same time twice as many as the number of Good Eggs besides Humpty Dumpty, who qualified, multiplied by the number of subjects.

There must have been at least five subjects, because the total number of marks necessary to qualify was four times the maximum obtainable in one subject and no marks were repeated in any one score.

In the case of five subjects, there are exactly seven ways to score:

$$60 = 15 + 14 + 13 + 12 + 6$$
$$60 = 15 + 14 + 13 + 11 + 7$$
$$60 = 15 + 14 + 13 + 10 + 8$$
$$60 = 15 + 14 + 12 + 11 + 8$$
$$60 = 15 + 14 + 12 + 10 + 9$$
$$60 = 15 + 13 + 12 + 11 + 9$$
$$60 = 14 + 13 + 12 + 11 + 10$$

In the case of more than five subjects, there are many more than seven ways to score.

Humpty Dumpty's mark in arithmetic, therefore, was 10.

283.

The two sides of the rectangle total 23 miles. Hence, if m miles be one side of the rectangle,

$$(m + 4)(23 - m + 5) = 2m(23 - m)$$

So m is either 14 or 8.

The Governor had had in mind a rectangle 15 miles by 8 miles (which is half the area of a rectangle 20 miles by 12 miles). The applicant selected a rectangle 14 miles by 9 miles (which is half the area of a rectangle 18 miles by 14 miles).

So the area in question was 126 square miles.

284.

The number of distinguishable dodecahedra is 96, subdivided thus, in respect of colour distribution:

Faces 12,0	2
11,1	2
10,2	6
9,3	10
8,4	24
7,5	28
6,6	24
Total	96

285.
The original scores of 6 points to each finalist must have come from a first, second and third placing each. When the three dishonest singers reversed their order of marking, the 3 points and 1 point scored by the honest singer were reversed, but his total remained at 6. The other three finalists, however, when the marks were reversed, gained 2, lost 2, or stayed the same, depending on whether they scored 1, 2 or 3 from the honest singer. So the final scores were 8, 6, 6 and 4, and the honest singer was tied second.

286.
If the first two notes are *mmmmmm-mmmmmm*, then it will settle down and play *mmmmmm* for ever. If the first two notes are anything else, then it soon settles into this rather over-simple tune:
ping-boing-ping-boing-ping-boing. . . .

287.
The phrase, 'it reads the same either way' did *not* mean that it was palindromic. It meant that it read the same upside down as the right way up! It was in fact 263^2 which is 69169. This was the code number.

288.
Yes, it is. Suppose the three friends have run thirty times with these results:
For the first ten days the order of finish is Timothy, Urban, Vincent.
For the next ten days it's Urban, Vincent, Timothy.
For the last ten days it's Vincent, Timothy, Urban.
Timothy finished before Urban twenty days out of thirty.
Urban finished before Vincent twenty days out of thirty.
Vincent finished before Timothy twenty days out of thirty.

289.

The last fact given means that no one married his son and daughter to the son and daughter of the same friend.

Let us call the five friends by their initials.

'Daughter-in-law of the father of A's son-in-law' means A's daughter. 'Son-in-law of the father of C's daughter-in-law' means C's son. Then A's daughter is the sister-in-law of B's son, which can only mean that her brother (A's son) married B's daughter. Similarly, C married his daughter to D's son.

Who is the husband of D's daughter? He cannot be C's or A's son. Let us suppose he is B's son. Then C's daughter's mother-in-law is Mrs D, while A's son's mother-in-law is Mrs B. So D's daughter can't have married B's son.

It follows that D's daughter married E's son. D's daughter and B's son have a common mother-in-law: Mrs E.

Eugene's daughter is married to Bernard's son.

290.

At the start, one inch of the yellow pencil gets smeared with wet paint. As the blue pencil is moved downward, a second inch of the blue pencil's length is smeared. After the next upward movement the second inch of the blue pencil smears a second inch of the yellow pencil.

Each pair of down-up moves of the blue pencil smears one more inch of each pencil. Five pairs of moves will smear five inches. This, together with the initial inch, makes 6 inches for each pencil.

(Looking at his boots, Leonid Mikhailovich noticed that their entire lengths were muddied where they usually rub each other while he walks.

'How puzzling,' he thought. 'I didn't walk in any deep mud, yet my boots are muddied up to the knees.'

Now you understand the origin of the puzzle.)

291.

He noticed that $\frac{7}{12} = \frac{1}{3} + \frac{1}{4}$, so he cut 4 sheets into 12 thirds, and 3 sheets into 12 fourths. Each worker got one third and one fourth, or $\frac{7}{12}$.

For the other distributions, he used:

$\frac{5}{6} = \frac{1}{2} + \frac{1}{3}$

$\frac{13}{12} = \frac{1}{3} + \frac{3}{4}$

$\frac{13}{36} = \frac{1}{4} + \frac{1}{9}$

$\frac{26}{21} = \frac{2}{3} + \frac{4}{7}$, and so on.

292.

They poured the shot into the jug and then poured in water, which filled all the spaces between the pellets. Now the water volume plus the shot volume equalled the jar's volume.

Removing the shot from the jar, they measured the volume of water remaining, and subtracted it from the volume of the jar.

293.
They will always reach the destination simultaneously, no matter where the bicycle is left behind for the last time.

294.
If you place the point of a compass at the centre of a black square on a chessboard with 2-inch squares, and extend the arms of the compass a distance equal to the square root of 10 inches, the pencil will trace the largest possible circle that touches only black squares.

295.
Several procedures have been devised by which *n* persons can divide a cake in *n* pieces so that each is satisfied he has at least $1/n$ of the cake. The following system has the merit of leaving no excess bits of cake.

Suppose there are five persons: A, B, C, D, E. A cuts off what he regards as $^1/_5$ of the cake and what he is content to keep as his share. B now has the privilege, if he thinks A's slice is more than $^1/_5$, of reducing it to what he thinks is $^1/_5$ by cutting off a portion. Of course if he thinks it is $^1/_5$ or less, he does not touch it. C, D and E in turn now have the same privilege. The last person to touch the slice keeps it as his share. Anyone who thinks that this person got less than $^1/_5$ is naturally pleased because it means, in his eyes, that more than $^4/_5$ remains. The remainder of the cake, including any cut-off pieces, is now divided among the remaining four persons in the same manner, then among three. The final division is made by one person cutting and the other choosing. The procedure is clearly applicable to any number of persons.

296.
The answer is that A's chances of being pardoned are ⅓, and that C's chances are ⅔.

Regardless of who is pardoned, the governor can give A the name of a man, other than A, who will die. The governor's statement therefore has no influence on A's survival chances; they continue to be ⅓.

What about prisoner C? Since either A or C must die, their respective probabilities for survival must add up to 1. A's chances to live are ⅓; therefore C's chances must be ⅔. This can be confirmed by considering the four possible elements in our sample space, and their respective initial probabilities:

1. C is pardoned, governor names B (probability ⅓)
2. B is pardoned, governor names C (probability ⅓)
3. A is pardoned, governor names B (probability ⅙)

4. A is pardoned, governor names C (probability $\frac{1}{6}$)

In cases 3 and 4, A lives, making his survival chances $\frac{1}{3}$. Only cases 1 and 3 apply when it becomes known that B will die. The chances that it is case 1 are $\frac{1}{3}$, or twice the chances ($\frac{1}{6}$) that it is case 3, so C's survival chances are two to one, or $\frac{2}{3}$.

297.

At nobody. Fire your pistol in the air, and you will have the best chance of all three of the truellists. Certainly you don't want to shoot at Black. If you are unlucky enough to hit him, Blue will polish you off on the next shot. Suppose you aim at Blue and hit him. Then Black will have first shot against you and his overall probability of winning the duel will be $\frac{6}{7}$, yours $\frac{1}{7}$. Not too good. (You are invited to confirm Black's winning probability of $\frac{6}{7}$ by summing the infinite geometric series: $\frac{2}{3} + (\frac{1}{3})(\frac{2}{3})(\frac{2}{3}) + (\frac{1}{3})(\frac{2}{3})(\frac{1}{3})(\frac{2}{3})(\frac{2}{3})\ldots$) But if you deliberately miss, you will have the first shot against either Black or Blue on the next round. With probability $\frac{2}{3}$, Black will hit Blue, and you will have an overall winning probability of $\frac{3}{7}$. With $\frac{1}{3}$ probability, Black will miss Blue, in which case Blue will dispose of his stronger opponent, Black, and your overall chance against Blue will be $\frac{1}{3}$.

Thus by shooting in the air, your probability of winning the truel is $\frac{25}{63}$ (about 40%). Black's probability is $\frac{8}{21}$ (about 38%), and poor Blue's is only $\frac{2}{9}$ (about 22%).

Is there a lesson in this which might have application to the field of international relations?

298.

Your strategy should be quite different from that best pursued in *Twenty Questions*. One way to proceed is to start with the question 'Is your number bigger than 1?' If you get a 'yes' response, your next question will be 'Is it bigger than 2?' and so on up the line. In this manner, the first 'no' answer you receive will pinpoint your opponent's number, which you will promptly guess the next time you assume the role of questioner.

The only way your opponent can win, therefore, is to guess your number on his first round of questions. His chance of doing so is 1 out of 100, so your advantage in this game, as first questioner is 99 to 1. As the size of the range of numbers increases, the first player's advantage increases correspondingly.

299.

Let P be the probability of winning for the first player who spins. In one out of six cases, he loses immediately. In the other five, the other player will have the same probability P of winning. Thus $P = \frac{5}{6}(1-P)$ and $P = \frac{5}{11}$. Now let N be the number of chambers remaining, assuming neither player has yet exercised the spin option. The chance of winning is not better than (N–1)(1–P)/N if no spin is made, and this chance is always less than $\frac{5}{11}$ except when N = 6, in which case it is equal to $\frac{5}{11}$. (Obviously spinning prior to the first shot does not affect the first player's odds, provided his opponent plans to spin on his turn.)

It follows that, after the first shot, it is always desirable to spin, and that prior to the first shot it apparently makes no difference! For if you elect not to spin and get a 'click', your opponent, who may not have worked out the game, is liable not to spin either, in which case (provided he also gets a 'click') you will spin prior to the third shot. By not spinning, you offer him the opportunity of foolishly lowering his odds by 4 per cent. Had you spun prior to the first shot, he would have had no opportunity of making a mistake, and would be compelled to adopt the best strategy. So your best chance is obtained by not spinning prior to the first shot, and spinning on all successive shots.

In the *misère* version, analysis is more difficult. Working backward, on the fifth shot, spinning gives odds of 6/11 against 1/2 without spinning. So spinning is superior at shot five. At shot four, spinning gives odds of 6/11 against 1/3 + 2/3 × 5/11 or 7/11 without spinning, so that no spinning is superior. At shot two, no spinning gives odds of 1/5 + (4/5 × 5/11) = 31/55, making no spinning the better percentage play. It follows that the first player should deny his opponent the opportunity of electing not to spin and should spin prior to his first shot, giving himself maximum odds of 6/11.

TOMORROW'S CLASSICS

300.

Apply 180-degree turns to each of the faces in the following sequence: top, bottom, right, left, front, back.

301.

Apply 180-degree turns to the following faces: front, right, back, front, right, back.

302.

Apply the following 90-degree turns: front clockwise, back anticlockwise, top clockwise, bottom anticlockwise, right clockwise, left anticlockwise, front clockwise, back anticlockwise.

303.
The answers are: 3784, 3159, 1395, 1827, 2187, 1435. The common factor is that in each multiplication, the answer consists of the same digits as the numbers being multiplied.

304.
The common factor is that each of the digits from 1 to 9 appears once and only once in the answer and the numbers being multiplied.

305.
Each of the answers, looked at upside down, spells out a word.
(a) 3704 (hole) (b) 5710 (oils) (c) 5733 (eels) (d) 7105 (soil)
(e) 7714 (hill) (f) 7734 (hell) (g) 53751 (isles)
(h) 317537 (Leslie)

306.
(1) The car's velocity steadily increases from zero at the start to maximum at the earth's centre, and steadily decreases thereafter to zero at the other end.
(2) The car's acceleration is maximum at the start (32 feet per second per second). It decreases as it approaches the earth's centre, where it becomes zero. After that it accelerates negatively until it reaches the other end.
(3) Halfway down the tube, in a stationary car, you would weigh much less than on the earth's surface because of the gravitational pull of the earth above you.
(4) You would be in free-fall throughout the entire trip, and therefore always in a state of zero gravity.
(5) The car reaches a top speed at the earth's centre of about 17,700 mph, or almost 5 miles per second.
(6) On the moon a car falling through the moon's centre would complete the trip in about 53 minutes; on Mars, in about 49 minutes.
(7) The story is 'When the Earth screamed' by Sir Arthur Conan Doyle. It tells how Professor George Edward Challenger, the hero of Doyle's novel *The Lost World*, penetrates the earth's 'skin', causing it to howl with pain.

307.
(1) Rocket ships are in 'free fall' as soon as they leave the earth. From the time the motors are turned off to the time they are used again for altering course or braking, there is zero gravity inside a rocket ship.
(2) Cigars won't stay lit in zero gravity unless you constantly wave them about. Gases produced by the burning of tobacco must be carried upward by the buoyancy of air, in turn caused by gravity pulling air down.

(3) Birds can't fly on the moon because there is no air against which their wings can push or support them when gliding.
(4) No air, no breezes, no rippling flags on the moon.
(5) Although in daytime the lunar sky is indeed dark, there is so much reflected light from the moon's surface that stars are not visible to unaided eyes. They *can* be seen through binoculars.
(6) Even at night, stars on the moon never twinkle. Twinkling on earth is caused by movements of the atmosphere.
(7) For stars to be visible inside the arms of a crescent earth they would have to be between earth and the moon.
(8) The moon does rotate once during each revolution around the earth, but since it always keeps its same face towards the earth, the earth does not rise and set. From any given location on the earth side of the moon, the earth remains fixed in the sky.
(9) Without air a boomerang can no more operate on the moon than a bird can keep itself aloft.
(10) Twitchell couldn't have heard the boomerang strike the boulder because sound requires an atmosphere to transmit its waves to a human ear.
(11) Before the first moon landing it was widely thought that objects would be invisible in moon shadows. Actually, so much light is reflected from the irregular lunar surface that this is not the case.
(12) Although the sun does rise and set on the moon, it takes it about 28 days to return to a former position. It could not have set as rapidly as the narrative indicates.
(13) The terminator moves at about 10 miles per hour. This is slow enough for a person to keep pace with its movement.
(14) Meteors leave glowing trails only when they are burned up by friction of the earth's atmosphere. On the atmosphereless moon, meteors would not produce such trails.
(15) As in mistake 12, the sun could not have risen until some two weeks after it set.

WORD GAMES

CONTENTS

PART ONE

SPOKEN GAMES

Party Games

I Love My Love

In the traditional version of this game the players take it in turn to describe their loved one using different letters of the alphabet, like this:

GEORGE: I love my love with an A because she is Arabella from Austria and amazingly ambitious.
BERNARD: I love my love with a B because she is Bernadette from Birmingham and bountifully buxom.
SHAW: I love my love with a C because she is Chloe from California and completely crazy.

In the wordsmith's version of the game the players continue with the same letter of the alphabet until they have exhausted it. Starting at A they take it in turn to think of adjectives beginning with A to describe their loved one and go on and on until one of them cannot think of a fresh adjective beginning with A or repeats an adjective already used. He loses a point and all the players move on to the next letter. When the players have reached the letter Z, or have stopped play after eight hours having only reached C, the player who has lost least points becomes the winner.

For those with rich vocabularies (and for those seeking to acquire them) this is a very entertaining game, as you can see from the first moments of this contest:

GEORGE: I love my love with an A because she is Abandoned!
BERNARD: – Able!
SHAW: – Amiable!
GEORGE: – Artful!
BERNARD: – Accommodating!
SHAW: – Acceptable!
GEORGE: – Adaptable!
BERNARD: – Accomplished!
SHAW: – Adulterous!
GEORGE: – Affluent!
BERNARD: – Advanced!
SHAW: – Amorous!
GEORGE: – Affable!
BERNARD: – Aristocratic!
SHAW: – Aromatic!
GEORGE: – Autonomous!
BERNARD: – Autocratic!
SHAW: – Available!
GEORGE: – Appealing!
BERNARD: – Astonishing!
SHAW: – Artful!
GEORGE: – Angelic!
BERNARD: – Altruistic!
SHAW: – Asleep!
GEORGE: – Ascetic!
BERNARD: – Aesthetic!
SHAW: – Amorous!

By making his love 'amorous' Shaw has repeated one of the attributes already ascribed to her, so the time has come to move on to B and we shall never know whether the young lady was also assured, attainable, awesome, audible, attenuated, artificial, acute, animated, acquiescent or abstinent.

Backwards Spelling

At the best of times, spelling words like Parallel, Separate, Embarrassed, Desiccate and Sacrilegious presents all but a few of us with problems. Spelling the words *backwards* would seem to be asking altogether too much – but that's just what this amusing party game is all about.

The players take it in turn to be given a word and have to spell it backwards. They must start to speak as soon as they have been told the word and they must not hesitate or correct themselves while they are speaking. Every time a player spells a word backwards correctly he scores a point. After ten rounds, the player with the highest score is the winner.

Inexperienced players will find even the simplest six- and seven-letter words a challenge and everyone will find words like these nearly impossible:

Abbreviation
Blunderbuss
Dilatory
Evangelistic
Fluorescence
Graphology
Hypocrisy
Ingratiating
Juvenescence
Kaleidoscope
Laryngitis
Nonconformity
Onomatopoiea
Quintessential
Rumbustious
Subpoena
Tautological
Unintentional
Vaporousness
Whomsoever
Yarborough
Zincograph

An umpire should be appointed before the game begins to select the words to be spelt and to make sure that they are being spelt backwards in the correct order.

The Last Shall Be First

The players decide on a category – Countries, Animals, Flowers, Scientists, Amino-acids or whatever. The first player calls out a word belonging in the chosen category, followed by each of the other players in turn. The catch is that the first letter of each word must be the same as the final letter of the preceding word. No word may be repeated. A player is out if he cannot think of a suitable word, if he repeats a word, or if he calls out a word that does not fit the category.

For example, with three players, and with Countries as the category, a game might begin like this:

DAVID:	Germany
HERBERT:	Yugoslavia
LAWRENCE:	Australia
DAVID:	Aden
HERBERT:	Nepal
LAWRENCE:	Luxembourg
DAVID:	Greece
HERBERT:	Egypt

Adverbs

One player leaves the room while the others agree among themselves on a suitable adverb. The player who has left the room then comes in again and has to guess the chosen word. To get some clues he or she may ask each of the other players in turn three questions (about any subject at all) to which the other player must reply in the manner suggested by the chosen adverb.

When each player has been asked three questions and all have replied in the appropriate manner, the outsider has to guess the adverb. As a refinement, he may be allowed three guesses, scoring three points if he gets the word right first time, two points if his second guess is correct, and one point if he guesses correctly at his last attempt. The other players then take it in turn to leave the room while another adverb is chosen.

The adverbs chosen should be descriptive and not too obscure, because everyone likes to guess words if they possibly can, and it's a good idea to let everyone have a go.

If you are stuck for ideas, here are some suggested adverbs, which might also suggest other suitable words to you:

angrily	hesitantly	proudly
childishly	humbly	rudely
conspiratorially	lazily	seductively
emotionally	lovingly	stridently
furtively	poetically	thoughtfully
gaily	pompously	timidly

Tennis, Elbow, Foot

The players take it in turn to call out a word which is either directly associated with the word previously called out or which rhymes with it. For example: Tennis, Elbow, Foot, Ball, Game, Bird, Third, Man, Handle, Candle, Light, Weight, etc.

Players are out if they hesitate, if they call out a word that neither relates to the previous word nor rhymes with it, or if they repeat a word that has previously been called out. A referee may be needed to settle any disputes. The last one left in is the winner.

Fizz-Buzz

FIZZ-BUZZ is a very silly game that is suitable for players of any age. The players take it in turns to call out numbers in ascending order, starting from 1, but replacing every multiple of 3 with the word 'Fizz', every multiple of 5 with the word 'Buzz', and every multiple of the two with the word 'Fizz-Buzz'.

So the sequence goes: One, Two, Fizz, Four, Buzz, Fizz, Seven . . . Fourteen, Fizz-Buzz, Sixteen . . . and so on.

A player is out if he calls a number instead of fizzing or buzzing (or vice versa) or if he confuses his fizzes with his buzzes. The last player left in the game is the winner.

Word Chain

Here is a game for two or more in which the players take it in turn to think of a two-word or three-word phrase, the first word of which must rhyme with the last word of the previous player's phrase. The opening player's first phrase is always 'Word Chain'.

To give you an idea of the game in action, here is a brief two-handed bout between Jack and Jill:

JACK: Word Chain
JILL: Grain of wheat
JACK: Heat wave
JILL: Slave trade
JACK: Laid back
JILL: Sack of coal
JACK: Pole vault
JILL: Malt whisky

At this point, Jack gives up because he cannot think of a phrase beginning with a rhyme for 'whisky'. Jill has won the round, and it is her turn to start the next round, again with the opening phrase 'Word chain'.

What constitutes an acceptable phrase and a legitimate rhyme must be left to the commonsense or whim of the individual players.

Word Chain may also be played as a solo game and, when played thus, is a perfect cure for insomnia.

Group Limericks

The first player makes up the opening line of a limerick; the second player has thirty seconds to come up with the next line; the third player another thirty seconds for the third, and so on until the limerick is complete. The verse does not need to make much sense, but it must rhyme and it should scan.

Here's an example of a group limerick created by five passengers flying from London to Madrid, shortly after they had been told the flight was being diverted to Paris. It took them just thirty-five seconds to come up with this:

There was a young man on a plane
Who wanted to travel to Spain,
But they led him a dance
And took him to France –
Next time he'll travel by train!

The Moulting Ostrich

A leader is chosen and all he has to do is make the other players smile or laugh. Grinning himself, he says to each player in turn, 'Alas, alas, my poor ostrich is moulting and I don't know what to do.' To this each player must make a reasonable suggestion, keeping a totally straight face all the while. Anyone caught smiling, smirking, giggling or bursting into wild hysterics is disqualified.

When he goes round the second time the leader says, 'Alas, alas, my poor ostrich is moulting and I've got a boil on the end of my nose.' Again each player must make, poker-faced, a reasonable helpful suggestion. For the third round the leader says, 'Alas, alas, my poor ostrich is moulting, I've got a boil on the end of my nose and my turkey's lost its stuffing.' Any player surviving all three rounds is a winner.

Word Order

The first player calls out a word at random, the second player follows with another word suggested by the first word, the third player with another suggested by the second, and so on around the group. If the first word were *apple*, it might be followed by *pie*, *sky*, *blue*, *colour*, *television*, *set*, *match*, *stick*, *cane*, *sugar*, and so on.

After a few rounds the first player suddenly shouts 'Reverse order!' at which point the last player to speak must remember the word before his and all the words are repeated around the groups in reverse order – from *sugar* to *cane* to *stick* to *match* to *set* to *television* to *colour* to *blue* to *sky* to *pie* to *apple*.

Anyone hesitating, getting the words in the wrong order, or forgetting a word loses a life. The player who has lost the fewest lives after five rounds is the winner.

Follow On

The first player calls out a two-word phrase or a word consisting of two separate parts. For example:

White Elephant	Skin Deep
Hard Times	Butterfly
Suitcase	Footpath
Pink Gin	High Tide
Foodstuff	Waterfall

Then each player in turn has to call out another word or phrase starting with the second part of the previous one. If a player cannot think of a suitable word or phrase he may throw out a challenge to the rest of the players. If anyone *does* provide a suitable word or phrase, the player whose turn it was drops out. Otherwise the player who called out the last word or phrase, that no one could follow, drops out. In either case, the next player starts another round with a fresh word or phrase. The last player left in is the winner.

Here is an example of how a game with four players might start:

Player 1:	Brief Case
Player 2:	Casebook
Player 3:	Bookmark
Player 4:	Mark Time
Player 1:	Timepiece
Player 2:	Piece Work
Player 3:	Work Place
Player 4:	Place Setting
Player 1:	Setting Sun
Player 2:	Sunspot

Performance Games

Peculiar Leader

Despite its name, this game has nothing to do with politics. It is a parlour game in which you as the leader get up and tell the other players what you do and don't like. Whenever one of the players feels he has caught on to the reason *why* you like this but you don't like that, he puts up his hand and gives an example of what he thinks you do and don't like. If he has indeed caught onto the gist of your peculiar likes and dislikes, congratulate him. The last player to put up his hand and show he has grasped the nature of your likes and dislikes is the loser.

See how long it takes you to discover why one thing is liked and another disliked in this list of examples:

I like coffee but I don't like tea.
I like trees but I don't like flowers.
I like yellow but I don't like blue.
I like balloons but I don't like party hats.
I like butterflies but I don't like moths.
I like bees but I don't like ants.
I like boots but I don't like shoes.
I like spoons but I don't like forks.
I like doors but I don't like windows.
I like swimmers but I don't like divers.
I like football but I don't like boxing.

As you no doubt guessed by the second or third example, the items I like all included double letters in their spelling.

Here is a different set of likes and dislikes, this one perhaps more difficult to catch on to than the last:

I like ants but I don't like bees.
I like the stupid but I don't like the wise.
I like beans but I don't like peas.
I like noses but I don't like eyes.
I like hard work but I don't like ease.
I like coffee but I don't like tea.
I like sheep but I don't like ewes.
I like lakes but I don't like the sea.
I like me but I don't like you.

Here all the things I don't like sound like letters of the alphabet: B's, Y's, P's, I's, E's, T, U's, C, U.

When playing the game with a group of three or more, the loser of one round should be the leader of the next and should think up his own formula for what he likes and dislikes.

Taboo

A very common word – like 'I' or 'and' or 'the' or 'this' or 'that' – is declared taboo and must not be spoken by any of the players. The leader of the group questions each player in turn, and any player uttering the forbidden word drops out. The last player left answering questions is the winner.

Forbidden Letter

This game is similar to TABOO, but a particular letter of the alphabet is banned, and the players must reply to the questions without using any word that contains the forbidden letter.

Tongue-Twisters

Each player is given a tongue-twister and just one minute in which to repeat it as many times as possible. An impartial observer is found to keep an eye on the stopwatch and an ear on the tongue-twisters, and the player who manages to cram the greatest number of correctly spoken twisters into his sixty seconds is the winner.

'The sixth sick sheik's sixth sheep's sick' is supposed to be the most difficult tongue-twister in the English language, but there are plenty of others that are simpler but just as much fun:

Truly rural.
Lemon liniment.
Cricket critic.
Preshrunk shirts.
Red lorry, yellow lorry.
Strange strategic statistics.
Twine three tree twigs.

Six slim slender saplings.
That bloke's back brake-block broke.
She sells sea-shells on the sea-shore.
The minx mixed a medicinal mixture.
They threw three thick things at three thrilled thrushes.
Frisky Freddy feeds on fresh fried fish.
The city sweep shook his sooty sheet in the city street.
Whistle for the thistle sifter.
Around the rugged rocks the ragged rascal ran.
Shiver and slither shovelling slushy squelchy snow.
The Swiss witch which bewitched this switch wished the switch bewitched.

Yarn-Spinning

This is one of those games that only works if someone has taken the trouble to prepare it properly. All you need to do is fill a cardboard box with a random selection of different and preferably slightly eccentric objects. For example: a revolver, a railway timetable, a jar of peanut butter, an egg-timer, some dice, a bible, a Mickey Mouse watch, a red flag, a broken telescope, a plant, some sweets, a foreign stamp and an empty toothpaste tube would do very nicely.

To play the game invite each player in turn to close his eyes and pick four objects out of the box. You then give him five minutes in which to tell a story, any story he cares to invent – the only condition being that he must bring each of his four objects into that story at some stage. When everyone has spun their yarn, the player who is considered to have told the most effective and entertaining tale is declared the winner.

Hobbies

The question-master prepares a list of names of famous people. This may be done mentally or with pencil and paper. Let us suppose the list begins with Ronald Reagan, Mia Farrow and Peter Sellers. The question-master then asks each player in turn, 'What's your hobby?', using one of the names on the list.

For example, he says to the first player, 'What's your hobby, Ronald Reagan?' to which that player, quick as a flash, must return an answer like 'Running races' or 'Reading romances' or any other answer in which the initial letters are the same as the name being used.

The second player is asked, 'What's your hobby, Mia Farrow?' and must immediately give a reply such as 'Making films' or 'Mending fences'.

The third player, having been asked, 'What's your hobby, Peter Sellers?' might reply without hesitation 'Playing snooker' or 'Polishing shoes'.

Any player who fails to give an appropriate reply (almost) immediately drops out. The last player left in the game is the winner.

Favourite Foods

FAVOURITE FOODS is an amusing variation of HOBBIES. The rules are the same but the question this time is 'What is your favourite food?'

Let's have a demonstration:

'What's your favourite food, Ronald Reagan?' 'Roast radishes.'
'What's your favourite food, Mia Farrow?' 'Mouse fillets.'
'What's your favourite food, Peter Sellers?' 'Pickled sausages.'
'What's your favourite food, Frank Sinatra?' 'Fried spaghetti.'
'What's your favourite food, Gyles Brandreth?' 'Gooey bananas.'

Coffee Pot

One player thinks of a word that has two or more meanings (e.g. Row) or a pair of words which have different meanings but which sound the same (e.g. Band and Banned). He then says aloud a sentence using both meanings but substituting the words 'coffee pot' for both of them – for example, 'I passed a coffee pot of trees as I was going for a coffee pot on the river' or 'The coffee pot was so rowdy that it was coffee pot from appearing again at the theatre.'

Each of the other players may then ask one question, and the first player's answer must include one or other of his words, or his word in one or another of its senses, again disguised as 'coffee pot'.

A player who manages to identify the 'coffee pot' word scores one point, otherwise the player who thought of the word scores the point. Each player takes it in turn to think of a 'coffee pot' word, and when everyone has had a go the player with the highest number of points is the winner.

Just A Minute

Players take it in turn to talk on a set subject for just a minute. They start with ten points apiece and when they have been talking for sixty seconds, without hesitating, repeating themselves or deviating from the subject, they are awarded another five points. However, if they *are* guilty of hesitation, repetition or deviation they *lose* two points. Before the game starts an impartial observer should be chosen to choose the subjects for discourse, impose the penalties and keep the score.

Some examples of suitable topics are:

A Visit To The Theatre
Crossing The Atlantic
The Decline And Fall Of The Roman Empire
A Stitch In Time Saves Nine
If I Ruled The World
The Changing Seasons

What Nonsense!

This game is similar to JUST A MINUTE – the difference is that the topics chosen are so ridiculous that only the best performers can speak on them for sixty seconds without hesitation, repetition or deviation.

For example:

I Was A Teenage Taxidermist
The Do-It-Yourself Heart Transplant
Werewolves I Have Met
The Differences Between Chalk And Cheese
Earthworm Farming In Mongolia

Balderdash

Whereas the topics in the previous game were ridiculous, the topics on which the performers have to expound in BALDERDASH are completely meaningless. Furthermore, they have to speak for two whole minutes on topics such as:

If I Am Here, Where Is Thursday?
How To Eat The Moon

The Cosmic Significance Of Custard
The Answer That Cannot Be Questioned
Algebra Versus Chicago And Why Not
If But Was
The Inverse Functionalism Of Sybaritic Dichotomy

This game is to be attempted only by those with the readiest of wits and the most fluent of tongues.

Shrewd Simon Short

This is the ideal game for a party when everyone has had a few drinks. The idea is to see who can read the following passage out loud in the shortest time without hesitating or stumbling over the words.

Shrewd Simon Short sewed shoes. Seventeen summers, speeding storms, spreading sunshine successively, saw Simon's small, shabby shop still standing staunch, saw Simon's selfsame squeaking sign still swinging silently, specifying:

SIMON SHORT, SMITHFIELD'S SOLE SURVIVING SHOEMAKER.
SHOES SEWED, SOLED SUPERFINELY.

Simon's spry, sedulous spouse, Sally Short, sewed shirts, stitched sheets, stuffed sofas. Simon's six stout sons – Seth, Samuel, Stephen, Saul, Silas, Shadrach – sold sundries. Sober Seth sold sugar, spices; simple Sam sold saddles, stirrups, screws; sagacious Stephen sold silks, satins, shawls; sceptical Saul sold silver salvers; selfish Shadrach sold salves, shoestrings, soap, saws, skates; slack Silas sold Sally Short's stuffed sofas.

Some seven summers since, Simon's second son Samuel saw Sophia Sophronia Spriggs somewhere. Sweet, smart, sensible Sophia Sophronia Spriggs. Sam soon showed strong symptoms. Sam seldom stayed storing, selling saddles. Sam sighed sorrowfully, sought Sophia Sophronia's society, sang several serenades slyly. Simon stormed, scolded severely, said Sam seemed so silly singing such shameful, senseless songs. 'Strange Sam should slight such splendid sales! Strutting spendthrift! Scatter-brained simpleton!'

'Softly, softly, sire,' said Sally. 'Sam's smitten; Sam's spied some sweetheart.'

'Sentimental schoolboy!' snarled Simon. 'Smitten! Stop such stuff.' Simon sent Sally's snuffbox spinning, seized Sally's scissors, smashed Sally's spectacles, scattering several spools, 'Sneaking scoundrel! Sam's shocking silliness shall surcease!' Scowling, Simon stopped speaking, started swiftly shopward. Sally sighed sadly. Summoning Sam, she spoke sweet sympathy. 'Sam,' said she, 'sire seems singularly snappy; so, solicit, sue, secure Sophronia speedily, Sam.'

'So soon? So soon?' said Sam, standing stock-still.

'So soon, surely,' said Sally, smiling, 'specially since sire shows such spirits.'

So Sam, somewhat scared, sauntered slowly, shaking stupendously. Sam soliloquized: 'Sophia Sophronia Spriggs, Spriggs – Short – Sophia Sophronia Short – Samuel Short's spouse – sounds splendid! Suppose she should say – she shan't – she shan't!'

Soon Sam spied Sophia starching shirts, singing softly. Seeing Sam, she stopped starching, saluting Sam smilingly. Sam stammered shockingly.

'Spl-spl-splendid summer season, Sophia.'

'Selling saddles still, Sam?'

'Sar-sar-tin,' Sam, starting suddenly. 'Season's somewhat soporific,' said Sam, steadily staunching streaming sweat, shaking sensibly.

'Sartin,' said Sophia, smiling significantly.

'Sip some sweet sherbert, Sam.' (Silence, sixty seconds.)

'Sire shot sixty sheldrakes, Saturday,' said Sophia.

'Sixty? Shot!' said Sam. (Silence seventy-seven seconds.)

'See sister Susan's sunflowers,' said Sophia socially, stopping such stiff silence.

Sophia's sprightly sauciness stimulated Sam strangely: so Sam suddenly spoke sentimentally: 'Sophia, Susan's sunflowers seem saying Samuel Short, Sophia Sophronia Spriggs, stroll serenely, seek some sequestered spot, some sylvan shade. Sparkling springs shall sing soul-stirring strains; Sweet songsters shall silence secret sighings; super-angelic sylphs shall – ' Sophia snickered; so Sam stopped.

'Sophia,' said Sam solemnly.

'Sam,' said Sophia.

'Sophia, stop smiling; Sam Short's sincere. Sam's seeking some sweet spouse, Sophia.'

Sophia stood silent.

'Speak, Sophia, speak; such suspense speculates sorrow.'

'Seek sire, Sam, seek sire.'

So Sam sought sire Spriggs; sire Spriggs said, 'Sartin.'

As reading this passage faultlessly from beginning to end is an almost impossible task, each player may be allowed to correct up to three mistakes before being disqualified. If none of the players manages to complete the passage, the winner will be the player who read most of the passage before being disqualified.

Games For Two

Yes No

Player One barrages Player Two with quick-fire questions, to which Player Two must reply without hesitation and without using the words Yes and No. For example:

STAN:	'Are you ready to start?'
OLIVER:	'I certainly am.'
STAN:	'You didn't nod your head, did you?'
OLIVER:	'I did not.'
STAN:	'Have you had your holiday this year?'
OLIVER:	'I have.'
STAN:	'Did you go abroad?'
OLIVER:	'That is so.'
STAN:	'You didn't hesitate just then, did you?'
OLIVER:	'Certainly not.'
STAN:	'Are you sure.'
OLIVER:	'Sure.'

Player Two wins if he can survive this interrogation for sixty seconds without using the words Yes or No, otherwise Player One wins. The players then change roles for another round.

Messing About In Quotes

One player comes up with a well-known phrase or quotation or cliché, and the other player has to suggest who might have said it. The players then swap roles. Nobody is awarded any points, penalties or prizes, but with quick-witted players the game can be a joy. To set you going, who said, 'Thank God it's Friday'? Why, Robinson Crusoe, of course!

Crambo

All the great masters of English literature have enjoyed tne occasional game of CRAMBO. To play it, one player thinks of a word and announces a word that rhymes with the secret word he has thought of. The other players are then allowed three attempts at guessing the word. If a player guesses the word correctly he has the honour of choosing the word for the next round. If none of the other players can guess the word or if they have all fallen asleep, the original player has another turn.

Stinkety Pinkety

In STINKETY PINKETY each player in turn offers a definition which the other player must translate into a noun followed by a rhyming adjective.

For example:

Definition: An obese feline.
Answer: Fat cat.

Definition: A very unmelodious group of singers.
Answer: Dire choir.

Definition: A cowardly shout.
Answer: Yellow bellow.

Definition: A comparatively tranquil agriculturist.
Answer: Calmer farmer.

Definition: A cactus in a bad mood.
Answer: Truculent succulent.

Definition: A self-denying art-lover.
Answer: Aesthetic ascetic.

(To connoisseurs of this game, an example using monosyllabic adjective and noun is known as a Stink Pink, with two syllables a Stinky Pinky, and with three syllables a Stinkety Pinkety.)

Proverbs

Player One chooses a secret proverb and tells Player Two the number of words it contains. Player Two has to guess the secret proverb by asking a series of questions, which may be about any subject under the sun. He gets his clues because Player One must include the first word of his proverb in his answer to the first question, the second word in his answer to the second question, and so, until all the words in the secret proverb have been accounted for.

With 'Too many cooks spoil the broth' as the secret proverb, the questioning might go something like this:

MATTHEW: 'Does this proverb express a basic truth about life?'
ARNOLD: 'Yes, definitely. If anything, I'd say it's almost *too* true.'
MATTHEW: 'How old are you?'
ARNOLD: 'So *many* years have passed since I was born that I'm afraid I have lost count.'
MATTHEW: 'What is your favourite colour?'
ARNOLD: 'Well, I like the red jackets worn by guardsmen, the white hats worn by *cooks*, and the black boots worn by policemen.'
MATTHEW: 'Where are you going for your holiday this year?'
ARNOLD: 'Oh, I think it would *spoil* the game if I gave you a straight answer to that question.'
MATTHEW: 'OK, back to the proverb – is it very well known?'
ARNOLD: 'Oh yes, I would say it is one of *the* most popular proverbs.'
MATTHEW: 'When did you first hear this proverb?'
ARNOLD: 'Oh, years ago, some old farmer told it to me over a dinner of chicken *broth*, meat balls and boiled cabbage.'

The crafty player will include in his answers plenty of red herrings, such as 'eggs', 'basket', 'cloud', 'lining', 'look', 'leap', etc.

The Railway Carriage Game

Two players are chosen and each of them is given a secret (and slightly absurd) phrase, sentence or expression. For example, the first player's phrase could be 'Pigs might fly' while the second player's phrase might be 'I did it my way'. Armed with their phrases, the players must climb into an imaginary railway carriage and chat to one another for the length of a two-minute journey. During the course of their conversation each player must slip his or her secret phrase into whatever he or she happens to say. It isn't easy – particularly when you remember that the aim of the game is to introduce your secret phrase without your opponent realizing you have done so.

When the journey is over, the first player must attempt to guess the identity of the second player's phrase, and vice-versa.

Questions! Questions!

In QUESTIONS! QUESTIONS! the first player begins with a question, his opponent must reply with another question, the first player puts a third question, the opponent responds with a fourth, and so on, until one of the players falters or forgets himself and fails to ask a question. Repetition is not allowed.

To give you a better idea of how the game can go, here is a brief bout between Lewis and Carol:

LEWIS: What time is it?
CAROL: Why do you want to know?
LEWIS: Why do you ask that?
CAROL: Why can't you answer a civil question?
LEWIS: Why can't you look at your watch?
CAROL: When are you going to get yourself a watch?
LEWIS: What's that got to do with it?
CAROL: Who do you think you are talking to me like that?
LEWIS: Where can I find someone who will tell me the time?
CAROL: Where can I find a husband who can afford a watch of his own?
LEWIS: When do you stop nagging?
CAROL: Why don't you stop going on like this?
LEWIS: Do you know something?
CAROL: What?
LEWIS: Do you know who you remind me of?
CAROL: Who?
LEWIS: Your mother!

Lewis managed to get his insult in, but he lost the game.

If you want to see how the game can be played at its most brilliant, get hold of a copy of Tom Stoppard's play *Rosencrantz and Guildenstern Are Dead*. The two characters play this game in the play and do so with breathtaking verve.

Ghost

There are few games as good as GHOST for sorting out those with impressive vocabularies from those without. It is a word game for two players in which they build up a series of letters to form a word but endeavour not to be the player that completes a word.

The first player begins by calling out a letter. The second player adds a second letter to the first, making sure that the two-letter combination could actually begin a valid word. The first player adds a third letter, again thinking of a valid word that begins with that letter combination. The second player adds a fourth letter, and so it goes on – until one of the players is forced to complete a word, in which case that player has lost the game.

Players must at all times have a valid word in mind, and one player may challenge the other if he feels that his opponent did not have a valid word in mind. If the challenged player cannot produce an acceptable word, he loses the round. If the challenged player, however, can produce an acceptable word, then it is the challenger who loses the round.

By the way, it is only when a word of four or more letters is completed that a player loses if he completes a word. If this rule did not apply, the range of possible openings to the game would be severely limited – no word, for example, beginning with HA, HE, HI, or HO.

Here is an example:

HENRY: G. (He is thinking of GARDEN)
JAMES: G-r. (He is thinking of GREAT)
HENRY: G-r-a. (He is thinking of GRADUATE)
JAMES: G-r-a-n. (He is thinking of GRAND or GRANT)
HENRY: G-r-a-n-u. (He is now thinking of GRANULAR)
JAMES: G-r-a-n-u-l. (He is thinking of GRANULE)
HENRY: G-r-a-n-u-l-a. (Still thinking of GRANULAR)
JAMES: G-r-a-n-u-l-a-t. (Thinking of GRANULATE).
HENRY: G-r-a-n-u-l-a-t-e. (Henry loses the round)

Superghost

SUPERGHOST is GHOST for masterminds. The principle of the game is the same. The difference is that in SUPERGHOST players may add their letters to either end of the group of letters as it is being built up! It requires a high degree of mental agility as well as an impressive vocabulary, as can be seen in this example:

JAMES: R. (He is thinking of RACK)
JOYCE: R-o. (She is thinking of ROBOT)
JAMES: T-r-o. (He is thinking of TROUBLE)
JOYCE: N-t-r-o. (She is thinking of INTRODUCE)
JAMES: O-n-t-r-o. (Thinking of CONTROVERT)
JOYCE: C-o-n-t-r-o. (Thinking of CONTROL)
JAMES: N-c-o-n-t-r-o. (Thinking of UNCONTROLLED)

JOYCE:	N-c-o-n-t-r-o-v. (Thinking of UNCONTROVERSIAL)
JAMES:	N-c-o-n-t-r-o-v-e. (Also thinking of UNCONTROVERSIAL)
JOYCE:	N-c-o-n-t-r-o-v-e-r. (Still thinking of UNCONTROVERSIAL)
JAMES:	I-n-c-o-n-t-r-o-v-e-r. (Realizing that with UNCONTROVERSIAL he will lose the round, he has thought of INCONTROVERTIBLE)
JOYCE:	I-n-c-o-n-t-r-o-v-e-r-t. (Unable to think of any alternative, she faces the prospect of imminent defeat)
JAMES:	I-n-c-o-n-t-r-o-v-e-r-t-i.
JOYCE:	I-n-c-o-n-t-r-o-v-e-r-t-i-b.
JAMES:	I-n-c-o-n-t-r-o-v-e-r-t-i-b-l.
JOYCE:	I-n-c-o-n-t-r-o-v-e-r-t-i-b-l-e.

Guessing Games

Dumb Crambo

Two teams are formed. Team A goes out of the room, while the members of team B confer among themselves to choose a mystery word. Once the word is chosen, team A returns and team B announces a word that rhymes with the word they have chosen.

Team A must now try to guess the mystery word. However, they are not allowed to speak – they must act out their guesses in dumb-show. Any player who speaks automatically loses the games for his team. Incorrect guesses are greeted with boos and hisses; correct guesses are greeted with applause and the successful team gains a point.

When the secret word has been guessed, or when teams A has made three incorrect guesses, the teams change roles for another round. The team with the most points after a pre-determined number of rounds is the winner.

Aesop's Mission

A player who is in the know plays the part of Aesop. Having secretly picked on a letter of the alphabet that is to be taboo, Aesop proceeds to ask a series of questions of the other players. If a player's reply contains the forbidden letter Aesop says 'Bad!', otherwise he says 'Good!'

Let's suppose the letter L is taboo.

AESOP (to JOHN):	'How old are you?'
JOHN:	'Twenty-three.'
AESOP:	'Good!'
AESOP (to George):	'How old are you?'
GEORGE:	'Eleven.'
AESOP:	'Bad!'
AESOP (to PAUL):	'Where did you go at the weekend?'
PAUL:	'Liverpool.'
AESOP:	'Bad!'
AESOP (to RINGO):	'What did you have for lunch today?'
RINGO:	'A hamburger.'
AESOP:	'Good!'

Those players who have encountered the game before have to try to work out what the taboo is; the others have first to try to work out what game is all about.

Clue Words

The questioner thinks of a mystery word containing seven letters with no letters duplicated. The other players have to try to guess the mystery word with the help of up to three clues.

The first clue is a three-letter word formed from three letters in the mystery word. Each player is allowed one guess at the mystery word. A successful guess is worth 3 points, but there is no penalty for failure.

If no one has guessed the word, the questioner gives a second clue. This is a four-letter word using letters in the mystery word. Again each player is allowed one guess, and correctly guessing the mystery word is now worth 2 points.

If the mystery word is still unguessed, the questioner gives the third clue, which is a five-letter word formed from letters in the mystery word. Each player again has one guess and if correct earns 1 point.

If a player guesses the mystery word at any stage he takes a turn as questioner for the next round. If no one has guessed correctly after the three clues have been given, the questioner scores one point and has another turn.

The player with the highest number of points, after an agreed number of rounds, is the winner.

How easy it is to guess the mystery word depends on how much information the questioner gives away in his clues. Let's say the mystery word is *coaster*. Clues of *act*, *cart* and *cater* leave two letters still undisclosed. But if clue 1 is *act* and clue 2 is *rose*, all the letters have been revealed and the word should be easily guessed.

Twenty Questions

One player thinks of an object – which may be anything from a dinosaur to Mickey Mouse's left shoe, from a tomato to a battleship – and announces whether it is Animal, Vegetable, Mineral or any combination thereof. The other players then fire questions which require only 'Yes' or 'No' answers and which are aimed at narrowing the field and eventually closing in on the mystery object. Only twenty questions are allowed, and if the mystery object has not been identified when twenty questions have been asked, the player who thought of it has won and chooses another mystery object.

Virginia Woolf

This is a variation of TWENTY QUESTIONS. All the players have to think of the person they would most like to be if they couldn't be themselves. You can choose to be a character from fact or fiction, alive or dead, male or female, but you should be someone whose name the other players are likely to know.

When everyone has chosen his or her ideal identity, each player takes it in turn to be quizzed by the remaining players whose aim it is to find out who the player in question would like to be. Twenty questions are allowed, requiring either 'Yes' or 'No' answers. When the secret identity has been revealed, the player whose choice it was must explain *why* he wanted to be whoever it was he happened to choose.

Where Am I?

In this variation of TWENTY QUESTIONS one player thinks of a place and an activity he might be doing there and then asks 'Where am I?'. The other players then have twenty questions, requiring 'Yes' or 'No' answers, to determine where the player has imagined himself to be and what it is he has imagined himself to be doing there.

Charades

CHARADES is a very popular game in which one team of players has to guess a word of several syllables presented in dramatic form by the other team.

The players divide into teams, and the first team disappears to another room to choose the word it is going to dramatize and to work out exactly how it is going to set about it. The word that is chosen must be of several syllables, and each part of the word must lend itself to dramatization, as must the word as a whole. Only the sound of the syllables or component parts of the word matters, not the spelling.

The word and the manner of presentation having been decided upon, the captain of the team returns and announces to the opposing team how many syllables there are in the word his team has chosen. Various members of the team then come into the room and act, with or without dialogue (it is far more entertaining without), a series of scenes designed to give clues to the sounds of the syllables they are dramatizing. Each syllable is acted out individually and finally the word is performed as a whole.

When the opposing team have guessed the word being presented it becomes their turn to leave the room and decide on a charade.

A variation of traditional CHARADES that has become quite as popular as the original involves the performers in dramatizing not merely an everyday word, but the name of a famous person, town, country, etc., or the title of a book, play, film or song. When this form of the game is played, the titles are normally broken down into individual words rather than syllables.

Another variation is SOLO CHARADES, in which individual players, rather than teams, take it in turn to perform the words or titles they choose.

If you would like to play CHARADES, but are stuck for ideas, here are a few suggestions, all of which should lend themselves to entertaining presentation:

abandon (a, band, don)
acrostic (a, cross, tic)
archery (arch, cherry)
assault (ass, salt)
barbecue (barber, cue)
bedlam (bed, lamb)
butterfly (butt, her, fly)
cabbage (cab, age)
caribou (carry, boo)
carnival (car, navel)
chauffeur (show, fur)
classic (class, sick)
correct (core, wrecked)
cucumber (queue, come, burr)
dinosaur (die, nose, sore)
discontent (disc, corn, tent)
domestic (dough, mess, stick)
dynamite (dine, aim, mite)
elastic (eel, last, tick)
excursion (eggs, cur, shun)
fahrenheit (far, wren, height)
fertilize (fur, till, eyes)
foreleg (fall, egg)
fundamental (fun, dam, mental)
grocer (gross, sir)
hallucination (halo, sin, nation)
harpsichord (harp, sick, cord)
holidays (holly, daze)
horizon (whore, rise, sun)
hospitality (horse, spit, alley, tea)
hydraulic (high, draw, lick)
hypnotic (hip, knot, tic)
illustrate (ill, lust, straight)
industry (in, dust, tree)
intelligence (in, telly, gents)
jasmine (jazz, mine)
khaki (car, key)
kidney (kid, knee)
lacrosse (lack, cross)
legionnaire (lee, John, air)
manicure (man, nick, cure)
manipulate (man, nip, you, late)
metronome (met, row, gnome)
misanthropy (miss, sand, throw, pea)
misunderstand (miss, under, stand)

mosquito (moss, key, toe)
navigator (navvy, gaiter)
nightingale (knight, tin, gale)
Olympics (o, limp, picks)
origin (awe, ridge, gin)
panorama (pan, or, armour)
pendulum (pen, duel, hum)
philosopher (fill, loss, offer)
psychology (sigh, collar, gee)
relief (reel, leaf)
renegade (wren, egg, aid)
robust (row, bust)
romantic (roam, antic)
sacrifice (sack, reef, ice)
sentry (scent, tree)
succeed (suck, seed)
telegram (tell, leg, ram)
trapeze (trap, ease)
universe (you, knee, verse)
valiant (valley, ant)
vampire (vamp, higher)
waitress (weight, tress)
waterfall (war, turf, all)
wholesaler (hole, sailor)
window (win, dough)
wonderful (one dare, full)

The African Queen
All Quiet On The Western Front
Blowin' In The Wind
The Blue Angel
Brave New World
Bridge Over Troubled Water
A Bridge Too Far
Carousel
Crime And Punishment
Duck Soup
Everything You Always Wanted To Know About Sex But Were Afraid To Ask
Far From The Madding Crowd
Fiddler On The Roof
A Fistful Of Dollars
From Russia With Love
The Good, The Bad And The Ugly
Great Expectations
Heart Of Glass
Horse Feathers
I'm Dreaming Of A White Christmas
The Jewel In The Crown
The King And I
Little Big Man
Look Back In Anger
Lord Of The Flies
Lord Of The Rings
The Man In The Iron Mask
Midnight Cowboy
My Fair Lady
The Naked And The Dead
One Flew Over The Cuckoo's Nest
Over The Rainbow
The Owl And The Pussycat
Penny Lane
Pop Goes The Weasel
River Deep, Mountain High
Rock Around The Clock
Sergeant Pepper's Lonely Hearts Club Band
Seven Brides For Seven Brothers
Silent Night
Star Wars
The Sting
Straw Dogs
The Taming Of The Shrew
Tie A Yellow Ribbon
Watership Down
What's My Line?

Botticelli

One player thinks of the name of a famous person or a well-known character from fiction. He reveals the first letter of his chosen subject's surname to the company, who must then try to discover who it is the player is thinking of.

They go about this task by asking the player two types of question: indirect and direct. They can only ask a direct question if the player has failed to come up with a satisfactory answer to an indirect question. For example, if the player chooses to be Winston Churchill, he will announce 'I am someone beginning with C', and the others will proceed to fire indirect questions at him, such as 'Are you a French painter?', 'Are you a castaway?' The player must reply along these lines: 'No, I am not Cezanne' or 'No, I am not Robinson Crusoe'. If he cannot think of appropriate answers, because he does not know of a French painter or a castaway beginning with C, or because his mind has gone blank at the crucial moment, the questioner can then ask a direct question –'Are you alive?', 'Are you fictional?', 'Are you Norwegian?' – to which a truthful 'Yes' or 'No' answer must be given. It is important, therefore, that the player chooses a character about whom he has some knowledge, or he may not be able to give correct answers to the direct questions.

Naturally, the questioners must do their best to ask awkward indirect questions in order to get as many opportunities as possible to put direct questions, which will lead them eventually to the secret identity they're after. The questioners can corner the player in one of two ways: either by asking an indirect question – 'Were you born in 1874 and were you Prime Minister of Britain between 1940 and 1945?' – which forces the player to reveal his identity, or by asking a direct question – 'Are you Winston Churchill?' – where the player has no alternative but to say 'Yes'.

Kolodny's Game

KOLODNY'S GAME is a rather strange game of induction. The players have to ask questions that can be answered with a 'Yes' or a 'No' and have to guess, from the answers, what the secret rule is that determines what the answers should be. Is that perfectly clear? No? Well, let's look at the start of a typical game, played by three players – Peter, Paul and Mary.

Peter decides on a secret rule that has to be discovered by Paul and Mary. The rule he chooses is: If the question consists of more than five words then the answer is 'Yes', otherwise the answer is 'No'. This is typical of the sort of rule used in the game. Here are a few more examples:

(a) If the question begins with the word 'Is' the answer is 'Yes', otherwise the answer is 'No'.
(b) If the age of the questioner is less than 25 the answer is 'Yes', otherwise the answer is 'No'.
(c) If the last letter of the question is in the first half of the alphabet the answer is 'Yes', if it is in the second half the answer is 'No'.

Paul and Mary now start asking questions:

'Are you stupid?' 'No.'
'Is anyone in this room stupid?' 'Yes.'
'Do you have a problem sleeping at night?' 'Yes.'
'Have you tried counting sheep?' 'No.'
'Is this an easy rule to guess?' 'Yes.'

Note that the actual meaning of the questions is irrelevant – it is the form of the question that is significant. The way to play successfully is to try to work out what the questions answered 'Yes' might have in common that is not shared by the questions answered 'No' (and vice versa), to form hypotheses, and to frame questions designed to test out your hypotheses.

For example, from the questions and answers above, you might form the hypothesis that the rule is: Questions starting with a two-letter word are answered 'Yes'. But if, to test your theory, you then ask 'Is coal black?' you will get the answer 'No', disproving the theory, so you will have to think again.

Alphabet And List Games

The Zoo Game

The first player names an animal beginning with A, and then starts counting to ten. Before he reaches ten, the next player must name a different animal beginning with A and start counting to ten. Before *he* reaches ten, the next player must name a different animal beginning with A, and so on until a player fails to come up with a name before he is counted out or until a player repeats a name that has already been used. That player drops out. The next player starts again with the name of an animal beginning with B.

For example, with four players the game might proceed like this:

MATTHEW: 'Ape. One, two, three . . .'
MARK: 'Alligator. One, two, three, four, five, six . . .'
LUKE: 'Antelope. One, two, three, four . . .'
JOHN: Ass. One, two, three . . .'
MATTHEW: 'Aardvark. One, two, three, four, five, six, seven, eight, nine, ten.'

Mark is out, as he could not think of another animal beginning with A (such as armadillo, ant-eater, aurochs, addax, agouti, ai, anoa, argali, aye-aye, acouchy, angwantibo or amon).

LUKE: 'Bear. One, two, three, four . . .'
JOHN: 'Buffalo. One, two . . .'
MATTHEW: 'Beaver. One, two, three . . .'
LUKE: 'Badger. One, two, three, four, five . . .'
JOHN: 'Bison. One, two, three, four, five, six, seven, eight, nine . . .'
MATTHEW (in desperation): 'Bear. One, two . . .'

Matthew is out, as 'bear' has already been used.

LUKE: 'Cat. One, two, three . . .'
JOHN: 'Cow. One, two, three, four . . .'
LUKE: 'Camel. One, two . . .'
JOHN: 'Chimpanzee. One, two, three, four . . .'
LUKE: 'Coyote. One, two, three, four, five, six, seven, eight, nine, ten.'

John is counted out before he can think of another name, so Luke is the winner.

When you are tired of animals, you can play the game with some other category: Birds, Composers, Rivers, or whatever.

The Preacher's Cat

The first player starts the game by declaring 'The preacher's cat is an amiable cat and his name is Archibald'. The next player then suggests, 'The preacher's cat is an amorous cat and his name is Andrew'. The third player avers, 'The preacher's cat is an abhorrent cat and his name is Alexander'. And so it goes on around the group until all the players have come up with an adjective and a name beginning with A.

Then they must each in turn find adjectives and names beginning with B, then with C, and so on, until they get to the fact that 'The preacher's cat is a zealous cat and his name is Zebediah'. The letters Q and X may be omitted, but anyone failing to come up with an adjective or name for any other letter drops out.

Traveller's Alphabet

The players sit in a circle and each player in turn asks the person on his left two questions: 'Where are you going?' and 'What will you do there?'. The replies consist of the name of a country and the description of an activity, using verb, adjective and noun – all beginning with the same letter of the alphabet. The first player's replies must begin with the letter A, the second player's with B, the third player's with C, and so on.

For example, a game might begin like this:

CHARLES: 'Where are you going?'
EDWARD: 'Algeria.'
CHARLES: 'What will you do there?'
EDWARD: 'Assist Arab archaeologists.'
EDWARD: 'Where are you going?'
STUART: 'Belgium.'
EDWARD: 'What will you do there?'
STUART: 'Buy beer bottles.'
STUART: 'Where are you going?'
CHARLES: 'Canada.'

STUART: 'What will you do there?'
CHARLES: 'Catch crazy criminals.'

Any player failing to come up with an answer within a reasonable time is disqualified, and the last player left in is the winner.

Word Lightning

The question-master chooses a victim and gives him a letter. The hapless victim then has sixty seconds in which to rattle off as many words as he can start with the chosen letter. The question-master keeps count. When all the players have been given a letter and a minute to do their best, the player with the highest word count is the winner.

It sounds ridiculously easy when you read it in print, but when you're put on the spot it's another matter.

Letters By Numbers

This game is suitable for any small number of players and is a good test of how quick their thinking is.

The question-master calls out, at random, a series of numbers between one and twenty-six. For each number called out, the aim is to see which player can be first to respond with the letter at that position in the alphabet.

For example:

'Seventeen!' 'Q.'
'Five!' 'E.'
'Twenty-three!' 'W.'

The first player to respond correctly to each number scores one point. Any player naming the wrong letter loses a point. After the game has been played for an agreed length of time, the player with the highest score is the winner.

Vowels Out

The question-master gives each player in turn an equally long and equally difficult word to spell. All the players have to do is spell the words correctly, remembering, however, that they must not utter any of the five vowels. When they get to a vowel they must adopt a special sign language: to indicate an A you raise your right arm; to indicate an E you raise your left arm; to indicate an I you point to your own eye; to indicate an O you point to your mouth; and to indicate a U you point to the question-master.

Any player spelling a word incorrectly, uttering a vowel or mixing up the signals is disqualified. The last player left spelling is the winner.

Leading Lights

For this game you need to prepare a list of names of well-known people, living or dead. For each name on the list the players have to think of an appropriate phrase that characterizes or defines that name beginning with the same initial letters as the name in question.

For example, a player might come up with the following phrases:

Frank Sinatra	– Famous Singer
Wolfgang Amadeus Mozart	– Wrote Appealing Melodies
Brigitte Bardot	– Beautiful Body
Albert Einstein	– Atomic Energy
William Shakespeare	– Wrote Sonnets
Paul McCartney	– Popular Musician

Games For Children And Others

I Went To Market

This game is suitable for younger children, and is educational in that it helps the children to learn the alphabet. Despite being educational, it is very popular with children!

The players have to think of nouns beginning with each letter of the alphabet in turn to complete the sentence 'I went to market and I bought . . .'.

For example:

Player 1: 'I went to market and I bought apples.'
Player 2: 'I went to market and I bought books.'
Player 3: 'I went to market and I bought cabbages.'
Player 4: 'I went to market and I bought dolls.'

Difficult letters like K, Q, X, and Z may be omitted. If you get to the end of the alphabet, the next player starts again with A, but words used previously must not be repeated.

A Was An Apple Pie

This game is similar to I WENT TO MARKET except that the players have to supply verbs for each letter of the alphabet in turn. Player 1 starts: 'A was an apple pie. A ate it'. The game might then proceed: 'B bought it', 'C cut it', 'D delivered it', 'E examined it', and so on through the alphabet. There is no need to repeat the first phrase 'A was an apple pie' each time.

I Packed My Bag

In this well-known memory game the players have to remember and repeat an ever-increasing list of items.

The game starts with one player saying, for example, 'I packed my bag and in it I put a pair of pyjamas.' The second player repeats the sentence and adds another item of his own. The third player does likewise, adding a further item. And so it goes on, each player in turn repeating the list and adding one more item.

For example:

Player 1: 'I packed my bag and in it I put a pair of pyjamas.'
Player 2: 'I packed my bag and in it I put a pair of pyjamas and a hard-boiled egg.'
Player 3: 'I packed my bag and in it I put a pair of pyjamas, a hard-boiled egg and a video recorder.'
Player 4: 'I packed my bag and in it I put a pair of pyjamas, a hard-boiled egg, a video recorder and a Mickey Mouse wristwatch.'
Player 1: 'I packed my bag and in it I put a pair of pyjamas, a hard-boiled egg, a video recorder, a Mickey Mouse wristwatch and a peanut butter sandwich.'
Player 2: 'I packed my bag and in it I put a pair of pyjamas, a hard-boiled egg, a video recorder, a Mickey Mouse wristwatch, a peanut butter sandwich and a compass.'

A player who forgets any of the items, or lists them in the wrong order, leaves the game. The winner is the last player left in the game.

I Spy

This must surely be the best-known and most popular word game for children.

One player starts the game by mentally selecting some object that is in his range of vision and announces its initial letter thus (assuming the initial letter is S): 'I spy with my little eye something beginning with S'. The other players have to guess the mystery object, and they can call out their guesses at any time – there is no requirement to play in turn.

'Sofa?'
'No.'
'Sandwich?'
'No.'
'Ceiling???'
'No!'
'Shoe?'
'No.'
'Sock?'
'Yes!'

The first player to guess correctly becomes the 'spy' in the next round.

Sausages

This is a silly game which relies for its effect on the inexplicable fact that the word *sausages* tends to make people laugh.

One of the players is chosen to be the victim, and the other players bombard him with questions. These should be personal questions about the victim, his family, school, teachers, holidays, favourite activities, etc. To every question the victim must reply simply 'Sausages' and must keep a perfectly straight face throughout, however ridiculous the answer sounds.

For example:

'What clothes do you wear in winter?' 'Sausages.'
'What do you like best at school?' 'Sausages.'
'What is your uncle's name?' 'Sausages.'
'What do you like watching on TV?' 'Sausages.'

The questioners may smile, laugh, giggle, chuckle, smirk or guffaw as much as they please, which makes it even harder for the victim to keep a straight face. When the victim betrays any sign of mirth – and even the hardiest cannot keep a straight face for long – he gives way to another victim.

Spelling Bee

One player is selected to be the question-master and calls out a word to each of the other players in turn, who must give the correct spelling of the word in question. For spelling a word correctly a player gets one point. At the end of the game, the player with most points is the winner.

For the game to be a success, it is important that the words to be spelled are suited to the ages and abilities of the players taking part. The question-master may use a prepared list of words to be spelled or may make up the list as he goes along – the former is normally preferable.

There are a number of possible variations, including the following:

Variation 1: The game is played as described above except that a player who spells a word incorrectly drops out. The last player left in is the winner.

Variation 2: A player spelling a word correctly is given another word to spell. He gets one point for each word spelled correctly and his turn ends only when he makes a mistake.

Variation 3: The players are divided into two teams, and the question-master offers a word to each player in turn, selecting each team alternately. If a player fails to spell a word correctly it is offered to that player's opposite number in the opposing team for a bonus point.

Action Spelling

This is a silly and amusing form of SPELLING BEE. It is played in the same way as that game except that in the spelling certain letters are not called out – instead, various actions are substituted. For example, it might be decreed that G should be represented by a growl, B by flapping one's arms, Y by scratching one's head, and so on. You can invent as many such actions to represent letters as you like, depending on how silly and how complicated you want the game to be.

Any player spelling a word incorrectly or failing to substitute the correct action for a letter loses a point or drops out of the game.

Spelling Round

The question-master calls out words to be spelled. Each word has to be spelled out around the circle of players, each player in turn calling out one letter of the word. For example, if the word in question was 'Parallel', the first player would call out 'P', the second 'A', the third 'R', and so on. Any player making a mistake or hesitating too long drops out. The last player left in is the winner.

Famous Fives

The question-master asks each player in turn to name five objects in a given category, each player being given a new category. For example, 'Name five ice hockey teams', 'Name five breeds of dog', 'Name five countries in Europe', 'Name five card games', 'Name five seaside towns', 'Name five Walt Disney films'.

Players score one point for each item named, with a bonus point for naming all five in a category, but they lose a point for each incorrect item.

The game ends when a pre-determined number of rounds have been played, and the player with the highest score is the winner.

Consonant Catalogue

This game is best if played with a stop-watch or, at least, a watch with a second hand. Each player in turn has to recite the alphabet from B to Z, leaving out all the vowels. The player who does so in the fastest time is the winner.

It's a simple idea, but the task is tricker than it seems. Try it and see!

I Want A Rhyme

This game is suitable for children of all ages, but may require an adult or older child to act as question-master.

The question-master says:

'I want a rhyme
In jolly quick time,
And the word I choose is: red'

The word, of course, does not have to be *red* – it can be any word that has a lot of other words that rhyme with it – *hat*, *mole*, *gate*, *pin*, *ride*, *clock*, *shoe*, etc. – but preferably not *wolf* or *orange*!

After the question-master has announced his word, each player in turn has to give a word that rhymes with it. So with *red* you might get *bed*, *head*, *led*, *fed*, *shed*, *bread*, *sled*, *wed*, *dread*, going round the players until one player fails to think of a word and has to drop out. The question-master then announces a new word for which the surviving players have to find rhymes. This continues until all but one of the players have been eliminated, the last surviving player being the winner.

Sentences

The game starts with one player choosing a word and announcing it to all the other players. Any word will do, but one with five or more letters makes for more fun.

Each player must then form a sentence consisting of words beginning with the letters of the given word. You can choose whether or not you make it a rule that the sentence must be connected in some way with the chosen word.

So, for example, if the chosen word was 'Games', suitable sentences would be:

'Girls and men enjoy sailing.'
'Golfers are meeting every Sunday.'
'Good archers make excellent soldiers.'

Chinese Whispers

The players sit in a circle, and the first player whispers a message into the ear of the player to the left; that player whispers the message into the ear of the player on *his* left, and so on around the circle until the message gets back to the player who started it. That player then declares out loud the original message and the message that came back to him. The two are usually widely different, causing much hilarity. After this, another player originates a message and the game continues until each player has had a turn.

For example, starting with the message 'Bring up the infantry, we are going to advance' you are quite likely to end up with 'Brick up the fruit tree, we are going to a dance'.

What Are We Shouting?

The players are divided into two teams. One team leaves the room to decide amongst themselves on a well-known phrase or saying. Film or television titles or names of books or songs are also acceptable. Ideally the phrase will consist of as many words as there are players in the team – in any case, there must not be more words than there are players. One word of the phrase is allotted to each player. Some players will have to share a word if there are fewer words than players.

The team then returns. Then all at the same time, after a count of three, they shout their words as loud as they can. The opposing team may, if they wish, ask for the shout to be repeated, but must then attempt to guess the phrase being shouted. If they guess wrongly, the other team has another go with a new phrase, but if they guess correctly it is their turn to choose and shout.

PART TWO
WRITTEN GAMES

Panel Games

Word Endings

Give all players a long list of word endings and let them race to see which one can be the first to find words that end with the given endings. You don't need to make the endings too obscure: the last three letters of a word invariably look a little unfamiliar when they are given without anything preceding them, and endings that are rare tend to slow down the game. Here are some examples of the types of ending that work well:

-don	-ask
-ppy	-ngs
-per	-eth
-the	-ket
-mum	-ssy
-tle	-nge

And here are complete words to match those endings:

abandon	flask
puppy	endings
hamper	Brandreth
breathe	market
maximum	messy
cattle	hinge

In the event of a tie, with two players declaring that they have completed their lists at the very same moment, the player whose list contains the longer words is declared the winner.

Alphabetic Narrative

Within a time limit of, say, ten minutes, each player has to compose a sentence, story or verse consisting of twenty-six words beginning with successive letters of the alphabet. The player whose effort is judged to be the best – the most logical or the most amusing – is the winner.

'X', as is often the case, is the stumbling block. Here is an example of one player's (mediocre) effort:

> All bandsmen carry drums, every flautist guards his instrument jealously. Knowing lots more notes, orchestral players quickly rehearse symphonies. Try using violins with xylophones, you zealots!

Short Story

The players are given a set period of time, say fifteen minutes, in which to write a simple story using only words with four or fewer letters. At the end of the time limit, the players read out their stories and the player who has written the longest, most lucid and most entertaining story is the winner.

It sounds simple, but it isn't – especially when you remember that one five-letter word inadvertently used will mean that you are disqualified. Here is a brief Love Story to give you an idea of the game's scope – and its limitations.

> It was in May a year or two ago that I met the fair Miss Anne Bun. She was just a slip of a girl and I was a man on the edge of ripe old age. We had tea on that cool May morn on the lawn at her Pa's seat near Deal by the sea. She was fun and full of life. I was grey and full of woe, but she did not seem to mind. I do not feel she fell in love with me just so that she and her vile Mama were able to have the vast sums of cash that I keep in a bank in town. She said that from the time she was a baby her wish had been to meet a man with a leg made of wood and with a red wig and that she was full of joy that at long last I had come to her. Yes, she said, to be my one and only wife was what she did want – and so did her Mama. (Her Papa was deaf and so had no say in the case, poor soul.) If I gave her all my cash she'd give me all her love. It was a fair deal and I was keen to say yes, but fate took a hand and said no, Miss Anne Bun is not to be your wife. She is to be run over by a big red bus on her way to the wee kirk on the hill. And that is what came to pass, alas, so that is the end of my sad tale. Take pity on me and weep for me as I lie all on my own in my old man's bed with only the idea of my lost love by me.

Short Short Story

If you thought the previous game was too easy, then this game should appeal to you. The rules are the same as before, except that no word used may contain more than *three* letters.

Here is an example of the sort of story that could be produced:

> A man had a pig in a sty. He fed it day by day. It ate all he fed it. But one day the pig bit the man on the leg. By gum, the man was mad! Now the pig is ham in a can.

(And if you think this is too easy, I'll leave you to write a story in which no word contains more than two letters!)

Stepping Stones

This is a mentally stimulating game of word associations, which may be played on any level from the banal to the esoteric. Each player in turn is given five themes by the other players. For example, a player may be told to get from 'Music' to 'Astronomy' via 'Cookery', 'Finance' and 'Automobiles'. He may use up to nine statements or phrases and must touch on each of the themes in the order given. The other players, acting collectively as umpires, must satisfy themselves that all the themes have been touched on, that the sequence of associations is valid, and that any puns, allusions and the like are not too far-fetched.

Here are two ways in which the example quoted might work out in practice:

1. A note may be flat or sharp. *(Music)*
2. Knives used in the kitchen should always be sharp. *(Cookery)*
3. Knives are used for cutting.
4. The government will soon cut interest rates. *(Finance)*
5. We can then afford to borrow more.
6. I first learned to drive in a Ford. *(Automobiles)*
7. I now drive a Rolls.
8. The Rolling Stones are rock stars.
9. Stars, in fact, are formed from gas not from rock. *(Astronomy)*

1. Musicians usually begin by learning scales. *(Music)*
2. Scales are found on fish.
3. Salmon is the fish most often served with salads. *(Cookery)*
4. Salmon may be caught from river banks.

5. Banks are financial institutions. *(Finance)*
6. Automatic cash dispensers are used in many banks.
7. Automatic transmission makes driving easier. *(Automobiles)*
8. When driving I like to listen to the radio.
9. Radio-telescopes are used by astronomers. *(Astronomy)*

Semordnilap

Semordnilap is, of course, *palindromes* spelled backwards. A semordnilap is defined as a word which, when spelled backwards, forms another word.

For example:

Liar – Rail
Tide – Edit
Evil – Live
Bard – Drab

The game of SEMORDNILAP may be played in two ways.

In the first version, the players are given a set amount of time in which they have to list as many semordnilaps as they can. The winner is the player who produces the longest list in the time allowed.

In the second version a question-master gives the players clues to specific semordnilaps. For example: 'Reverse an eastern ruler to get frost' (answer: Emir & Rime), 'Reverse a beast to get a thin plate or layer' (answer: Animal & Lamina).

Word Ladders

In 1879 Lewis Carroll wrote a letter to *Vanity Fair* introducing a new kind of puzzle: 'The rules of the puzzle are simple enough. Two words are proposed of the same length; and the puzzle consists in linking these together by interposing other words, each of which shall differ from the next word *in one letter only*. That is to say, one letter may be changed in one of the given words, then one letter in the word so obtained, and so on, till we arrive at the other given word. The letters must not be interchanged among themselves, but each must keep to its own place. As an example, the word 'head' may be changed into 'tail' by interposing the words "heal, teal, tell tall".'

This now well-known puzzle forms the basis of an excellent game. Two related words with the same number of letters are chosen – *sleep* and *dream*, *flour* and *bread*, *poor* and *rich*, *black* and *white*, *chin* and *nose* – and the aim is to see which player can transform one word into the other in the fewest steps.

For example, I have transformed *winter* into *summer* in nine steps – perhaps you can do it in fewer.

WINTER
WINDER
WANDER
WARDER
HARDER
HARPER
HAMPER
HAMMER
HUMMER
SUMMER

Acrosticals

A word of six or seven letters is chosen, and each player writes the word in a column on the left side of his sheet of paper. He then writes the same word in another column some distance to the right of the first one, but this time with the letters in reverse order. Let us say the chosen word is Dreamer, then each player's sheet of paper should look something like this:

D	R
R	E
E	M
A	A
M	E
E	R
R	D

The players are then given a set time – five or ten minutes – in which they have to write the longest word they can think of, beginning and ending with each pair of letters provided by the two columns.

The players score one point per letter for each of their words, and the player with the highest total score is the winner.

With this particular example, my best effort is shown below. Can you beat my total score of 106?

DEMISEMIQUAVER	=	14
RECONNAISSANCE	=	14
ELECTROENCEPHALOGRAM	=	20
ABRACADABRA	=	11
MULTIMILLIONAIRE	=	16
ELECTRODYNAMOMETER	=	18
RECAPITULATED	=	13

Stairway

A letter of the alphabet is chosen (avoiding difficult letters like K, X or Z) and the players have a set time – ten minutes, say – in which to form a 'Stairway' of words beginning with that letter. The stairway consists of a two-letter word, then a three-letter word, then a four-letter word, and so on. Here is an example for the letter L:

L
LO
LOT
LONG
LEAST
LAGOON
LONGBOW
LIMERICK
LAMPSHADE
LOCOMOTION
LEGISLATION
LIFELESSNESS
LIBRARIANSHIP
LIBERTARIANISM

The winner is the player who forms the longest stairway within the set time.

Twisting Stairway

In the game of STAIRWAY the words forming the steps are not related to one another except in that they all begin with the same letter and are of increasing length. In TWISTING STAIRWAY, on the other hand, each step is formed by rearranging the letters of the previous step and adding one more letter. This makes it a somewhat more difficult game.

A letter is called out, and the players have a set time – about fifteen minutes would be appropriate – in which to attempt to build the longest twisting stairway they can.

For example, starting with the letter R:

R
RE
ARE
REAL
ALTER
RETAIL
RELIANT
ENTRAILS

Telegrams

A word of seven or more letters having been chosen, it is written down by each of the players. The players then have five minutes in which each of them has to compose a telegram, the words of which must begin with the letters of the chosen word in the correct order. For example, if the chosen word is *telegrams*, a player might produce:

TAKE EACH LETTER: EXPAND: GENERATE REALLY APPROPRIATE MESSAGE SPEEDILY

The telegram need not necessarily be relevant to the chosen word, but if it is then so much the better.

When the five minutes is up, each player reads out what he has written, and the player whose telegram is judged to be the cleverest or most amusing is the winner.

Initials

Two words are chosen – any words will do, provided that they are both the same length and contain at least seven letters. Each player writes the words in two vertical columns, side by side, on the left side of his sheet of paper.

Say, for example, the words chosen were *weeping* and *spanner*.

Each player's sheet of paper should look something like this:

W S
E P
E A
P N
I N
N E
G R

The object of the game is to use these letters as sets of initials, and to think of the name of a famous person (living or dead) to fit each set of initials. The first player to complete his list of names matching the initials is the winner.

In this particular example, one possible solution would be as follows:

W S – William Shakespeare (poet)
E P – Elvis Presley (singer)
E A – Edward Albee (dramatist)
P N – Paul Newman (film star)
I N – Isaac Newton (scientist)
N E – Nelson Eddy (actor-singer)
G R – George Robey (music-hall comedian)

Convergence

CONVERGENCE is a very entertaining game for two players in which each player thinks of a four-word sentence which his opponent has to guess.

Each player writes down a four-word sentence without letting the other player see what it is – the only restriction is that the sentence must not contain any proper nouns. Then player 1 makes his first guess at the other player's mystery sentence by calling out a test sentence. Player 2 tells him how near his guess was by saying, for each of the four words in the test sentence, whether the corresponding word in the mystery sentence is before or after it in alphabetical or dictionary sequence. Player 2 then makes his guess at the first player's mystery word and is given similar information.

Play continues in this way, with each player guessing in turn, until one of them wins the game by correctly identifying his opponent's mystery sentence.

Here, as an example, is one player's first few guesses from a typical game, showing how quickly you can home in on your opponent's sentence:

Mystery sentence: RED ROSES LOOK PRETTY.

Guess 1: MY HAIR IS GREY. – After, After, After, After

Guess 2: TRAMS SEEM RATHER NOISY – Before, Before, Before, Before

(1st. word is between MY & TRAMS)
(2nd. word is between HAIR & SEEMS)
(3rd. word is between IS & RATHER)
(4th. word is after NOISY)

Guess 3: NEVER READ MAD ROMANCES – After, After, Before, Before

(1st. word is between NEVER & TRAMS)
(2nd. word is between READ & SEEMS)
(3rd. word is between IS & MAD)
(4th. word is between NOISY & ROMANCES)

Guess 4: POET'S RUN LIKE PANTHERS – After, Before, After, After

(1st. word is between POETS & TRAMS)
(2nd. word is between READ & RUN)
(3rd. word is between LIKE & MAD)
(4th. word is between PANTHERS & ROMANCES)

Guess 5: ROUGH ROBBERS LOVE QUICHE – Before, After, Before, Before

(1st. word is between POETS & ROUGH)
(2nd. word is between ROBBERS & RUN)
(3rd. word is between LIKE & LOVE)
(4th. word is between PANTHERS & QUICHE)

Guess 6: RAINBOW RUGS LOOK PLEASANT – After, Before, Correct, After

(1st. word is between RAINBOW & RUGGED)
(2nd. word is between ROBBERS & RUGS)
(3rd. word is LOOK)
(4th. word is between PLEASANT & QUICHE)

Orthographic Invigilation

First gather together a group of people who pride themselves on their vocabulary and spelling ability. Then tell them that you are about to conduct an orthographic invigilation. Of course, they will know that this is what lesser mortals call a spelling test.

What you do is dictate the following passage to them, and then check their transcriptions. A result of more than 25 errors is poor, 15 is average, 5 is exceptional, and anyone who transcribes it faultlessly must surely have cheated.

> The infectious proclivity for polysyllabic interchange of incomprehensible and occasionally irrefutable and unanswerable ratiocination, invective and oftentimes laryngeal trivialities is a poltroonery that is permissible of the most censorious and punitive retaliation. To possess an aggrandized vocabulary is a mental endowment transcending the encyclopaedical attributes of pedadogues who must investigate, peruse, and burrow for the scintillating segments of verisimilitude normally secreted from those whose knowledge is enchorial and whose verbiage is enclitic.
>
> Exuberant and exultant propensities in phraseology continually lead to cerebral extradition for malefactors guilty of philological pyrotechnics. Perspicacious pundits scrupulously shun irreverent behaviourism and invariably take innocent refuge in the incontestable sanctuary of benign blandiloquence. Or by way of antithetical alternative, in mundane myopia.
>
> Malicious malingerers in the realm of obsequious vacuity intermittently and agonizingly bewail the punctiliousness of those superlatively heirloomed with the gifts of psychic penetration. To their pettifogging mentalities any laboriously contrived device so minutely registering a mechanism as a micro-motoscope would loom gargantuan by invidious comparison. To elucidate for the benefit of such individuals would parallel the espousal of eudaemonics by Italo-Ethiopian aesthetes. One unmitigated and undisputed contention is that philological parsimoniousness is particularly preferable to loquacious laxity, especially as demonstrated by evanescent nincompoops of the lower cerebral classification.

Grid Games

Alphabet Race

This is a pencil and paper game for two players in which they race to see who can use all twenty-six letters of the alphabet first.

Each player has a piece of paper on which he has written out the complete alphabet, and there is a third piece of paper which serves as the 'board'. The players take it in turn to write words on the board, making sure that the word they play attaches (crossword-fashion) at some point to a word already played. A player may use each letter only once, and when he has written it on the board he must cross it off his list. For example, if the opening player begins by writing OPEN on the board, he then crosses the letters O, P, E and N off his list. His opponent must now write a word that he can attach to OPEN, for example ZOO:

```
Z
O
O P E N
```

He now crosses the letters Z and O off his list, because they are the two letters he has played.

The first player to use all twenty-six of his letters wins the game. If a stage is reached when neither player can play, the player who has used most of his letters at that point is the winner. The words themselves do not score points: the sole aim of the game is to be the first one to use up the alphabet.

Here is how the board might look at the end of a game. The first player's words are written in capitals. His opponent's words are in lower-case letters.

```
  d                 W
f u r               I
  m         c a b l e
  p         h       L     Z
  S C Y T H E       D o z i n g
            s         x   p
            t
            Y O U N G
                    R
                  W A X
                    B
```

When the stalemate was reached, the player using capitals still had five letters unused and the player using lower-case letters had only four, thus becoming the winner.

Trackword

Choose a nine-letter word, perhaps by opening a book at random and taking the first nine-letter word that appears. Then write the chosen word in a three-by-three grid. If, for example, the chosen word was Elephants, it would appear thus:

E	L	E
P	H	A
N	T	S

Each of the players then has to compile a list of as many words as he can, of at least three letters, from the word in the grid. Words are formed by tracking from letter to letter, up, down, across or diagonally. In this example, a player's list could include the following words:

lea	heal
least	hale
east	eat
ale	shale
stale	sale
last	plea
lathe	pleat

A time-limit, say ten minutes, should be set up. At the end of that time, the player with the most words on his list is the winner.

Crossword

To prepare for the game a square grid is drawn with nine squares across and nine squares down. A larger grid may be used if a longer game is required.

The first player writes a word anywhere in the grid, either across or down, scoring one point for each letter used. The players then play alternately, each player forming another word which must interlock with one or more of the words already entered in the grid, scoring 1 point for each letter added. For example if a player writes in the word ANAGRAM, intersecting with the G and M or previously entered words, he scores 5 points – he cannot claim points for the G and M already entered.

Play continues until neither player can find further letters that can be inserted to form new words. The player with the highest score is the winner.

Five By Five

This is a game for two players. Each player draws a grid five squares wide and five deep. The players do not let each other see their own grids until the game is over.

The two players take it in turns to call out letters. When a player calls out a letter he puts it into one of the squares on his grid. His opponent must also put the called-out letter somewhere on his grid. This continues until twenty-five letters have been called out, when the two grids will be full.

The object of the game is to fill your own grid with three-, four- and five-letter words going horizontally and vertically. At the end of the game you score 3 points for every three-letter word, 4 for every four-letter word, and 5 for every five-letter word.

Of course, the letters you call out will be ones designed to help you make words in your grid. Your opponent will have to accommodate the letters you call out in his grid as best he can. When he calls out his letters they will be ones he thinks will help him make words for his grid and you will then have to try to make the most of the letters he gives you.

Here is what the two grids looked like at the end of a game between Adam and Eve, in which Adam called out the letters R, G, E, L, A, S, O, L, I, P, E, L and S, and Eve called out A, N, C, H, O, R, E, A, E, N, D, and V.

Adam's grid	Eve's grid
R A N C H	G R A P E
O G R E A	R O E L A
P E E L S	O L V I C
E N D L V	A L E E H
S O L I A	N S N D S

Here is what each player scored:
ADAM: Words across – RANCH (5), OGRE (4), PEELS (5), END (3); Words down – ROPES (5), AGE (3), RED (3), CELL (4), HAS (3). Total: 35 points

EVE: Words across – GRAPE (5), ROE (3), ALE (3);
Words down – GROAN (5), ROLLS (5), EVEN (4), PLIED (5), EACH (4).
Total: 34 points.

One- and two-letter words do not count, and each letter can only be counted once in either direction. For example, in her top horizontal line Eve can only score for GRAPE, she cannot also score for RAPE, RAP or APE.

To add an extra dimension to the game, a bonus of 10 points can be awarded to any player who manages to form a five-letter word running diagonally from the top left-hand corner of his grid to the bottom right-hand corner.

Scramble

Each player draws – or is supplied with – an empty grid consisting of ten squares across and ten squares down. A theme is then chosen – which should be a fairly general one, such as Music, Transport, Art, Science, Food or Sport.

What each player has to do is to fill in his grid with interlocking words, blanking out unused squares where appropriate, so as to form a crossword. All the words entered must have some relevance to the chosen theme.

A crossword is deemed to be complete when at least half the squares – 50 in the case of a 10 × 10 grid – have been filled with letters and the remaining squares blanked out. The first player to complete his crossword calls out 'Stop!'. The other players may then finish any word they happen to be writing at that time, but must not start entering any new words.

Each player then passes his crossword to the player on his left for checking. A word is only valid if it interlocks with others, is correctly spelled and is relevant to the theme. Words of doubtful relevance should be put to a vote. If all the words are valid, a player scores 1 point for each letter entered in the grid. In the case of an invalid word, no points are scored for its letters except for those that interlock with, and thus form part of, a valid word.

To avoid arguments, certain rules should be agreed before you start. For example, supposing the theme is Music:

(a) Do you allow proper names such as *Ravel*?
(b) Do you allow abbreviations such as *pp* (for pianissimo)?
(c) Do you allow the same word to be used twice in a crossword – or variations of the same word, e.g. *drum* and *drums*?

(d) Do you allow phrases such as *in tune*?

If you like, you can add the refinement that the player who stops the game gets an extra 10 points if his is the highest letter score but loses 10 points if any other player has a higher letter score.

Here is an example with Music as the theme.

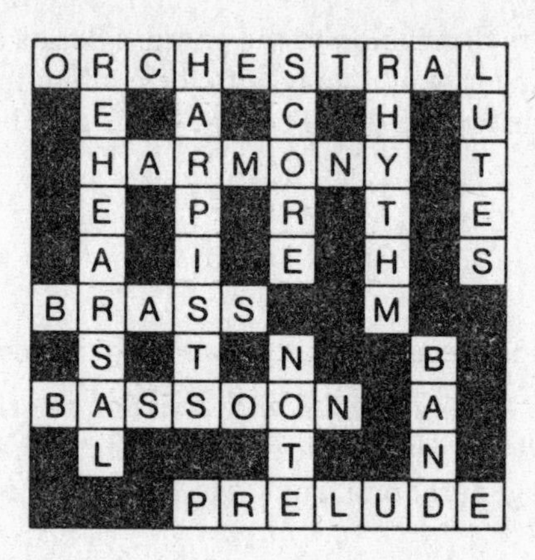

Sinko

SINKO is a game for two players that sounds simple but is challenging and stimulating to play.

A 5 × 5 grid is drawn, and the first player enters a five-letter word in any one of the five rows or five columns. The second player then enters another five-letter word either parallel to the first or interlocking with it.

Then each player in turn enters another five-letter word, either horizontally or vertically. The game ends when a player is unable to fill in another word, either because the grid is full, or because he cannot find a word that will fit in with any of the letters previously entered.

Here, as an example, is the grid from a game in which the words played were as follows:

Player 1: PLAIN
Player 2: TAKEN
Player 1: MINOR
Player 2: SHEET
Player 1: VIDEO
Player 2: SPASM

S		T	V	
P	L	A	I	N
A		K	D	
S	H	E	E	T
M	I	N	O	R

Player 1 has lost because, understandably, he could not think of a word in the form S-TV-, A-KD-, -L-HI or -N-TR.

Letter Games

The Initial Letter Game

'Delightful, delicious, delectable, dainty Deborah Diamante, dare-devil Danny Diamante's dimpled daughter, demanded desperate decisions, despising diffident doubters.'

That is the intriguing opening of one player's effort in the INITIAL LETTER GAME, the aim of which is to write the longest story using words beginning all with the same letter.

You can play the game on your own, or you can give all the players pencil and paper and let them have ten minutes in which to concoct their stories. When the time is up, the player with the longest story that makes sense wins the game.

A, B, C, D, E, F, G, H, L, M, N, R, S, T and W are the letters to use. If you try playing with the other letters, the game is almost impossible.

Say It With Letters

How do you spell 'vacant' in two letters? Answer: MT. How do you spell 'disintegration' in two letters? Answer: DK.

SAY IT WITH LETTERS is a game in which the players have to identify 'words' like MT and DK (and IV and NRG and XLNC) and may be played in two ways.

In the first version the players are given clues as above, from which they have to guess the correct answers. The player getting the most correct answers is the winner.

The other way to play is to set the players the task of listing as many such 'words' as they can think of in a given amount of time. The winner is the player producing the longest list.

Jotto

JOTTO is a game of logical deduction for two players in which each player has to guess a mystery word chosen by the other.

Each player writes down a five-letter word without letting the other player see what it is. Then each in turn calls out a five-letter word and the other player responds by saying how many letters of the test word correspond with letters in the word to be guessed.

For example:

Mystery word:	SLEEP	
Guess 1:	THROW	– no letters in common
Guess 2:	CREST	– 2 letters
Guess 3:	STYLE	– 3 letters

Play continues, with each player guessing alternately, until one or the other wins the game by correctly identifying his opponent's mystery word.

Here, as an example, are one player's guesses from a typical game, showing the sort of reasoning that is required:

1.	DANCE	1 letter	
2.	SANDY	2 letters	
3.	HANDY	1 letter	(So there must be an S and no H)
4.	SOUND	1 letter	(Eliminating O, U, N, D – from guess 2 there must be an A or Y)
5.	SUNNY	1 letter	(That eliminates Y. The word contains S, A – from guess 1, that eliminates C, E)
6.	FAILS	2 points	(Eliminating F, I, L)
7.	STRAP	4 letters	(The word must contain two of the letters of T, R, P)
8.	GRASP	3 letters	(So there's T and no G – we now have S, A, T plus either R or P and one other or a repeated letter)
9.	STAMP	3 letters	(So it's S, T, A and R and another – no M or P)
10.	STRAW	5 letters	– that's it!

Bulls And Cows

BULLS AND COWS is a variation of JOTTO. It is played in the same way except that each time a player calls out his test word he is told:
(a) how many letters of his test word correspond with letters in the mystery word *in the same position* (number of bulls);
(b) how many letters of his test word correspond with letters in the mystery word *but in different positions* (number of cows).

For example:

Mystery word:	TRAIN	
Guess 1:	ABOVE	1 cow
Guess 2:	PRINT	1 bull, 2 cows
Guess 3:	GRAND	2 bulls, 1 cow

Double Jeopardy

DOUBLE JEOPARDY is another variation of JOTTO, which was invented by Don Laycock, an Australian games designer. The rules are the same as for JOTTO, except that when a player calls out his test word he must at the same time declare how many letters of the test word correspond with letters in *his own* mystery word.

This means that test words need to be selected with great care – because you want to glean as much information as you can about your opponent's mystery word while at the same time revealing as little as possible about your own.

Crash

CRASH is yet another variation on the JOTTO theme, and in fact it could be described as BULLS AND COWS without the cows.

Rules are as for JOTTO, except that when a player calls out his test word he is told only the number of 'crashes' – that is, the number of matching letters in the same position in both the test word and the mystery word.

For example:

Mystery word:	STARE	
Guess 1:	ASTER	– no crashes
Guess 2:	STONE	– 3 crashes

Uncrash

A 'crash' may be defined as the situation in which two words of equal length have the same letter in the same position. For example, in the case of *stop* and *pest*, there is no crash – although they have letters in common, they do not occur in the same position in each word. In the case of *last* and *hose*, however, they both have the letter s in the third position – that is a 'crash'.

UNCRASH is a game for two to four players. Player 1 writes down a word of an agreed length, say three letters. The second player then writes underneath it another three-letter word that does not have any crashes with the previous word. The players then continue, in turn, each placing at the end of the list a new word that has no crashes with *any* of the previous words. This goes on until a player is unable to add a new word without causing a crash. That player loses the round and is eliminated. The remaining players continue to play further rounds until the winner has eliminated all his opponents.

Here is a sample game, in which player 2 lost because he could not think of a word to add after *emu*:

Player 1:	RUB
Player 2:	ASK
Player 3:	TRY
Player 1:	DIN
Player 2:	OLD
Player 3:	LET
Player 1:	WAR
Player 2:	HOG
Player 3:	BYE
Player 1:	EMU

Ten-Letter Challenge

A ten-letter word is chosen as a starter – preferably one that does not have many duplications of letters. *Orchestral*, *tambourine*, *aerobatics*, *diagnostic*, *balustrade*, *stimulated* and *hinterland*, for example, would all make suitable starter words. Each player writes the chosen starter word in a column down the left side of his sheet of paper.

A time limit is set – say, ten minutes – and in that time each player has to find the longest word he can starting with each letter of the starter word, but using only letters contained in the starter word itself. For the first letter of the starter word you may not use the starter itself or any word derived from the same root. That is, if the starter word is *orchestral*, for example, your word beginning with the letter O cannot be *orchestral* or *orchestra*. If a letter is duplicated in the starter word, you must have a different word for each occurrence of that letter.

When the time is up, the players score 1 point per letter in each of the words they have formed, and the player with the highest total is the winner.

Here is what one player achieved with *orchestral* as his starter word:

Others	= 6	Starch	= 6
Reacts	= 6	Torches	= 7
Chortles	= 8	Reach	= 5
Harlots	= 7	Arches	= 6
Earths	= 6	Lathers	= 7

Total 64

Centurion

The game of CENTURION was invented by David Parlett and is an excellent two-player game for those adept with numbers as well as with words.

The letters from A to Z are assigned numerical values according to their position in the alphabet.

A	1	N	14
B	2	O	15
C	3	P	16
D	4	Q	17
E	5	R	18
F	6	S	19
G	7	T	20
H	8	U	21
I	9	V	22
J	10	W	23
K	11	X	24
L	12	Y	25
M	13	Z	26

Player 1 starts off by writing down any three-letter word which has a total value of 10 or less – which tends to mean the choice is between *ace*, *add*, *aga*, *aha*, *bad*, *bag*, *cab*, *cad*, *dab*, *dad*, and *fad* – and writes the values of the word beside it.

Player 2 then writes under the first word another three-letter word which must start with the last letter of the first word. Beside that he writes the value of the word and the cumulative total.

For example:

ADD	9
DIE	18 + 9 = 27

The players then continue, in turn, adding another three-letter word that starts with the final letter of the previous word, keeping count of the cumulative value. The first player to make the total go over 99 is the loser.

ADD	9
DIE	18 + 9 = 27
EEL	22 + 27 = 51
LOP	43 + 51 = 94

Since the lowest-scoring word that can be used to continue is PAD, scoring 21, Player 1 loses in this sample game.

Double Centurion

DOUBLE CENTURION is a variation of CENTURION that may be played by up to four players. Rules are the same as for the previous game except that it is the player making the total reach 200 who loses.

Letter Nim

NIM is an old-fashioned game in which two players alternately take a number of objects from a pile, the winner being either the player who takes the last object or the player who forces his opponent to do so. LETTER NIM is a tactical word game for two players, based on the same principle.

The alphabet is written out from A to Z. The first player then writes down a word beginning with A, and A is crossed off the alphabet to show it has been used. If the word contains a B, that letter is also crossed off. If the word contains a C following the B, C is crossed off. The same applies to a D following the C, and so on.

Thus *anchor* would delete only the A; *album* would cause the A and B to be deleted; *ambulance* the A, B and C; *abscond* the A, B, C and D; *absconder* the A, B, C, D and E.

The next player then writes a word beginning with the first letter in the alphabet that has not yet been crossed off. As before, he crosses off that letter and any consecutive letters of the alphabet after that which appear in the correct sequence in his word.

Here is a sample game:

Player 1:	ABACUS	(deleting A, B, C)
Player 2:	DEFENDING	(deleting D, E, F, G)
Player 1:	HIJACK	(deleting H, I, J, K)
Player 2:	LEMON	(deleting L, M, N)
Player 1:	OPAQUE	(deleting O, P, Q)
Player 2:	REST	(deleting R, S, T)
Player 1:	UNDER	(deleting U)
Player 2:	VOW	(deleting V, W)
Player 1:	XYLOPHONE	(deleting X, Y)
Player 2:	ZAP	(deleting Z)

You can decide which way you prefer to play the game – whether the player using the Z is the winner or the loser. It is preferable, however, if both players come to the same decision!

Word Ping-Pong

This two-player game was invented by P. Perkins and first published in *Games and Puzzles* magazine. The basic idea of the game is the same as that of WORD LADDERS (see page 45) – that is, a list of words is formed by changing one letter at a time to form a new word. I have altered the original rules of this game somewhat, and I think the result is a very enjoyable game.

The first player 'serves' by writing down a four-letter word, in which the letters are all different. Then each player in turn alters one letter to form a new word which is written underneath the previous word. The first player may change only the first or second letter, and the second player may change only the third or fourth letter. In each turn the letter that is changed must be changed to a completely new letter – one that has not appeared anywhere in any of the previous words.

A valid 'serve' must give the second player a chance to respond – that is, it must consist of a word that is capable of having its third or fourth letter changed to form a new word. So serving *cyan* or *cwms*, for example, would be a fault, and one point would go to the opposite player. Also, the same word may not be served more than once in a game.

A player loses when he is unable to form a new word in accordance with the rules.

Here is a sample rally:

LONG	(Player 1 serves)
LONE	(Player 2 – new letter E)
LINE	(Player 1 – new letter I)
LINK	(Player 2 – new letter K)
MINK	(Player 1 – new letter M)
MINT	(Player 2 – new letter T)
HINT	(Player 1 – new letter H)
HIND	(Player 2 – new letter D)
HAND	(Player 1 – new letter A)
HARD	(Player 2 – new letter R)
CARD	(Player 1 – new letter C)
CARP	(Player 2 – new letter P)
WARP	(Player 1 – new letter W)
WASP	(Player 2 – new letter S)

Player 1 loses because he cannot follow on from *wasp*. I, G, H and R have already appeared in previous words, so he cannot play *wisp*, *gasp*, *hasp* or *rasp*.

In keeping with the name of the game, you can use the scoring system of Ping-Pong (otherwise known as Table Tennis). A rally is a round of play starting with a service and ending with one player scoring a point. Each player serves (goes first) for five successive rallies, and then there is a change of service. The winner is the first player to score 21 points, except that if the score reaches 20–20, service alternates with each rally and the winner has to establish a 2-point lead over his opponent.

Verbal Sprouts

To start, a four-letter word is formed by each player in turn writing a circled letter in a horizontal line. The letters must be all different and must form a word. The circled letters are then joined by arrows, like this:

(H) → (A) → (R) → (E)

Then each player in turn adds a new circled letter to the diagram and connects it with arrows to one or more existing letters to form further words. The letter added must be different from any letters already entered in the diagram. The player then scores one point per letter for each word he can make, using his newly entered letter and following the arrows in the diagram.

For example, from the starting position shown above, the first player could insert the letter T and add the appropriate arrows to form the words *hart*, *hate*, *tear* and *earth*, scoring 17 points.

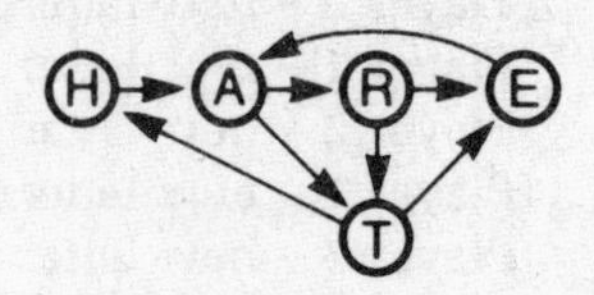

The second player might then add the letter D to the diagram.

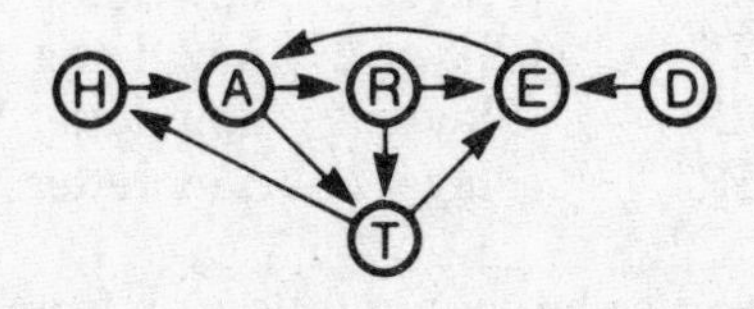

This enables him to make the words Dearth and Death, giving him 11 points.

The game continues in this way until neither player is able to add a new letter to form further words. The player with the highest score is then the winner.

There are a few additional rules to bear in mind:

(a) Arrows may not cross one another.
(b) There can never be more than one arrow between any given pair of letters. Thus, in our example, where there is an arrow from A to R, you could not add an arrow going from R to A.
(c) Words may only be made by following the direction of the arrows.
(d) No letter may have more than four arrows attached to it (whether leading to or from the letter). Thus, in our example, T has its full complement of arrows after it has been connected to the H.
(e) Points may not be scored for words entirely contained within a longer word. So the player scoring 6 points for Dearth, for example, could not also claim 4 points for Dear.

Collection Games

Categories

The players decide on a list of categories – preferably about twenty. The fairest way to choose them is to let each player propose an equal number of categories.

Each player writes down the list of categories on his sheet of paper, and then a letter of the alphabet is chosen at random. A time limit is agreed – ten minutes, let us say. The players then have to write down as many words as they can that begin with the chosen letter for each of the categories.

When the time is up, each player passes his list to the person on his left for checking. The words listed for each category are read out. A word which has not been thought of by any other player scores 2 points; a word which one or more other players have also listed scores only 1 point. The player with the highest total is the winner.

For subsequent rounds a new initial letter is chosen.

Guggenheim

A list of categories is chosen and each player writes the list down the left-hand side of his sheet of paper. A keyword of five or more letters, all different, is then chosen, and each player writes the keyword, well spaced out, along the top of his sheet of paper.

A time limit is set, and each player must then attempt to write down one word beginning with each letter of the keyword for each category.

For example, with a keyword of Track, one player's list might look something like this:

	T	**R**	**A**	**C**	**K**
Countries	Turkey	Russia	Austria	Canada	Kenya
Birds	Turkey	Raven	Auk	Coot	Kite
Rivers	Thames	Rhine	Aire	Coquet	Kennet
Novelists	Trollope	Roth	Asimov	Conrad	Kafka
Weapons	Torpedo	Rifle	Assegai	Club	Kris
Boats	Trawler	Raft	Ark	Canoe	Ketch
Drinks	Tea	Retsina	Ale	Cider	Kummel
Flowers	Thistle	Rose	Aster	Camellia	Kingcup

Animal Magic

Equip all the players with pencil and paper and give them ten minutes in which to write down all the adjectives they can think of that have their origin in birds and beasts but which, as adjectives, may be applied to human beings. Here are some examples:

Asinine	Foxy
Bitchy	Lousy
Bovine	Mulish
Catty	Ratty
Dogged	Sheepish
Elephantine	Sluggish
Fishy	Swinish

When the time is up the player with the longest list of adjectives wins the game.

Since, curiously, so many of the adjectives refer to what are generally regarded as unpleasant or unattractive characteristics, any player who manages to include adjectives that have a pleasant connotation (Kittenish, for example) will be allowed 2 points for that one adjective.

Build-Up

The players are given a simple word onto which they must build up as many other words as they can think of. For example, if the given word is Head here are just some of the words that can be built up from it: headhunter, head-over-heels, headstrong, headlong, headquarters, headdress, headline, heading, heady, headache, headfast, header, headmost, headsman, headband, headgear.

If the players are given a set time-limit, say five or ten minutes, the player with the longest list when the time is up is the winner of the game.

To give the players even greater scope, as well as starting with short words that can be built up into longer ones, it is possible to start with prefixes. Here, for example, is a *very* small selection of the words you can build up from EX: exacerbate, exact, exactly, exaggerate, exalt, examine, example, exasperate, excavate, exceed, excel, except, exhibit, exhilarate, exhort, exigence, exiguous, exile, exist, exit, exorbitant, exotic, expand, expatiate.

Consecutives

The players, each armed with pencil and paper, have to list as many words as they can which contain two consecutive letters of the alphabet. A time-limit of, say, ten minutes is set for the performance of this task.

Among the words that might be listed are:

ABOUT	TUNE
DETAIL	OXYGEN
EFFORT	HYMN
GHOST	OPPOSITE

Scoring may be based on the total number of words listed or, alternatively, the number of *different* consecutive letter pairs in a player's list.

A variant of this game involves listing words which contain *three* consecutive letters of the alphabet, for example:

DABCHICK	FIRST
DEFY	STUDY
PLOUGHING	AFGHAN

This game, in either variation, is also suitable as an entertaining solo pastime.

Personal Words

Within the given time-limit, the players have to compile a list of words which are not only boys' or girls' names but are also common nouns that may be found in the dictionary without a capital initial letter.

Some examples are:

Lee	– the sheltered side
Lance	– a cavalry weapon
Warren	– a maze of narrow passages
Gene	– a unit of DNA
Ruth	– pity, sorrow
Carol	– a song

You should decide before starting the game whether or not you are going to allow the many girls' names that are also names of flowers or trees – Daisy, Violet, Rose, Olive, Hazel etc.

The player with the longest list is the winner.

Palindromic Words

Palindromic words are words that read the same when written backwards: Gag, Deed, Kayak etc.

Within a given time limit see which of the players can form the longest list of such words.

(Can you find a longer palindromic word than my nine-letter word Malayalam (an Asian language)?)

Animal Words

The objective of this game is to see who can form the longest list of words, each word to contain within it the name of an animal. Only one word per animal is allowed.

Some words that may be listed are: Kayak; Benevolent; Catch; Drapery; Foxglove.

Irregular Plurals

The aim is to see who can form the longest list of words which, in their plural form, do *not* end with the letter S.

Some typical examples are:

Die / Dice
Stigma / Stigmata
Cherub / Cherubim
Lied / Lieder

Before playing this game you should decide whether or not to allow words that are the same in the singular and plural – Fish, Sheep, etc.

Alpha

In this game each player is given a time-limit – ten minutes, say – in which to write down a list of words that begin and end with the same letter of the alphabet. Here are some examples: Clinic, Evade, Gag, Hash, Mum, Rider, Stress, Yesterday, and, of course, Alpha.

Naturally, you increase the potential number of words if you allow proper names (Cadillac, Xerox), foreign words (Uhuru), colloquialisms (zizz) and exclamations (Aha!, Wow!).

There are two different versions of the game.

In the first version, the players just list as many acceptable words as they can and, at the end of the set time, the player with the longest list is the winner.

In the second version, which is a more demanding test of vocabulary, each player first writes the letters of the alphabet down the left-hand margin of his piece of paper. Then for each letter he has to find the longest word which begins and ends with that letter. When the time-limit has expired, the players score 1 point for each letter of each word they have listed and the winner is the player with the highest total score. Thus Minimum (7 points) is preferable to Maim (4 points), and Metamorphism (12 points) is preferable to both.

Arena

The players are given a time-limit in which to form as long a list as possible of five-letter words which have vowels as their first, third and fifth letters, and consonants as their second and fourth letters.

Such a list might include the following words:

Arena	Opera	Unite
Aroma	Abide	Amuse
Evade	Image	Okapi

The player who produces the longest list is the winner.

Vowels

A particular vowel is chosen, and the players are given a set time in which to produce a list of words which must contain the given vowel at least twice and must contain no other vowels.

For example, if A is the chosen vowel, the following words would qualify: Ballad, Data, Atlas, Salad, Ballast, Anagram, Catamaran.

Players score one point for each occurrence of the chosen vowel in their words – thus Data scores 2 points but Catamaran scores 4. The player with the highest number of points is the winner.

Six And Two Threes

The players are given a set amount of time in which to list as many six-letter words as they can which can be split in half to form separate three-letter words.

For example:

Carpet – Car & Pet
Carton – Car & Ton
Season – Sea & Son
Redraw – Red & Raw
Catkin – Cat & Kin

The winner is the player with the longest list at the end of the time allowed.

Roman Numeral Words

What do the words below have in common?

LID	MILD
CIVIL	MIX

The answer is that they are all formed entirely from letters that are also Roman numerals: I, V, X, L, C, D, M.

In this game the players are allowed five minutes in which they have to list as many words of this type as they can. The player with the longest list at the end of the time allowed is the winner.

Combinations

For this game you need to prepare a list of ten or more two-letter or three-letter combinations which could occur within words. Such a list might contain letter combinations such as these:

gn	ido
tr	rew
mf	ump
hn	tic
bl	rve
rp	

Each of the players writes down the list on his sheet of paper. A time-limit is set –of ten minutes, say – in which each player has to find as long a word as possible containing each letter combination in the list. The scoring is 1 point per letter for each word, and the player obtaining the highest total number of points is the winner.

Using the combinations shown as an example a good player might achieve a result like this, giving a total score of 147:

Indignation	= 11
Theatrically	= 12
Circumferences	= 14
Pyrotechnical	= 13
Incorrigibleness	=16
Anthropomorphism	= 16
Kaleidoscopes	= 13
Wherewithal	= 11
Presumptuousness	= 16
Statisticians	= 13
Surveillance	= 12

Sequentials

A fixed time is set – say, ten minutes – in which each player has to list as many words as he can that contain two consecutive letters that are consecutive in the alphabet.

For example: Alphabet; Child; Elm.

The player producing the longest list is the winner.

That version of the game is probably more suitable for younger players – most adults would find it too easy as there are so many suitable words – words containing *de*, *no*, *st*, *tu*, etc – that it could become merely a test of how fast one can write. A more demanding version is to list only words containing *three* consecutive letters of the alphabet, for example: Defy; Sighing; First.

Beheadings

No, BEHEADINGS is not a variation of HANGMAN – it is a completely different game.

The players are given a set time in which they have to list as many words as they can which have the property of forming another word when the initial letter is removed.

For example:

Blight	(may be beheaded to form Light)
Every	(may be beheaded to form Very)
Stone	(may be beheaded to form Tone)
Hand	(may be beheaded to form And)

When the time is up, the players add up the number of words they have found, and the player with the longest list is the winner.

Children's Games

Hangman

This is a classic paper-and-pencil game for two players. One player thinks of a word, preferably of six or more letters, and the other player has to discover the word by guessing individual letters.

The first player writes down a series of dashes to indicate the number of letters in the mystery word, thus: – – – – – – – – –. The second player then starts guessing the letters in the word, calling out one letter at a time. If the letter occurs anywhere in the word the first player writes that letter above the appropriate dash (or dashes) wherever the letter occurs. But for each letter called out that does *not* occur in the mystery word, the first player adds an extra bit to the drawing of a gallows. The player who is doing the guessing has eleven lives to lose, in that the gallows consists of eleven parts:

1. The base of the gallows
2. The upright of the gallows
3. The arm of the gallows
4. The support
5. The rope
6. The victim's head
7. The victim's body
8. The victim's right arm
9. The victim's left arm
10. The victim's right leg
11. The victim's left leg

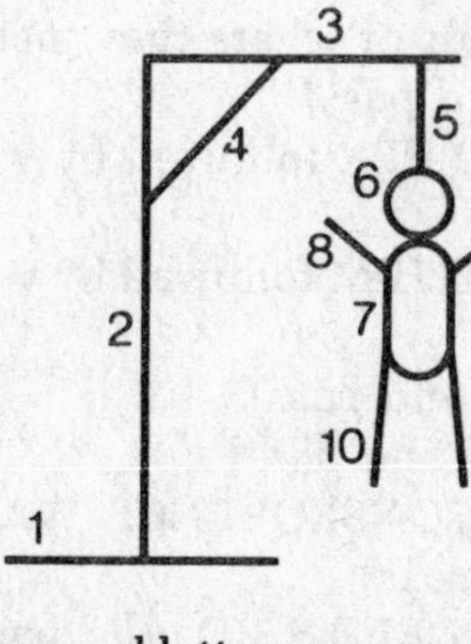

The incorrectly guessed letters are usually recorded underneath the gallows so that the second player can see which letters he has already tried.

If the gallows is completed before the second player has identified the word he is 'hanged' and loses, and the first player has another go at choosing a mystery word.

The second player wins if he correctly identifies the word before the gallows is completed. He then chooses a word for the other player to guess.

Sometimes the game is played using agreed themes, such as Book Titles or Names of TV Programmes, in which case the name or title to be guessed may consist of more than one word. In this case the first player will draw the dashes to show the number of letters in each word with spaces between the words.

Consequences

CONSEQUENCES is a classic word game that has been played around the world for generations and yet still manages to retain its peculiar charm. To play it, equip everyone with a pencil and a long sheet of paper. Then tell the players to write down certain pieces of information, and each time they have done so get them to fold the top of their pieces of paper forward (so as to conceal what they have written) and pass the paper to the player sitting on their right. Gradually the pieces of information build up into a story, and at the end of the game all the different stories are read out and the wittiest is given the warmest applause.

Traditionally a dozen pieces of information are called for, but you may amend these or add your own should you feel so inclined:

1. An adjective *(fold and pass)*
2. A girl's name *(fold and pass)*
3. The word MET plus and adjective *(fold and pass)*
4. A man's name *(fold and pass)*
5. The word AT plus details of where they met *(fold and pass)*
6. When they met *(fold and pass)*
7. The words HE SAID TO HER followed by what he said *(fold and pass)*
8. The words SHE SAID TO HIM followed by what she said *(fold and pass)*
9. What he then did *(fold and pass)*
10. What she then did *(fold and pass)*
11. The words AND THE CONSEQUENCE WAS plus details of the consequence *(fold and pass)*
12. The words AND THE WORLD SAID plus details of what the world did say.

First Names First

Each player is given a sheet of paper and a pencil, and a boy's or girl's name is called out. This should be a name of six or more letters, like Roland, for example.

Each player writes the letters of this name, well spaced out, across the top of his sheet of paper, and then has to list under each letter as many names as he can think of that begin with that letter. A time-limit is set, and when the time is up the player with the longest list of names is the winner.

In the case of Roland, a typical list might start like this:

R	**O**	**L**	**A**	**N**	**D**
Roland	Oliver	Luther	Anne	Neil	Dawn
Richard	Olive	Lucy	Abe	Natalie	Denis
Rachel	Oscar	Lesley	Andrew	Nicholas	David
Ruth		Laura	Arthur	Norma	Don
Rhoda			Alice	Norman	Daisy
Ralph			Amy	Nancy	Dwight
Rebecca					

Mirror Writing

Each player has his own sheet of paper and a pencil. The question-master reads out a sentence, and each player has to write that sentence in mirror writing. That is, when the paper is held up in front of a mirror, the writing reflected in the mirror has to appear the normal way round. It is surprising how difficult it can be to do this perfectly without a lot of practice.

The results are checked with the aid of an actual mirror, and the player whose effort is judged the best is declared to be the winner.

Sounds The Same

This game is based on homonyms – pairs of words that sound the same but are different in spelling and meaning: *throne* and *thrown*, *herd* and *heard*, *bough* and *bow*, for example.

The question-master reads out a list of such words, and the players have to write down the two different spellings for each word. The winner is the player who manages to write down the largest number of correct pears. I'm sorry, I mean pairs.

Other suitable pairs of words are:

Coarse & course	Links & lynx
Assent & ascent	Suede & swayed
Foul & fowl	Baize & bays
Allowed & aloud	Lax & lacks
Bold & bowled	Ball & bawl
Cereal & serial	Packed & pact
Clause & claws	Quarts & quartz
Colonel & kernel	Bolder & boulder
Council & counsel	Altar & alter
Signet & cygnet	Grown & groan
Muscle & mussel	Side & sighed
Pray & prey	Their & there
Soared & sword	Waist & waste
Pole & poll	Wood & would
Medal & meddle	Plain & plane

Synonyms

This game is an entertaining way of getting children to extend their vocabularies. A list of twenty words is read out, which the players must copy down on the left-hand side of their sheet of paper. The players are then given a time-limit in which they have to write down synonyms (words with the same meaning) for each of the given words. Some words may have more than one acceptable synonym, in which case the players may list as many as they like. When the time is up, the player with the longest and most accurate list of synonyms is the winner.

A suitable list of words for this game might include some of these:

Abide	Convey	Jump	Sailor
Adorn	Deadly	Keep	Sundry
Afraid	Educate	Lie	Tear
Aid	Error	Mild	Throw
Allow	Fall	Near	Under
Bad	Forbid	Observe	Vanish
Beat	Gift	Pull	Victory
Branch	Haste	Quiet	Wander
Careful	Huge	Rescue	Yokel
Choose	Idle	Rogue	Zero

Partners

This game requires a little preparation on the part of the question-master. He has to prepare a list of well-known pairs of partners. Suitable pairs might include:

Jack & Jill	Starsky & Hutch
Adam & Eve	Antony & Cleopatra
Tom & Jerry	Bonnie & Clyde
Laurel & Hardy	Abbott & Costello
Romeo & Juliet	The Owl & The Pussycat

The list might be extended to include phrases such as sugar and spice, bat and ball, stars and stripes, etc.

To play the game each player is given a sheet of paper and a pencil. The question-master reads out the first name of each pair, allowing a few seconds before moving on to the next pair. The players have to try to write down the name of the missing partner for each name read out. The player who correctly lists the most partners is the winner.

Nation Game

This game may be played in two ways. The players can either list as many words as they can that end with 'nation' or they can be given clues that lead them to the answers.

In the first version the players should be given a set amount of time to list words like: Designation, Donation, Examination, Imagination. The player who produces the longest list of words is the winner.

To play the game in the second way, the players need to be given clues to point them towards the 'nation' words. For example, 'Which nation is a flower?' (answer: Carnation), or 'Which nation sleeps through the winter?' (answer: Hibernation). Again the winner is the player with the longest list of correct answers at the end of the time allowed.

Ship Game

Like the NATION GAME, this game may be played in two ways.

The players may be given a set amount of time in which to list as many words as they can that end with ship – words like: Worship, Friendship, Ownership, Partnership, Scholarship. The player who produces the longest list of words is the winner.

Alternatively, the players may be given clues to point them to the 'ship' words. For example: 'Which ship commands others?' (answer: Leadership), or 'Which ship is shared by somebody else?' (answer: Partnership). Again the winner is the player with the longest list of correct answers at the end of the time allowed.

Jumbled Proverbs

Give each player a sheet of paper and a pencil and then read a list of proverbs to them. In every case the proverb has been jumbled, and the players have to unjumble the words and put them into the right order before writing down the proverb as it should read. These are some examples of proverbs you might include:

Shines hay while the make sun.

A silver has every lining cloud.

The bush worth is a hand in bird two the in.

Children, especially those who may not know the proverbs well, will enjoy puzzling over ten to fifteen of these, trying to unscramble them. The player with the most correct answers wins.

Licence-Plate Words

This is an ideal game for keeping children amused on long car journeys. Tell them to keep their eyes open for complete words on the licence-plates of vehicles they see. For example:

CAT MAT
MUM FOR
LET BAR
TOP TON

A list should be kept of the words seen. The player with the longest list at the end of the journey is the winner.

Solo Games

Starting Point

You begin by writing any word of your choice on the middle of a blank piece of paper. Then give yourself ten minutes in which to build up a series of other words based on the starting word. The words must not only be physically linked to one another, they must also be broadly related to the theme set by the starting word. Here is an example in which the starting word is Entertainment:

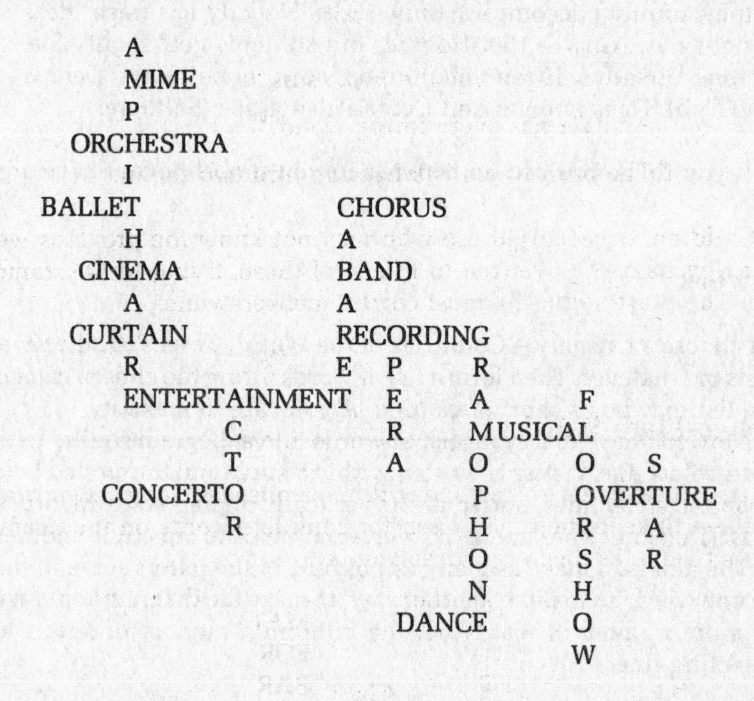

Twenty words in ten minutes isn't bad going, but the ease or difficulty of the game depends largely on the word you start with. Holidays, Animals, Pastimes and Education are easy starting words: Taxidermist, Follicle and Battery aren't. If you want to cheat, you can always start with the word Dictionary, in which case every word you choose to add could be said to be in some way linked to it!

One Hundred Word Challenge

Could you write a hundred words that make sense and not repeat a single word once? If you can, then you have mastered the game already because that's all it involves. Here is how Mrs Pearl Feldman and her pupils managed at Pompton Lakes High School, New Jersey, where the game originated:

> 'Let's go! The challenge is to write a composition without using any word more than once. Do you think that it can be done? If not, give one reason for doing this. While we are sitting here in English class at Pompton Lakes High School, Lakeside Avenue, New Jersey, all of us figure out something which makes sense. Mrs Feldman helps her pupils because another teacher said they couldn't accomplish such tasks. Nobody has fresh ideas right now. Goal – 100! How far did students get? Eighty-five done already; fifteen left. 'Pretty soon none!' says Dennis O'Neill. Gary Putnam and Debra Petsu agree. So there!'

If you think you can do better (and you probably can) have a go.

Network

First choose a category – Countries of the World, Towns, Birds, Rivers, Artists or whatever. Then form a list of words fitting the chosen category – the list may be as short or as long as you care to make it.

Now you have to fit your list of words into a diagram similar to that shown below. Each letter is written within a circle and the circled letters are connected by lines, horizontally, vertically or diagonally to form the words. (Diagonal lines are not, however, allowed to cross one another.)

The aim is to make as many as possible of the letters serve in more than one word, or, to put it another way, to make the diagram contain the maximum number of words but the minimum number of letters and connecting lines.

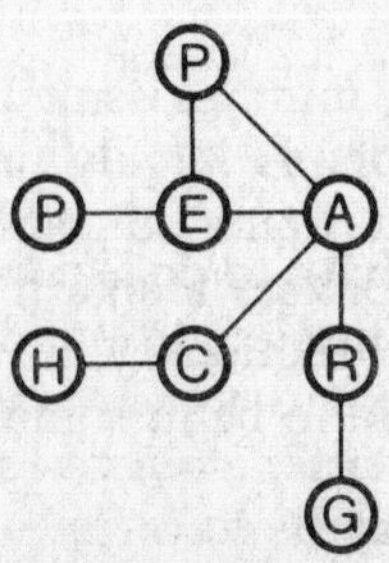

One suggested method of scoring is to score 10 points for each word in the network, minus 2 points for each letter used and minus 1 point for each connecting line.

So this simple example would score 8 points:

3 words (PEAR, PEACH, GRAPE) = 30 points
7 letters = − 14 points
8 connectors = − 8 points

Here is a more advanced example, scoring 27 points. See if you can work out for yourself how that score is reached.

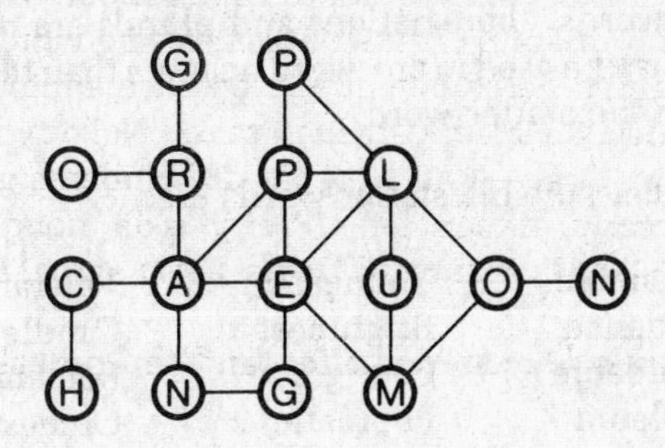

Safari For Literati

See how many names for species of mammal you can find that end with the letter I. (There are more than you probably think there are!)

My personal list includes seventeen species (not counting Yeti) ranging from Agouti – a South American rodent – to Wistiti (a type of marmoset). Can you do better than that?

Wordbuilder

To play this game all you have to do is take a word – any word will do, but preferably one of medium length – and form a list of as many other words as you can think of that may be formed from the letters in the given word. For example, if the starter word was Accidental, the following are some of the words that may be formed:

Acid	Cant	Dale	Tale
Aide	Candle	Date	Talc
Antic	Clan	Data	Tidal
Accident	Clad	Dace	Tide
Accent	Cent	Dental	Teal
Alien	Clean	Diet	Tail

The following rules are usually applied (but of course, you may modify the rules as you wish):

(a) Each word must contain at least four letters.
(b) Proper nouns are not allowed.
(c) Foreign words, abbreviations and plurals are not allowed.
(d) A letter may be used in any word no more than the number of times it occurs in the starter word.

Some other suitable starter words are:

Reasonable	Youngster	Tolerance
Avoidance	Brightness	Candlewick
Formidable	Centigrade	Remainder
Petroleum	Population	Orchestra
Promenade	Newspaper	Headstrong
Manifesto	Disastrous	Introduce

To play the game as a solo game, just choose your word and start scribbling. To play it as a game for two or more, give everyone the same word and the same amount of time, and see which player manages to come up with the longest list of acceptable words.

Category Crosswords

For this game you need a blank crossword grid. You can draw your own but it is much easier to cut out a crossword grid from a newspaper or magazine. Now choose a category – Countries, Birds, Book titles, Animals, Rivers, Artists, or whatever you like.

The aim of the game is to fill in the crossword grid, using only words connected with your chosen category. Entering the first few words is easy enough, but the task becomes progressively harder as you have to put in words that will connect with the letters of the words you have already entered. You will probably find that you often have to backtrack, and therefore a pencil (and eraser) will be found to be more suitable than a pen.

Half The Alphabet

What do the following words all have in common?

Called	Climbed
Ballad	Milkmaid
Alibi	Defiled
Deface	Gamble

The answer is that they use only letters from the first half of the alphabet – *a* to *m*. See how many words you can find that have the same property. What is the longest such word you can discover?

When you have done that you might like to consider words that use only letters from the second half of the alphabet.

Typewriter Words

The top row of letters on a standard typewriter keyboard consists of Q, W, E, R, T, Y, U, I, O, P. How many words can you find that contain only these letters?

Here are a few words to start you off:

Pert	Pour
Pretty	Totter
Quip	Poetry
Quite	Tripper

The letters on the second row of the typewriter are: A, S, D, F, G, H, J, K, L. I shouldn't think there are so many words to be found using only these letters, as only one vowel is included. But have a go and see how many you can discover.

On the third row we have: Z, X, C, V, B, N, M. I think we can forget about finding words that use only these letters!

Theme Songs

Set yourself the task of seeing how many song titles you can think of to fit a given theme. Here are some examples, but you can, no doubt, make up many more of your own.

Song titles including the name of a country: *America*, *From Russia With Love*, *Slow Boat To China*, etc.

Song titles including a colour: *White Christmas*, *Yellow Submarine*, *Green Grow The Rushes-O*, etc. (If you want to make it more difficult you can restrict the theme to one particular colour such as red, green, white or blue.)

Song titles including or consisting of a girl's name: *Laura*, *Lucy In The Sky With Diamonds*, *Eleanor Rigby*, etc.

Song titles including a number: *Tea For Two*, *Three Coins In The Fountain*, *Ten Green Bottles*, etc.

Song titles including the name of a town or city: *Chicago*, *I Left My Heart In San Francisco*, *April In Paris*, etc.

This game may also be played with the titles of books or films if your tastes are literary or cinematic rather than musical.

Newspaper Headline Search Game

The language of newspaper headlines is quite different from English.

The vocabulary is different. There are no articles, definite or indefinite. In headlines people don't criticize or condemn, they rap or slam – 'Industry Boss Raps Unions', 'Reagan Slams Soviets'. They don't investigate, they probe – 'Police Probe Jewel Theft'.

The tenses are different too. For actions in the past, the present tense is used – 'Boy Saves Drowning Man'. And for actions in the future the infinitive is used – 'Film Star To Quit'.

But the aspect of headlines that appeals to me most is the noun-cluster. In my newspaper today there is the headline 'Gang Boss Trial Verdict'. Doubtless, I will soon be reading 'Gang Boss Trial Verdict Appeal' or even 'Gang Boss Trial Verdict Appeal Shock'. I might even see 'Gang Boss Trial Jury Corruption Probe Sensation'.

It is an amusing game to collect actual examples from your daily newspaper. What is the longest noun-cluster you can find? What is the funniest?

I haven't yet seen the headline 'Heart Boy Mercy Dash Plane Crash Report Cover-up Denial', but I live in hope.

Multiple Beheadings

The game of BEHEADINGS was described on page 73. An interesting solo variation is to try to find as many words as you can that are capable of multiple beheading.

For example:

Spin – Pin – In
About – Bout – Out
Strap – Trap – Rap
Gland – Land – And
Amorally – Morally – Orally – Rally – Ally

How many words of this type can you discover? What is the longest chain of beheadings you can find?

Word Squares

For anyone fascinated by words, creating word squares is among the most absorbing of pencil-and-paper pastimes. The idea is simply to form a square of different words reading the same vertically and horizontally.

Word squares date back thousands of years. Socrates and Aristotle loved them, and the ancient Romans enjoyed them, too. When a Roman site at Cirencester in Gloucestershire was being excavated, this Latin word square was discovered on a piece of wall plaster:

R O T A S
O P E R A
T E N E T
A R E P O
S A T O R

This word square is extra special: it is palindromic; you can read the five words backward or upward and it is still a perfect word square – the same words in another arrangement. Arepo is a proper name, but the other words are legitimate Latin and actually form a sentence which, when translated, means something like 'Arepo, the sower, controls the wheels with an effort'.

Devising word squares of your own with up to five-letter words is relatively easy.

One-letter word square:

I

Two-letter word square:

T O
O N

Three-letter word square:

T A N
A R E
N E T

Four-letter word square:

O P A L
P I N E
A N O N
L E N S

Five-letter word square:

B L I S S
L U N C H
I N T E R
S C E N E
S H R E W

Devising squares with six- and seven-letter words is much more difficult, though it can be done.

Six-letter word Square:

E S T A T E
S H A V E N
T A L E N T
A V E R S E
T E N S E R
E N T E R S

Eight-letter word square:

A G A R I C U S
G E N E R A N T
A N A C O N D A
R E C A N T E R
I R O N W O R T
C A N T O N A L
U N D E R A G E
S T A R T L E D

Darryl Francis and Dmitri Borgmann are the world's leading authorities on word squares. They say that about 900 squares of nine-letter words have been constructed. Here is one of them:

Nine-letter word square:

F R A T E R I E S
R E G I M E N A L
A G I T A T I V E
T I T A N I T E S
E M A N A T I S T
R E T I T R A T E
I N I T I A T O R
E A V E S T O N E
S L E S T E R E D

The ultimate achievement is a ten-letter word square. Darryl and Dmitri managed to construct one after hitting on the brilliant idea of using tautonyms – words, like *yoyo*, *cancan* and *beri-beri*, that consist of two identical halves. Even so, they had to use the same word more than once within the word square.

Ten-letter word square:

O R A N G U T A N G
R A N G A R A N G A
A N D O L A N D O L
N G O T A N G O T A
G A L A N G A L A N
U R A N G U T A N G
T A N G A T A N G A
A N D O L A N D O L
N G O T A N G O T A
G A L A N G A L A N

Definitions:

Orangutang: orangutan. A spelling given by *Funk and Wagnalls New Standard Dictionary* (1946).

Rangaranga: In the Caroline Islands, a name for parsley fern growing in the cracks of old walls. Taken from *The Caroline Islands* by Frederick Christian (1899).

Andolandol: A Chinese fly, a tincture of which is used as a blistering agent. Taken from *An Illustrated Encyclopedic Medical Dictionary* by Frank Foster (1888).

Ngotangota: Town on the western shore of Lake Nyasa, now spelled Kota Kota. Taken from *Longman's Gazetteer of the World* by George Chisholm (1902).

Galangalan: A mountain in Sorsogon Province, Luzon Island, Philippines. Taken from *A Pronouncing Gazetteer and Geographical Dictionary of the Philippine Islands* by the U.S. War Department (1902).

Urangutang: The orangutan again – spelling given in *Oxford English Dictionary* (1933).

Tangatanga: A name for the trinity of ancient Peruvian divinities – Pachama, Virakotcha and Mamakotcha. Taken from *The Reader's Handbook of Allusions, References, Plots and Stories* by E. Cobham Brewer (1880).

The world still awaits the first eleven-letter word square. However, if you are new to the game, I suggest you stick initially to the five- or six-letter variety.

Alphabeticar

One way to make a tedious journey less tiresome is to study the number plates on the cars that pass you or that you pass. In this game the aim is to form the alphabet from A to Z from the letters in the number plates that you see. DAL782X or A268COF will give you A, BKX222W or B190DCW will give you B, and so on. You can collect two or three letters at a time from one number plate, providing they appear on the number plate both alphabetically and consecutively – which means that YAB547T will give you A *and* B but AYB547T will not.

When you have completed the alphabet from A to Z, you can then go on to complete the alphabet in reverse order from Z to A.

PART THREE

WORD PLAY

Anagrams, Palindromes, Pangrams and Lipograms

Anagrams

When you have turned the word *Pepsi-Cola* into *episcopal*, or the word *cart-horse* into *orchestral* or *dishonest* into *hedonists*, you have created an anagram – an arrangement of the letters in a word or phrase to form another word or phrase. Anagrams are said to have originated in the fourth century BC with the Greek poet Lycophron, and they have been popular in every period of history since then.

Among the longest one-word anagrams are the following:

Containerised – Inconsiderate
Discriminator – Doctrinairism
Cephalometric – Petrochemical
Interrogatives – Tergiversation
Vicepresidents – Predictiveness
Interosculates – Sansculotterie

The largest group of mutual one-word anagrams is:

Arets – Aster – Astre – Earst – Rates – Reast –
Resat – Stare – Strae – Tares – Tears – Teras

('Arets' is an obsolete word meaning 'assigns'; 'astre' means hearth or home; 'earst' means 'formerly'; 'strae' is a Scots word for straw; and 'teras' is a medical word meaning 'monstrosity'.)

Anagrams become more interesting, however, when they relate in some way to the original word or phrase. Here is a selection of my favourite anagrams which change a word into something spectacularly apt:

ALPHABETICALLY	I play all the ABC
ANIMOSITY	Is no amity
ASTRONOMER	Moon-starer
CONSIDERATE	Care is noted
CONVERSATION	Voices rant on
DESEGREGATION	Negroes get aid
DISCONSOLATE	Is not solaced
ENDEARMENT	Tender name

LUBRICATION	Act – rub oil in
MEASUREMENTS	Man uses meter
MISREPRESENTATION	Interpret one amiss
PARISHIONER	I hire parson
PITTANCE	A cent tip
PREDESTINATION	I pertain to ends
PRESBYTERIAN	Best in prayer
PUNISHMENT	Nine thumps
REVOLUTION	Love to ruin
SAINTLINESS	Least in sins
SCHOOLMASTER	The classroom
SEPARATION	One is apart
SOFTHEARTEDNESS	Often sheds tears
STAGHOUNDS	A hunt's dogs
SUGGESTION	It eggs us on
TEMPESTUOUS	Seems put out
TRAGEDIAN	Egad, I rant
TRIBULATIONS	Is but on trial
UNDIPLOMATIC	Mad, unpolitic
UNIFORMITY	I form unity
UPHOLSTERERS	Restore plush
WAITRESS	A stew, sir?

And here are a few more, where a phrase is the subject of the anagram:

THE ARISTOCRACY	A rich Tory caste
BATHING GIRLS	In slight garb
THE BOARDING HOUSE	This abode o' hunger
CIRCUMSTANTIAL EVIDENCE	Actual crime isn't evinced
THE COUNTRYSIDE	No city dust here
FOOL'S PARADISE	So ideal for sap
FRENCH REVOLUTION	Violence run forth
HMS PINAFORE	Name for ship
INTEGRAL CALCULUS	Calculating rules
THE IRISH NATION	Oh, that is in Erin
MIDWINTER WEATHER	Wind, rime, wet earth
THE MONA LISA	No hat, a smile
THE MORSE CODE	Here come dots
THE NUDIST COLONY	No untidy clothes
POLICE PROTECTION	Let cop cope in riot
A SENTENCE OF DEATH	Faces one at the end
SILVER AND GOLD	Grand old evils
SLOT MACHINES	Cash lost in 'em

SUSPENDED ANIMATION	Supine man is not dead
WESTERN UNION	No wire unsent

The names of the great and famous are, of course, prime targets for the anagrammatist:

CLINT EASTWOOD	Old West action
DANTE GABRIEL ROSETTI	Greatest idealist born
FLORENCE NIGHTINGALE	Flit on, cheering angel!
HENRY WADSWORTH LONGFELLOW	Won half the new world's glory
INDIRA GANDHI	Had Indian rig
MADAME CURIE	Radium came
MARGARET THATCHER	Great charm threat
ROALD AMUNDSEN	Laud'd Norseman
RONALD REAGAN	An oral danger
WILLIAM SHAKESPEARE	We all make his praise

It is possible to spend many happy hours taking a popular phrase or the name of a well-known person and shuffling the letters to see if you can produce an apt and amusing anagram. Try it also with the names of your friends and acquaintances.

Anagrams are truly Ars Magna – the great art.

Antigrams

An antigram is a special sort of anagram which has a meaning opposite to that of the word or phrase from which it is derived. Thus *real fun* is what you don't have at a *funeral* and *enormity* is not *more tiny*.

Here are a few of my favourite antigrams:

FILLED	Ill-fed
VIOLENCE	Nice love
INFECTION	Fine tonic
MISFORTUNE	It's more fun
MILITARISM	I limit arms
EVANGELISTS	Evil's agents
DISCRETION	Is no credit
ADVERSARIES	Are advisers
PROTECTIONISM	Nice to imports
OLD MAN WINTER	Warm, indolent
A PICTURE OF HEALTH	Oft pale, I ache, hurt
THE MAN WHO LAUGHS	He's glum, won't ha-ha

Palindromes

It is sometimes claimed that the first palindrome was created in the Garden of Eden, when Adam introduced himself to Eve with the words 'Madam, I'm Adam' (and Eve replied, simply, 'Eve'). In fact, the first palindrome was even earlier than this, when Adam said to his creator 'Name me Man'.

A palindrome is a word, like *did*, *noon*, *level*, *civic*, *kayak*, *tenet* or *repaper*, or a phrase or sentence, like 'Enid and Edna dine', that reads the same backwards as forwards.

The longest known palindromic word is *saippuakauppias*. It is a 15-letter Finnish word meaning 'soap-seller'. In the language of the Cree Indians is the 12-letter *kinnikkinnik* – the name of a tobacco substitute made from dried leaves and bark.

The longest palindromic word in everyday English is *redivider*, with nine letters. Also with nine letters are *Malayalam* (a language spoken in southern India) and *Rotavator* (a registered trademark that has found its way into the dictionary). *Detartrated*, with eleven letters, is a contrived scientific term that has not yet reached the dictionary.

It is not easy to create palindromic sentences, if it is a requirement that they make sense. The palindromist works with a greatly reduced vocabulary – you might see the word *red* in a palindrome, for example, but you are not likely to see *black*, *brown* or *blue*. Nevertheless, there are some extremely ingenious palindromic sentences. Here is a selection of my favourites:

Evil I did dwell; lewd did I live.

No lemons, no melon.

Pull up if I pull up.

Yawn a more Roman way.

Deer frisk, sir, freed.

'Tis Ivan, on a visit.

Was it a car or a cat I saw?

Now, Ned, I am a maiden won.

Ten animals I slam in a net.

Was it Eliot's toilet I saw?

Some men interpret nine memos.

A rod, not a bar: a baton, Dora.

Draw no dray a yard onward.

Sums are not set as a test on Erasmus.

Evil is a name of a foeman, as I live.

Goddesses so pay a possessed dog.

No mists reign at Tangier, St. Simon!

He lived as a devil, eh?

Marge lets Norah see Sharon's telegram.

A man, a plan, a canal – Panama.

Some palindromes are attributed to the famous. The composer Henry Purcell is said to have remarked:

Egad, a base tone denotes a bad age.

And of course there is this palindrome attributed to the emperor Napoleon in exile:

Able was I ere I saw Elba.

Billy Graham, the evangelist, *might* have said:

'Amen' I call if I fill a cinema.

When palindromes get longer, sense tends to disappear. These, however, are very creditable:

Doc, note I dissent. A fast never prevents fatness. I diet on cod.

Mirth, sir, a gay asset? No, don't essay a garish trim.

Are we not drawn onwards, we Jews, drawn onward to new era?

Desserts I desire not, so long no lost one rise distressed.

Too far away, no mere clay or royal ceremony, a war afoot.

Now saw ye no mosses or foam, or aroma of roses. So money was won.

What must surely be the best long palindrome ever penned was the work of Joyce Johnson, and was written as an entry for a competition in the *New Statesman* in 1967. Here it is, all 467 letters of it:

HEADMASTER'S PALINDROMIC LIST ON HIS MEMO PAD

Test on Erasmus
Deliver slap
Royal: phone no.?
Ref. Football.
Is sofa sitable on?
XI – staff over
Sub-edit Nurse's order
Caning is on test (snub slip-up)
Birch (Sid) to help Miss Eve
Repaper den
Use it
Put inkspot on stopper
Prof. – no space
Caretaker (wall, etc.)
Too many d— pots
Wal for duo? (I'd name Dr O)
See few owe fees (or demand IOU?)
Dr of Law
Stop dynamo (OTC)
Tel: Law re Kate Race
Caps on for prep
Pots – no tops
Knit up ties ('U')
Ned (re paper)
Eve's simple hot dish (crib)
Pupil's buns
T-set: no sign in a/c
Red roses
Run Tide Bus?
Rev off at six
Noel Bat is a fossil
Lab to offer one 'Noh' play
– or 'Pals Reviled'?
Sums are not set.

Pseudodromes

Pseudodromes are palindromes in which words, rather than individual letters, read the same backwards or forwards. Pseudodromes may not be true palindromes but they can be quite as entertaining, as these examples demonstrate:

So patient a doctor to doctor a patient so.

Does milk machinery milk does?

Bores are people that say that people are bores.

Women understand men; few men understand women.

Dollars make men covetous, then covetous men make dollars.

You can cage a swallow, can't you, but you can't swallow a cage, can you?

Girl, bathing on Bikini, eyeing boy, finds boy eyeing bikini on bathing girl.

Pangrams

The quick brown fox jumps over a lazy dog.

That well-known sentence, often used as a typing test, is an example of a pangram – a sentence that uses every letter of the alphabet. That particular pangram uses 33 letters, but there are shorter pangrams:

Pack my box with five dozen liquor jugs.	(32 letters)
Quick waxy bugs jump the frozen veldt.	(31 letters)
The five boxing wizards jump quickly.	(31 letters)
Jackdaws love my big sphinx of quartz.	(31 letters)
How quickly daft jumping zebras vex.	(30 letters)

To get below 30 letters, you have to introduce proper names:

Quick wafting zephyrs vex bold Jim.	(29 letters)
Waltz, nymph, for quick jigs vex Bud.	(28 letters)

The ultimate, of course, is a pangram consisting of only 26 letters. These are examples, but they use either initials and funny names or obscure archaic and dialect words:

Blowzy night-frumps vex'd Jack Q.

J. Q. Schwartz flung D. V. Pike my box.

Cwm fjord-bank glyphs vext quiz.

This latter may be translated as 'Ancient inscriptions on the side of a fjord in a Welsh valley annoyed an eccentric'.

If *you* can devise the perfect 26-letter pangram, it may not make you rich but it will certainly make you famous.

If you can't devise pangrams of your own, you can look for them in pieces of literature. When reading the Book of Ezra, Chapter 7, Verse 21, you will have been struck by the following sentence:

> And I, even I Ataxerxes the king, do make a decree to all the treasurers which are beyond the river, that whatsoever Ezra the priest, the scribe of the law of the God of heaven, shall require of you, it be done speedily.

That is an imperfect pangram because it lacks the letter J. Also imperfect as a pangram, lacking the letter Z, are these lines from Shakespeare's *Coriolanus*:

O! a kiss
Long as my exile, sweet as my revenge!
Now, by the jealous queen of heaven, that kiss
I carried from thee, dear, and my true lip
Hath virgin'd it ever since.

A true pangram, however, may be found in the following lines from Milton's *Paradise Lost*:

Likening his Maker to the grazed ox,
Jehovah, who, in one night, when he passed
From Egypt marching, equalled with one stroke
Both her first-born and all her bleating gods.

There must be many more pangrams waiting to be found in works of great literature, so get those neglected classics down from the shelf and start searching. Then you might be able to say:

By Jove, my quick study of lexicography won a prize.

Lipograms

A lipogram is a literary text in which one or more letters of the alphabet have been deliberately excluded.

Among the great lipograms of the past were the poet Tryphiodorus who wrote an epic poem about the adventures of Ulysses, omitting a different letter of the Greek alphabet from each of its 24 books; and Lope de Vega, the prolific Spanish dramatist, who wrote five novels excluding the letters A, E, I, O and U in turn.

Coming to the present century, the 50,000 word novel *Gadsby* by Ernest Vincent Wright, published in 1939, was written completely without the use of the letter E.

There is not enough space to reproduce any of these works here. But we can show some of the work of the contemporary lipogrammarian A. Ross Eckler, who rewrote the nursery rhyme *Mary Had A Little Lamb* in several versions, omitting various common letters.

Here, to remind you, is the original verse:

Mary had a little lamb,
Its fleece was white as snow,
And everywhere that Mary went
The lamb was sure to go;
It followed her to school one day,
That was against the rule;
It made the children laugh and play
To see a lamb in school.

Now here are three of Mr Eckler's versions, omitting the letters H, T and E in turn:

Mary owned a little lamb,
Its fleece was pale as snow,
And every place its mistress went
It certainly would go;
It followed Mary to class one day,
It broke a rigid law;
It made some students giggle aloud,
A lamb in class all saw.

Mary had a pygmy lamb,
His fleece was pale as snow,
And every place where Mary walked
Her lamb did also go;
Her lamb came inside her classroom once,
Which broke a rigid rule;
How children all did laugh and play
On seeing a lamb in school.

Mary had a tiny lamb,
Its wool was pallid as snow,
And any spot that Mary did walk
This lamb would always go;
This lamb did follow Mary to school,
Although against a law;
How girls and boys did laugh and play,
That lamb in class all saw.

Composing lipograms, as well as being great fun, is a valuable exercise in that it teaches one to express the same idea in different ways. Why not see if you can do as well with other works? Try producing alternative versions of other nursery rhymes or short poems, omitting some common letter. Then perhaps you might care to tackle the works of

Shakespeare. I myself have had a go at *Hamlet*, from which I scrupulously excluded the letter I. Here is part of it:

> To be, or not to be; that's the query:
> Whether you would be nobler to suffer mentally
> The stones and arrows of outrageous fortune,
> Or to take arms to oppose a sea of troubles,
> And through combat end them? To pass on, to sleep:
> No more . . .

I cannot leave the subject of the lipogram without including the following example which, I am sure, must be unique. This work, by an unknown author, is a pangrammatic lipogram – or is it a lipogrammatic pangram? Each stanza of this poem has been written so that it includes all the letters of the alphabet except E.

THE FATE OF NASSAN

Bold Nassan quits his caravan,
A hazy mountain grot to scan;
Climbs craggy rocks to spy his way,
Doth tax his sight, but far doth stray.

Not work of man, nor sport of child,
Finds Nassan in that mazy wild;
Lax grow his joints, limbs toil in vain –
Poor wight! why didst thou quit that plain?

Vainly for succour Nassan calls,
Know, Zillah, that thy Nassan falls;
But prowling wolf and fox may joy,
To quarry on thy Arab boy.

Clangers

Spoonerisms

A spoonerism is the transposition (either accidentally or deliberately) of the initial letters of the words in a phrase so as to change the phrase's meaning or make nonsense of it.

A well-boiled icicle.

The Lord is a shoving leopard.

Please sew me to another sheet.

Let us toast the queer old dean.

I have in my bosom a half-warmed fish.

You were fighting a liar in the quadrangle.

The cat popped on its drawers.

You have hissed my mystery lectures; you have tasted a whole worm. You will leave Oxford by the town drain.

These classic spoonerisms have all been attributed to the Reverend William Spooner, Warden of New College, Oxford from 1903 to 1924, but it is doubtful if any of them ever issued from his lips. Despite being a shrewd man of considerable personal dignity, he was apparently what most people would consider 'an absent-minded professor'. He did, it seems, give out a hymn in chapel as *Kinquering Kongs Their Titles Take*, and he did use the words 'In a dark, glassly'. On meeting Stanley Casson in the quadrangle, Dr Spooner said to him 'Do come to dinner tonight to meet Casson, our new Fellow.' 'But, Warden, I *am* Casson,' said Casson, to which Spooner replied 'Never mind, come all the same.'

Spooner, however, vigorously denied authorship of the classic spoonerisms attributed to him, and it is almost certain that they are the invention of Oxford undergraduates who, inspired by the verbal infelicities of the Doctor, enthusiastically took up the idea of creating spoonerisms by design rather than accident.

Why not have a go at inventing some spoonerisms of your own? I can assure you the exercise will provide plots of leisure.

Malapropisms

A malapropism, named after the character Mrs Malaprop in Sheridan's play *The Rivals*, is a ludicrous misuse of words, especially by confusion with similar words. Here are a few highlights from the conversation of Mrs Malaprop herself:

'A progeny of learning.'

'Make no delusions to the past.'

'She's as headstrong as an allegory on the banks of the Nile.'

'Illiterate him, I say, quite from your memory.'

'An aspersion upon my parts of speech! Was ever such a brute! Sure, if I reprehend anything in this world, it is the use of my oracular tongue, and a nice derangement of epitaphs!'

Here are a few of my favourites among the more modern malapropisms I have heard or read:

'White as the dripping snow.'

'I was so surprised you could have knocked me over with a fender.'

'I was so hungry that I gouged myself.'

'My sister uses massacre on her eyes.'

'He had to use biceps to deliver the baby.'

'I don't like him and he doesn't like me, so it's neutral.'

'I had an idea that would happen – I must be psychopathic.'

If you want to form your own collection of malapropisms, I can recommend disc jockeys and sports commentators on TV or radio as a good source of erogenous phraseology.

Goldwynisms

Sam Goldwyn, the Hollywood movie mogul, was renowned for his verbal clangers. It is impossible to define the essence of a Goldwynism – each one is unique. All one can do is regard them with awestruck admiration.

'Include me out.'

'In two words: im-possible!'

'A verbal contract isn't worth the paper it's written on.'

'We're overpaying him, but he's worth it.'

'We have all passed a lot of water since then.'

'I'll give you a definite maybe.'

'If Roosevelt were alive, he'd turn over in his grave.'

'It's more than magnificent – it's mediocre.'

'Anybody who goes to see a psychiatrist ought to have his head examined.'

'Every director bites the hand that lays the golden egg.'

'Yes, my wife's hands are very beautiful. I'm going to have a bust made of them.'

'I read part of it all the way through.'

'Let's have some new clichés.'

'A bachelor's life is no life for a single man.'

'Going to call him William? What kind of a name is that? Every Tom, Dick and Harry's called William. Why don't you call him Bill?'

Mixed Metaphors

We all mix metaphors all the time. Even Shakespeare was susceptible. In Hamlet's great soliloquy the words 'to take arms against a sea of trouble' are a classic example of a mixed metaphor.

Mixed metaphors are part of everyday speech and usually we don't even notice. 'To hog the limelight', 'galloping inflation', 'a fully-fledged star', 'to latch on to a new hobby' are examples. It is only when the metaphors that are mixed present a startlingly incongruous image in our minds that the mixed metaphor becomes worthy of our notice. Like these gems:

He is a rough diamond with a heart of gold.

It is the thin end of a white elephant.

The sacred cows have come home to roost with a vengeance.

All these white sepulchres are tarred with the same brush.

The views of the grass roots are not hearing the light of day.

Wild horses on their bended knees would not make me do it.

The whole chain of events consists entirely of missing links.

I strongly protest against the attack on my absent friend, for surely it is not right to hang a man behind his back.

One of the most famous of all mixed metaphors comes from a speech made in the House of Commons by the eighteenth-century Irish politician Sir Boyle Roche:

Mr. Speaker, I smell a rat: I see him forming in the air and darkening the sky: but I'll nip him in the bud.

Poetry And Rhyme

Limericks

The limerick is furtive and mean;
You must keep her in close quarantine,
Or she sneaks to the slums
And promptly becomes
Disorderly, drunk and obscene.

A limerick is a five-line nonsense verse that originated with the eighteenth-century ale-house chorus 'Will you come up to Limerick' and was later made famous by Edward Lear.

Although at the limericks of Lear
We may be tempted to sneer
We should never forget
That we owe him a debt
For his work as the first pioneer.

It must be said that the majority of limericks are lewd and indecent. There are some, though, that are amusing without being offensive. Here is a very brief selection of my favourites:

There was an old fellow of Tring
Who, when someone asked him to sing,
Replied 'Ain't it odd?
I can never tell God
Save The Weasel from *Pop Goes The King*.

There was a young fellow of Perth
Who was born on the day of his birth;
He married, they say,
On his wife's wedding day,
And he died when he quitted the earth.

There was an old man of Madrid
Who ate sixty eggs – yes, he did!
When they asked 'Are you faint?'
He replied 'No, I ain't.
But I don't feel as well as I did.'

I sat next to the Duchess at tea;
It was just as I feared it would be.
  Her rumblings abdominal
  Were simply phenomenal,
And everyone thought it was me!

There was a faith-healer of Deal
Who said 'Although pain isn't real,
  If I sit on a pin
  And it punctures my skin,
I dislike what I fancy I feel.'

Some of my favourite limericks take liberties with spelling:

Said a maid 'I will marry for lucre'
And her scandalized ma almost shucre.
  But when the chance came
  And she told the good dame,
I notice she did not rebucre.

There was a young lady named Wemyss
Who, it semyss, was afflicted with dremyss.
  She would wake in the night
  And in terrible fright
Shake the bemyss of the house with her scremyss.

Writing limericks of your own can provide a great deal of fun, and it is not too difficult to produce an acceptable result – that is, if you avoid the error made by the young man from Japan:

There was a young man from Japan
Whose limericks never would scan.
  When asked why that was,
  He replied 'It's because
I always try to cram as many words into the last line
  as I possibly can.'

Clerihews

Edmund Clerihew Bentley is remembered mainly for his classic detective story *Trent's Last Case* and for the verse form that was named after him – the clerihew.

Bentley's first collection of verse in this vein was published in 1905 as *Biography For Beginners*. Further collections appeared in 1929 and in 1939. It was soon after the publication of the first volume that the name 'clerihew' became applied to this particular form of light verse.

What exactly is a clerihew? Frances Stillman in *The Poet's Manual and Rhyming Dictionary* defines it as 'a humorous pseudo-biographical quatrain, rhymed as two couplets, with lines of uneven length more or less in the rhythm of prose'. Add to this, that the name of the subject usually ends the first or, less often, the second line, and that the humour of the clerihew is whimsical rather than satiric, and that it is a verse form comparatively unknown outside the UK, and there you have a complete definition.

Here are a few of my favourite Bentley clerihews:

The people of Spain think Cervantes
Equal to half-a-dozen Dantes;
An opinion resented most bitterly
By the people of Italy.

Although Machiavelli
Was extremely fond of jelly,
He stuck religiously to mince
While he was writing *The Prince*.

George the Third
Ought never to have occurred.
One can only wonder
At so grotesque a blunder.

Among the contemporaries of Shakespeare
There were few who regarded him as Drake's peer.
Spoiling paper was so much less strain
Than spoiling the Spanish Main.

Sir Humphrey Davy
Abominated gravy.
He lived in the odium
Of having discovered sodium.

And here are three clerihews by Michael Curl:

Alexander Selkirk
Did not like hotel work.
He informed a maid
That he was monarch of all he surveyed.

James Joyce
Had an extremely loud voice;
In the morning he'd shout and make
Finnegans Wake.

E. C. Bentley
Mused while he ought to have studied intently;
It was this muse
That inspired clerihews.

Sententious Verse

The object of the game is to write the longest piece of verse that you can, consisting of *only one sentence*. To give you something to aim for, here is a forty-eight-line example by John Slim:

DEATH SENTENCE

Have you heard how Cuthbert Hatch
To find a gas leak, struck a match
And thereby hastened his despatch
To realms unknown to you and me,
Who have not yet been foolishly
Inclined to leave posterity
To puzzle for itself just why
We chose to make our fragments fly
For ever upwards to the sky,
As Cuthbert did when in the dark
He smelled a smell and sparked a spark
Which sent him rising like a lark
– A very shattered fowl, it's true,
With no lump large enough to stew
And nothing any cat could chew –
Into the unresisting space
Where there is never any place
To rest one's feet or wash one's face,
Though this, for faceless, feetless folk,
As Cuthbert was by then, poor bloke,
Is not by any means a yoke
Which is impossible to bear,
For it's with truth that I declare
That cases are extremely rare

Of people ceasing to exist
And then, assuming they'll be missed,
Proceeding forthwith to insist
On spreading sadness with their pen
Among their former fellow-men
With news of things beyond their ken
By writing letters to the Press
To say that they are in a mess
Which words in print cannot express,
For they're aware that we below
Quite rarely care just how they go
And, once they've gone, don't want to know
The finer details of the fate
Which suddenly transformed their state
From Man Alive into The Late
Lamented such as Cuthbert Hatch,
Who found that leak with lighted match
And who thereafter failed to catch
The interest of the public eye
Or stir mankind to spare a sigh
– Which may explain precisely why
I think that Cuthbert Hatch (The Late)
Would not expect to read (or rate)
A second sentence on his fate?

By Apt Alliteration's Artful Aid

We are all familiar with alliteration as one of the weapons in the poet's armoury. Few poets, however, used alliteration to the same extent as the writer of that epic ballad *The Siege Of Belgrade* – that great poet Anon.

THE SIEGE OF BELGRADE

An Austrian army, awfully arrayed,
Boldly, by battery, besieged Belgrade;
Cossack commanders cannonading come –
Dealing destruction's devastating doom;
Every endeavour, engineers essay,
For fame, for fortune – fighting furious fray: –
Generals 'gainst generals grapple – gracious God!
How honours heaven, heroic hardihood!
Infuriate – indiscriminate in ill,

Kindred kill kinsmen, – kinsmen kindred kill!
Labour low levels loftiest, longest lines –
Men march 'mid mounds, 'mid moles, 'mid murderous mines:
Now noisy, noxious, noticed nought
Of outward obstacles opposing ought:
Poor patriots, partly purchased, partly pressed;
Quite quaking, quickly quarter, quarter quest,
Reason returns, religious right redounds,
Sorrow stops such sanguinary sounds.
Truce to thee, Turkey – triumph to thy train!
Unjust, unwise, unmerciful Ukraine!
Vanish vain victory, vanish victory vain!
Why wish ye warfare? Wherefore welcome were
Xerxes, Ximenes, Xanthus, Xaviere?
Yield! ye youths! ye yeomen, Yield, your yell!
Zeono's, Zapater's, Zoroaster's zeal,
And all attracting – arms against acts appeal.

As an example of alphabetical alliteration this is not quite perfect – note that the author skipped *j* and there is a *ye* in among the *w*'s. But could you do any better?

Acrostics

An acrostic is a verse in which a word or a message or (most commonly) a name is spelled out by the initial letters of the lines.

Lewis Carroll loved to create acrostics, and here is his most famous example, dedicated to Alice Pleasance Liddell, the little girl who inspired *Alice's Adventures in Wonderland*:

A boat, beneath a sunny sky
Lingering onward dreamily
In an evening of July –

Children three that nestle near,
Eager eye and willing ear,
Pleased a simple tale to hear –

Long has paled that sunny sky;
Echoes fade and memories die:
Autumn frosts have slain July.

Still she haunts me, phantomwise,
Alice moving under skies
Never seen by waking eyes.

Children yet the tale to hear,
Eager eye and willing ear,
Lovingly shall nestle near.

In Wonderland they lie,
Dreaming as the days go by,
Dreaming as the summers die:

Ever drifting down the stream –
Lingering in the golden gleam –
Life, what is it but a dream?

Single-Rhymed Verse

An interesting exercise is to see what is the longest piece of verse one can produce using only a single rhyme. Clearly you have to pick your rhyme carefully – you would get further if you ended your first line with the word *man*, for example, than you would if it ended with *rhythm* or *silver*!

Here, to show you what can be achieved, is a single-rhyme alphabet dating from the nineteenth century.

A was an Army, to settle disputes;
B was a Bull, not the mildest of brutes;
C was a Cheque, duly drawn upon Coutts;
D was King David, with harps and with lutes;
E was an Emperor, hailed with salutes;
F was a Funeral, followed by mutes;
G was a Gallant in Wellington boots;
H was a Hermit who lived upon roots;
I was Justinian his Institutes;
K was a Keeper, who commonly shoots;
L was a Lemon, the sourest of fruits;
M was a Ministry – say Lord Bute's;
N was Nicholson, famous on flutes;
O was an Owl, that hisses and hoots;
P was a Pond, full of leeches and newts;
Q was a Quaker, in whitey-brown suits;

R was a Reason, which Paley refutes;
S was a Sergeant with twenty recruits;
T was Ten Tories of doubtful reputes;
U was Uncommonly bad cheroots;
V Vicious motives, Which malice imputes;
X an Ex-King driven out by emeutes;
Y is a Yarn; then, the last rhyme that suits,
Z is the Zuyder Zee, dwelt in by coots.

Univocalics

Univocalic verse restricts itself to the use of only one vowel. Here is a well-known, though brief example, of the art:

Persevere, ye perfect men,
Ever keep the precepts ten.

And here is a Victorian production, on the theme of the Russo-Turkish war, using A as the only vowel:

War harms all ranks, all arts, all crafts appal;
At Mars' harsh blast, arch, rampart, altar fall!
Ah! hard as adamant a braggart Czar
Arms vassal-swarms, and fans a fatal war!
Rampant at that bad call, a Vandal band
Harass, and harm, and ransack Wallach-land.
A Tartar phalanx Balkan's scarp hath past,
And Allah's standard falls, alas! at last.

Puns And Riddles

Puns

The glorious paradox of the pun is that the worse it is the better it is. When you have heard a pleasing pun you don't show your appreciation by laughing – you groan instead. Puns are plays on words using the same or similar sounds, and they come in all shapes and sizes.

There are short, snappy ones:

A yes-man is one who stoops to concur.

When I'm stoned I get a little boulder.

Corporal punishment smacks of sadism.

There are long rambling puns:

Little Jimmy was looking forward to going to the circus with his Uncle Alf. When the day arrived, his father said 'I'm afraid Uncle Alf can't take you to the circus today. He's gone to Wimbledon to watch the tennis instead.' 'But I didn't even know Uncle Alf liked tennis' wailed little Jimmy. 'Oh yes,' said his father, 'I've often heard Alfred laud tennis, son.'

A newspaper editor was dining in a very grand French restaurant in Mayfair, and he enthused about the Coq au Vin. Summoning the proprietor of the restaurant, he asked if he could have the recipe. 'Oh no,' replied the proprietor. 'In the restaurant business we are just like you journalists – we never reveal our sauces.'

There are heavenly puns:

Saint Peter: And how did you get here?
Latest arrival: Flu.

And hellish puns:

Latest arrival: Do you mind if I smoke?
Little devil: I don't mind if you burn.

There are alcoholic puns:

'Orange juice sorry you made me cry?'
'Don't be soda pressed – them martini bruises.'

And there are philosophical puns:

Better to have loved a short girl
Than never to have loved a tall.

Few great writers have resisted altogether the temptation to indulge in the occasional pun and some, like Shakespeare, revelled in it. In that play, Lady Macbeth says:

'If he do bleed
I'll gild the faces of the grooms withal;
For it must seem their guilt.'

If punning is not to your taste, don't worry. It's well known that one man's Mede is another man's Persian.

Tom Swifties

Named after a character in a series of books by Edward Statemeyer, published in the 1920s, Tom Swifties are a type of pun for which there seems to be a craze every few years. The idea is to make a pun on an adverb or adverbial phrase, as in the following examples:

'Let's trap that sick bird,' said Tom illegally.

'Pass the cards,' said Tom ideally.

'I like to go camping,' said Tom intently.

'That's a very large herring,' said Tom superficially.

'I've just had a serious operation,' said Tom half-heartedly.

'Drop that gun!' said Tom disarmingly.

'The bacon is burnt,' said Tom with panache.

'Turn on the radio,' said Tom with a short wave.

'How about a game of draughts?' asked Tom airily.

'Try looking in the attic,' said Tom loftily.

'I've swallowed a lot of hay,' said Tom balefully.

Croakers

The croaker is a close relative of Tom Swiftie, and in this case the pun is purely verbal, as these examples demonstrate:

'I'm dying,' he croaked.

'The fire is going out,' he bellowed.

'Someone is at the door,' she chimed.

'I ordered raspberry ripple not vanilla,' I screamed.

'Watch the birdie!' he snapped.

'We've struck oil,' he gushed.

'I think company's coming,' she guessed.

Terse Verse

The world's greatest punster is Alan F. G. Lewis, who has made creating puns his life's work. Many of his puns are cast in a form he calls Terse Verse. Here are some of my favourites:

Soupçon is French for a small amount, only morceau.

Schnapps and hock are my favourite Teutonics.

If his new secretary isn't sweet in the daytime and a little tart at night, he'll saccharin the morning.

Why piccolo profession like music that's full of viol practices, confirmed lyres, old fiddles, and bass desires?
For the lute, of course.

I'll be with you –
in two sex, said the hermaphrodite
in half a tick, said the vivisectionist

in two shakes, said the freemason
in half a mho, said the electrician
in a trice, said the Third Man
in necks to no time, said the executioner
in a flash, said the magician
in an instant, said the marketing man
in a twinkling, eye said.

I Told Her

I told her no sensible man
would take her dancing
in her bikini.
So she went
with a little moron.

Valentine Rhyme

My heart and I
Call to you
But you're too deaf
To Eros.

The Tree of Love

Yew witch Hazel
It's plane
I'm sycamore poplar girls
And aspen alder time
On the beech
And pine to cedar day
When I maple to say
'Hazel lime yours,
Cumquat may.'

Please Be Seated

When she said 'Howdah do
Take a pew
You look divan'
I thought 'This is sit'
But I was throne aside
When she decided to settle
For a pouffe.

A sort of plinth charming
Who promised to support her
For the rest of her dais,
Next time I'll be more chairy.

The Poet's Dilemma

Once upon a time I used
To mispel
To sometimes split infinitives
To get words of out order
To punctuate, – badly
To confused my tenses
To deem old words wondrous fair
to ignore capitals
To employ common or garden clichés
To miss the occasional out
To indulge in tautological repetitive statements
To exaggerate hundreds of times a day
And to repeat puns quite by chants
But worst of all I used
To forget to finish what I

Not The Nine O'Clock News

The clichés used in news reports on radio and television often provide material for the inveterate punster:

Hundreds of stray dogs disappeared yesterday. Police say they have no leads.

A truck carrying strawberries spilled its load at a busy intersection today. The result was a large traffic jam.

Two men robbed a city bank today. One of the men is described as being seven feet tall, and the other is said to be four feet six inches. The police are looking high and low for them.

After a Japanese motor factory was hit by a tornado earlier this week, witnesses say it has been raining Datsun cogs.

A lorry carrying onions has shed its load on the motorway. Motorists are advised to find a hard shoulder to cry on.

Thieves stole a van containing bottles of hair restorer, but their getaway ended when it crashed over a bridge. Police are now combing the area.

Dismissals

When a man loses his job he may be dismissed, sacked, fired or kicked out; he may be out on his ear or on his neck; he may be shown the door; or he may be given his cards, his marching orders, the push, the elbow, the old heave-ho or the order of the boot.

Some professions, however, have their own individual terminology for this situation: a clergyman is defrocked, a lawyer disbarred, an army officer cashiered.

Why should not people in other walks of life also have their own terms for dismissal? Thus:

An office-worker could be defiled.
A salesman could be disordered.
A writer could be described.
A journalist could be depressed.
A wine merchant could be deported.
A celebrity could be defamed.
A climber could be dismounted.
A jailer could be excelled.
A policeman could be unwarranted.
A judge could be dishonoured.
A bishop could be disgraced.
A model could be deposed.
A prostitute could be delayed.
A Moonie could be dissected.
A conjuror could be disillusioned.
A rabble-rouser could be demobbed.
A musician could be denoted, disbarred, disbanded, decomposed or disconcerted!

See how many more 'dismissals' you can think of.

Awful Authors

This is a form of word play, especially popular among children, which involves inventing the name of an imaginary author punningly alluding to the name of an equally imaginary book.

The most satisfactory results are obtained when the names of the authors are reasonably credible while at the same time containing the most outrageous puns.

Here are some of my favourites, but no doubt you can come up with better examples:

Dog's Dinner by Nora Bone
The Gardener by Moses Lawn
Slimming by Lena Boddy
The Open Window by Eileen Doubt
The Debtor by Owen Munny
Crime Does Pay by Robin Banks
The Funeral by Paul Bearer
The Female Ghost by Sheila Peer
The Lion Tamer by Claude Face
Frankenstein Meets Dracula by Horace Tory
King Kong by Hugh Jape
The Singer by Barry Tone
Big White Bird by Albert Ross
A Visit To The Dentist by Phil McAvity
The Cavalryman by Rhoda Norse
A Continental Breakfast by Roland Coffy
Where's My Hat by Sonia Head
Prehistoric Reptiles by Terry Dactyl & Dinah Soar
Tolstoi by Warren Peace
D-Day by Norman D. Landing
At The Eleventh Hour by Justin Time

Riddles

Riddles are the most ancient and most widespread type of word game. They have been popular in every civilization and every culture, both ancient and modern.

Having said that, it must be admitted that the traditional riddle is not quite the same as the wordplay we know by that name today. The traditional riddle is a cryptic or enigmatic utterance which the hearer has to try to interpret. An example is in the Story of Samson who, having seen a swarm of bees making honey in the carcass of a lion, proposed the riddle:

> Out of the eater came something to eat;
> Out of the strong came something sweet.

By contrast, the modern riddle is usually based on a pun, and the aim is amusement rather than mystification.

There are riddles based on letters of the alphabet:

Q. Which letter is like a Roman emperor?
A. P – because it is near O.

Q. Which other letters are like a Roman emperor?
A. The C's are.

Q. Why is the letter D like a naughty child?
A. Because it makes ma mad.

One popular form may be styled the 'Difference' riddle:

Q. What's the difference between a poor man and a feather bed?
A. One is hard up, the other is soft down.

Q. What's the difference between a woman and a postage stamp?
A. One is a female, the other a mail fee.

Q. What's the difference between an ornithologist and someone who can't spell?
A. One is a bird-watcher, the other is a word-botcher.

Q. What's the difference between a cat and a comma?
A. A cat has claws at the end of its paws, a comma is a pause at the end of a clause.

Another popular type is the 'Crossing' riddle:

Q. What do you get if you cross an elephant with a kangaroo?
A. Great big holes all over Australia.

Q. What do you get if you cross a hyena with a stallion?
A. Hoarse laughter.

Q. What do you get if you cross a weasel with a nightingale?
A. A pop singer.

In fact there is a wide variety of riddles, covering just about every subject one can think of.

Q. Where do sheep go to have their hair cut?
A. The baa-baa shop.

Q. What lies on the sea-bed and trembles?
A. A nervous wreck.

Q. What's a Grecian urn?
A. About ten drachmas a week.

Q. How do you use an Egyptian doorbell?
A. Toot-and-come-in.

Q. Why do devils and ghosts get on well together?
A. Because demons are a ghouls best friends.

Q. Why were the Dark Ages dark?
A. Because there were so many knights.

Q. Do any metals float on water?
A. Tin can but stainless steel sinks.

Q. Why does a calendar have only a year to live?
A. Because its days are numbered.

Q. What flies the Atlantic and climbs the Empire State Building?
A. King Kongcorde.

Q. What colours are the sun and wind?
A. The sun rose and the wind blue.

ACKNOWLEDGMENTS

The author and publishers would like to thank the following people for permission to reproduce material which is their copyright. They have made every effort to trace copyright holders. If they have inadvertently omitted to acknowledge anyone they would be most grateful if it could be brought to their attention for correction at the first opportunity.

The Observer for nos 241 and 243 (crosswords by Torquemada and Ximenes).

A. F. Ritchie for no 242 (crossword by Afrit).

Michael Curl for nos 191–3, 217, 220, 221, 223, 230, 236–7, 244–6, 249–51, 309–11.

Bantam Books Inc. for nos 247–8 from *Fifty Great Crossword Puzzles 10*, © 1974.

Dover Publications, Inc. for nos 282–4 from *My Best Puzzles in Mathematics* (© 1961) by Hubert Phillips; and for nos 285–7 from *Recreations in Logic* (© 1979) by D. G. Wells.

Charles Scribner's Sons and George Allen & Unwin Ltd for nos 288 and 290 from *100 Geometric Games* (1976) and *100 Logic Games* (1977) by Pierre Berloquin, © 1973 Libraire Generale Francaise.

Charles Scribner's Sons for nos 291–4 from *The Moscow Puzzles* by Boris Kordemsky, © 1971, 1972.

Martin Gardner for nos 295–7 from *More Mathematical Puzzles and Diversions*, published by Simon and Schuster Inc., © 1961.

William Heinemann Ltd for nos 298–300 from *Your Move* (Kaye and Ward, © 1973) by David Silverman.

Penguin Books Ltd and Clarkson N. Potter Inc., for puzzles 307–8 from *Science Fiction Puzzle Tales* by Martin Gardner, © 1981.

St Louis Post for no 238.

ALPHABETICAL LIST OF PUZZLES AND WORD GAMES